Microbial Transformation

of

Steroids and Alkaloids

MICROBIAL TRANSFORMATION

OF

STEROIDS AND ALKALOIDS

by

HIROSHI IIZUKA, Ph. D.
Professor
Institute of Applied Microbiology
University of Tokyo

ATSUSHI NAITO, Ph. D.
Central Research Laboratories
Sankyo Co. Ltd.

UNIVERSITY OF TOKYO PRESS
Tokyo
UNIVERSITY PARK PRESS
State College, Pennsylvania

Published jointly by
UNIVERSITY OF TOKYO PRESS
Tokyo
and
UNIVERSITY PARK PRESS
State College, Pennsylvania
LIBRARY OF CONGRESS CATALOG CARD NUMBER 68–19102

Preface

In recent years, the most striking and significant development in the field of synthetic chemistry has been the application of biological systems to chemical reactions. Biological systems display a far greater specificity than the more conventional forms of organic chemical reactions, and of all the systems available, that which has the greatest immediate potential in organic synthesis is microbial transformation.

The first application of such a system was reported in 1937, in the work of Luigi Mamoli and Alberto Vercellone on the oxidative transformation of steroid compounds, using yeast and bacteria. The next few years saw little progress in the field, but in the mid 1950's there was a sudden interest in research on the problems of producing steroid hormones by microbial transformation. The method is significant both for basic research and for its industrial possibilities. At present, scientists are attempting the application of microbial transformation not only in the synthesis of steroid compounds, but more broadly for other organic compounds, such as alkaloids, etc., and a number of results have already been reported. Inevitably such efforts have led to an increased interest on the part of microbiologists in discovering and breeding of new strains, and these are constantly being searched for or developed in the laboratory. Thus it would seem that the new field of microbial transformation will develop more and more in the near future.

The present authors have been carrying out their studies on microbial transformation of steroids and alkaloids in the Institute of Applied Microbiology, the University of Tokyo, since 1956. This book presents a summary of the data which has been accumulated up to 1966.

The book itself is divided into ten chapters according to the type of substrate used in the microbial reactions. Within each chapter, the various transformation reactions are grouped by type. To simplify usage, representative substrates dealt with in each chapter are listed at the beginning, along with their chemical structures and structural names. For each specific reaction, the substrate is given on the left, and the reaction product on the right, as shown in Examples 1 and 2.

Below the substrate, the scientific name and strain name or number of the microorganism responsible for the particular reaction are given, followed by the percentage yield in parentheses. Below the reaction product, the name or names of the researchers and the reference for the

Example 1

Hydroxylation

Progesterone

Aspergillus saitoi IAM R-1216

6β, 11α-Dihydroxyprogesterone

Iizuka, H., A. Naito and M. Hattori, J. Gen. Appl. Microbiol. (Japan), **4**, 67 (1958)

Example 2

Dehydrogenation

Cortisol

Bacillus pulvifaciens IAM N-19-2

11β, 17α, 21-Trihydroxypregna-1, 4-diene-3, 20-dione (Prednisolone)

Iizuka, H., A. Naito and Y. Sato, J. Gen. Appl. Microbiol (Japan), **7**, 118 (1961)

particular reaction are listed. In the section on steroid hormones, the hormones are arranged in order from C_{18}-steroids to C_{21}-steroids, within similar reaction patterns. Hydroxylation is shown according to the carbon number.

The microorganisms are identified by their scientific names, and the author's names of species are omitted, but the particular strains to which the strain name and number refer in the original reports are given. The index at the end of the book lists personal names, microorganisms, and compounds.

Because of the tremendous amount of work being done in the field at the present time, this book, by the time it leaves the press, will inevitably have a number of gaps in its coverage of recent research, making the subsequent publication of a revised edition imperative. In view of this, the authors would like to request anyone who has obtained any significant results on new microbial reactions relating to steroids, alkaloids or other substrates to send a copy of the paper or report to Hiroshi Iizuka, at the Institute of Applied Microbiology, the University of Tokyo, Bunkyo-ku, Tokyo, Japan.

The authors would also like to thank Dr. Hiroshi Okazaki for his kind advice with respect to collecting the materials for the present volume, and are deeply gratefull to all others who aided in the publication of this book.

Tokyo
September, 1967

HIROSHI IIZUKA
and
ATSUSHI NAITO

Contents

CONTENTS

Microbial Transformation
of
Steroids and Alkaloids

I. MICROBIAL TRANSFORMATION OF STEROID HORMONES

Common names and systematic names of typical steroids

Common name	Systematic name
Androstenedione	Androst-4-ene-3,17-dione
Androsterone	3α-Hydroxy-5α-androstan-17-one
Corticosterone	11β, 21-Dihydroxypregn-4-ene-3,20-dione
Cortisol (Hydrocortisone)	11β, 17α, 21-Trihydroxypregn-4-ene-3,20-dione
Cortisone	17α, 21-Dihydroxypregn-4-ene-3,11,20-trione
11-Dehydrocorticosterone	21-Hydroxypregn-4-ene-3,11,20-trione
Dehydroepiandrosterone	3β-Hydroxyandrost-5-en-17-one
1-Dehydrotestololactone (Δ¹-Testololactone)	13α-Hydroxy-3-oxo-13,17-secoandrosta-1,4-dien-17-oic lactone
11-Deoxycorticosterone	21-Hydroxypregn-4-ene-3,20-dione
11-Deoxycortisol	17α, 21-Dihyroxypregn-4-ene-3,20-dione 17α-Hydroxy-11-deoxycorticosterone
Estradiol	Estra-1,3,5(10)-triene-3, 17β-diol
Estrone	3-Hydroxyestra-1,3,5(10)-trien-17-one
Prednisolone	11β, 17α, 21-Trihydroxypregna-1,4-diene-3,20-dione
Prednisone	17α, 21-Dihydroxypregna-1,4-diene-3,11,20-trione
Pregnenolone	3β-Hydroxypregn-5-en-20-one
Progesterone	Pregn-4-ene-3,20-dione
Testololactone	13α-Hydroxy-3-oxo-13,17-secoandrost-4-en-17-oic lactone
Testosterone	17β-Hydroxyandrost-4-en-3-one

Structures of typical steroid hormones

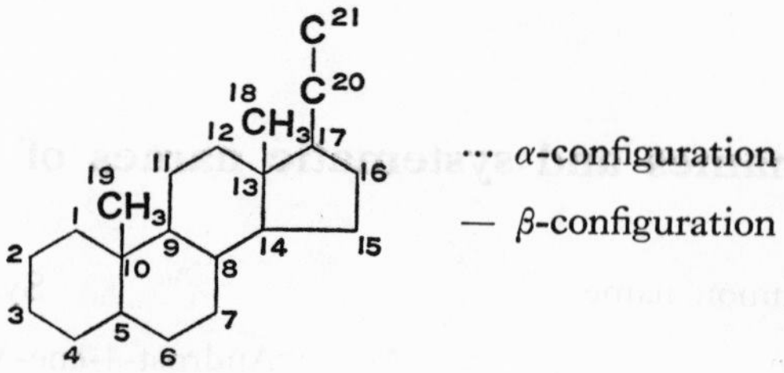

$\cdots$ α-configuration

— β-configuration

Basic skeleton of steroids

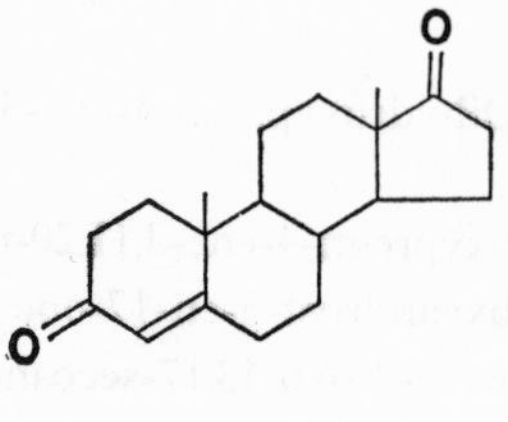

Androstenedione

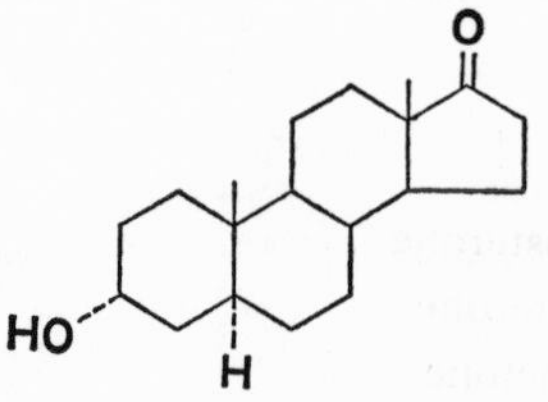

Androsterone

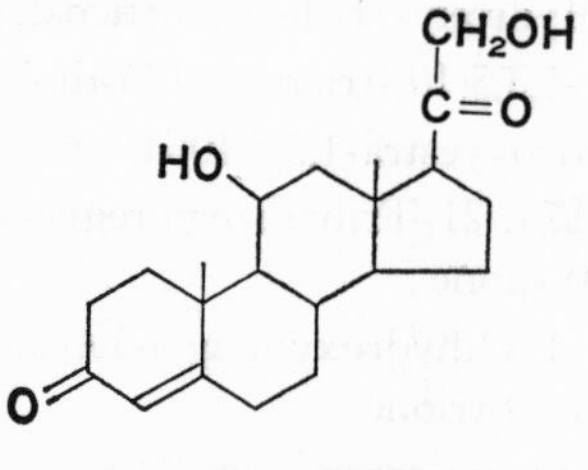

Corticosterone

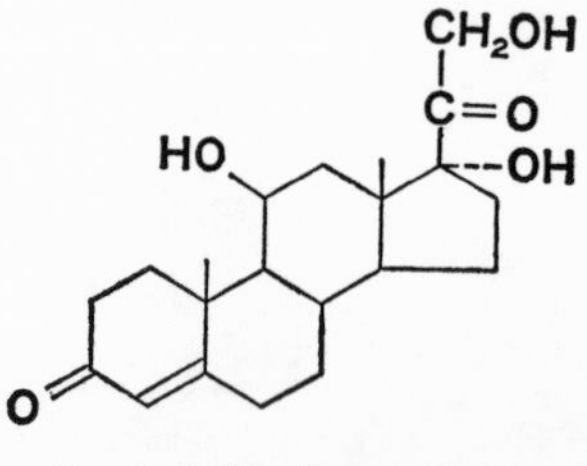

Cortisol (Hydrocortisone)

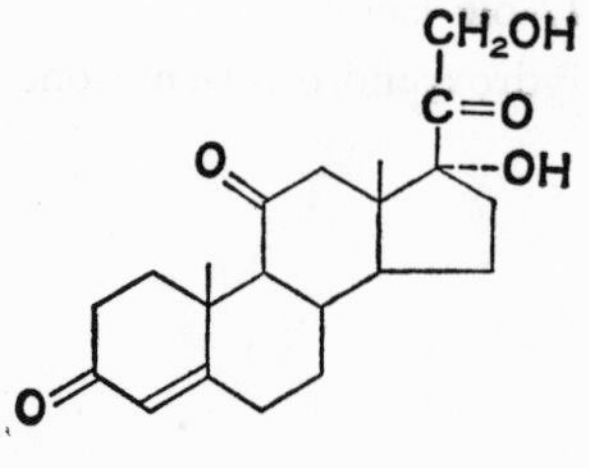

Cortisone

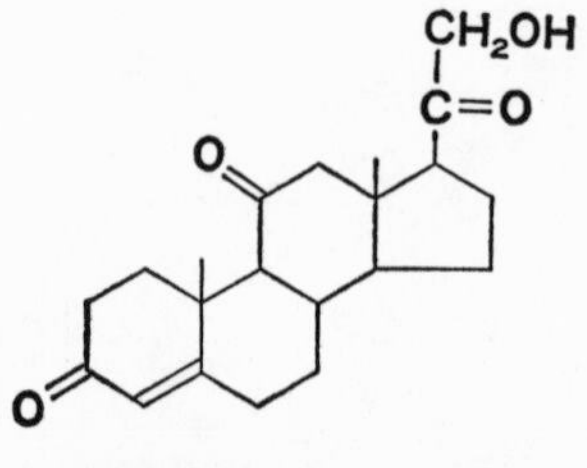

11-Dehydrocorticosterone

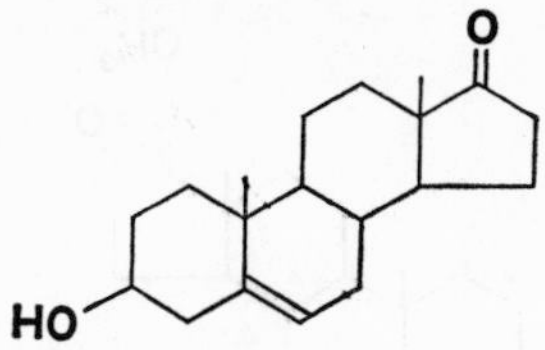

Dehydroepiandrosterone

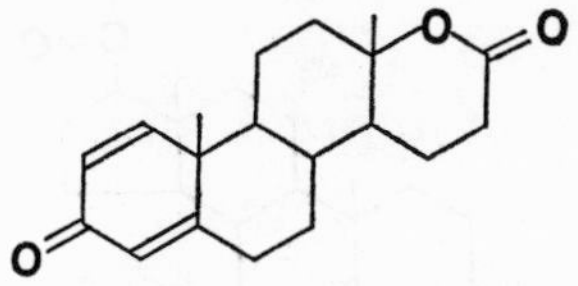

1-Dehydrotestololactone

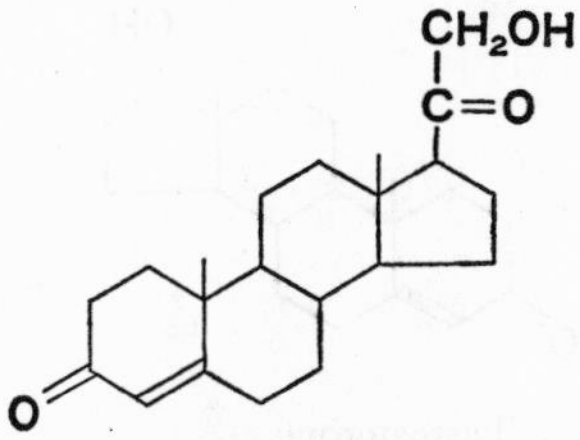

11-Deoxycorticosterone

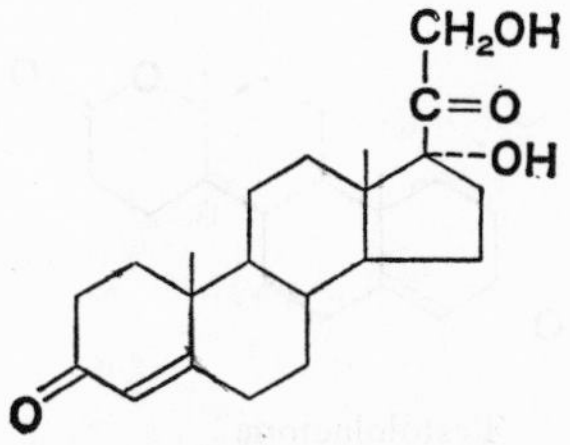

11-Deoxycortisol

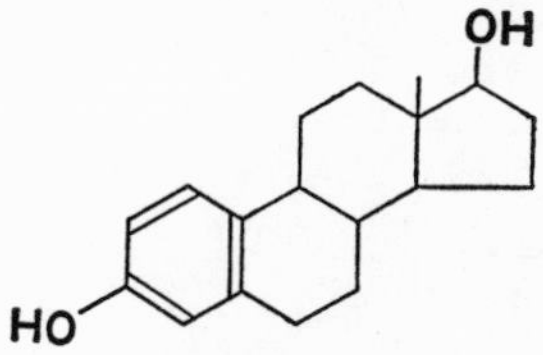

Estradiol

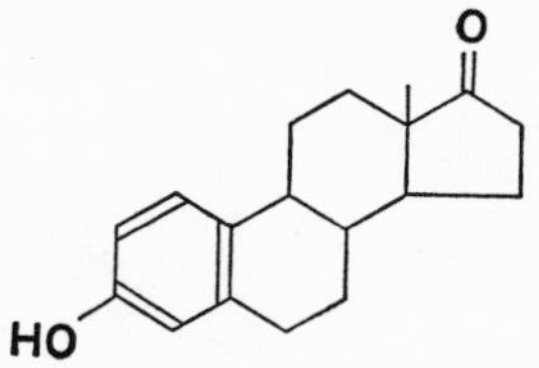

Estrone

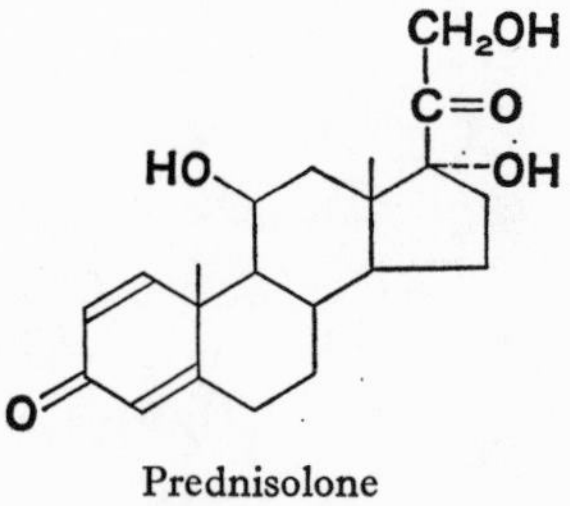

Prednisolone

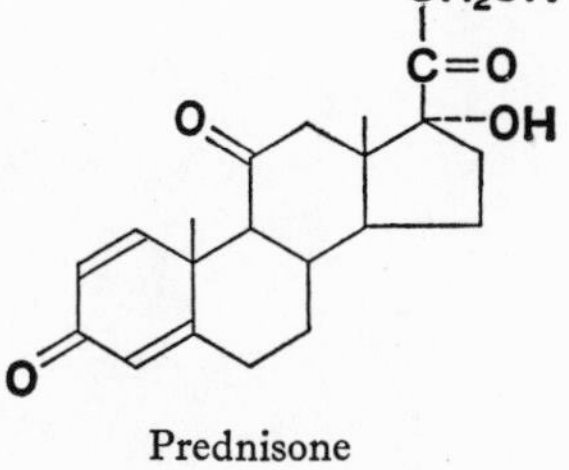

Prednisone

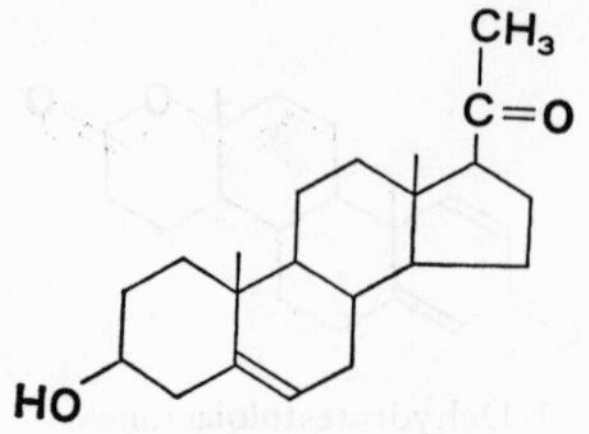

Pregnenolone

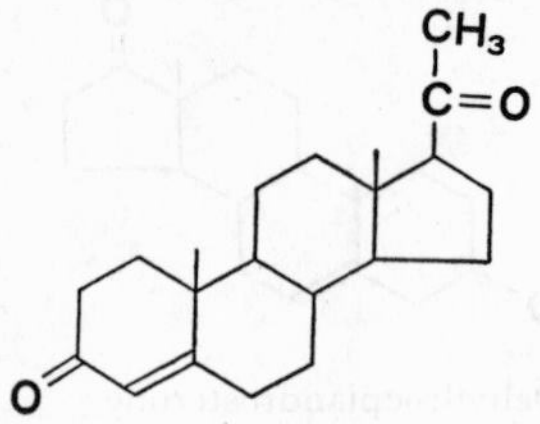

Progesterone

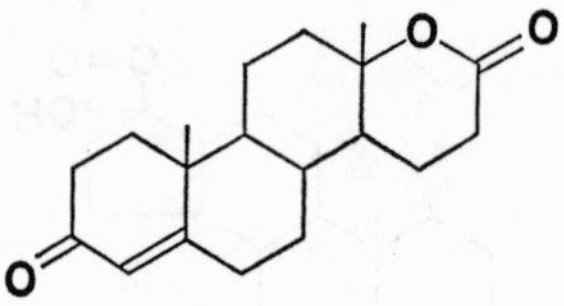

Testololactone

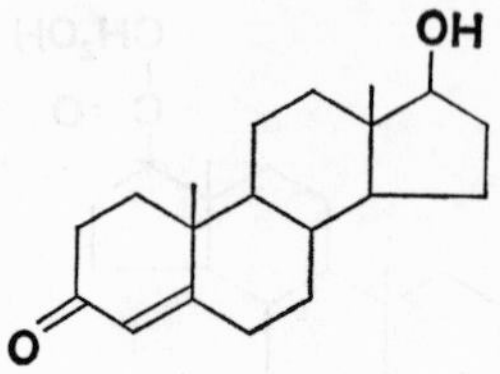

Testosterone

A. HYDROXYLATION

(a) 1-Hydroxylation

19-Nortestosterone 17-acetate

1 or 2-Hydroxy-19-nortestosterone
17-acetate

Corynebacterium simplex ATCC 6946
(25%)

Kushinsky, S., J. Biol. Chem., **230**, 31 (1958)

9α-Fluoro-17α-methyl-11β, 17β-
dihydroxyandrost-4-en-3-one

9α-Fluoro-17α-methyl-1α, 2α, 17β-
trihydroxyandrost-4-ene-3, 11-dione

Nocardia corallina ATCC 999 (18%)

Sax, K. J., C. E. Holmlund, L. I. Feldman, R. H.
Evans, Jr., R. H. Blank, A. J. Shay, J. S. Schultz
and M. Dann, Steroids, **5**, 345 (1965)

17α-Ethinyltestosterone

17α-Ethinyl-1α, 2α, 17β-
trihydroxyandrost-4-ene-3-one

Nocardia corallina ATCC 999 (21%)

Sax, K. J., C. E. Holmlund, L. I. Feldman, R. H.
Evans, Jr., R. H. Blank, A. J. Shay, J. S. Schultz
and M. Dann, Steroids, **5**, 345 (1965)

— 7 —

Androst-4-ene-3, 17-dione

1α-Hydroxyandrost-4-ene-3, 17-dione

Penicillium sp.

Dodson, R. M., A. H. Goldkamp and R. D. Muir, J. Am. Chem. Soc., **79**, 3921 (1957)

Penicillium sp. ATCC 12556

Dodson, R. M., A. H. Goldkamp and R. D. Muir, J. Am. Chem. Soc., **82**, 4026 (1960)

Androst-4-ene-3, 17-dione

1α-Hydroxy-5α-androstane-3, 17-dione

Penicillium sp. ATCC 12556

Dodson, R. M., A. H. Goldkamp and R. D. Muir, J. Am. Chem. Soc., **82**, 4026 (1960)

Androst-4-ene-3, 17-dione

1α, 3β-Dihydroxy-5α-androstan-17-one

Penicillium sp. ATCC 12556

Dodson, R. M., A. H. Goldkamp and R. D. Muir, J. Am. Chem. Soc., **82**, 4026 (1960)

Dehydroepiandrosterone

1α, 3β-Dihydroxyandrost-5-en-17-one

Penicillium sp.

Dodson, R. M., A. H. Goldkamp and R. D. Muir, J. Am. Chem. Soc., **79**, 3921 (1957)

Penicillium sp. ATCC 12556

Dodson, R. M., A. H. Goldkamp and R. D. Muir, J. Am. Chem. Soc., **82**, 4026 (1960)

Dehydroepiandrosterone

1α-Hydroxyandrost-4-ene-3, 17-dione

Penicillium sp.

Dodson, R. M., A. H. Goldkamp and R. D. Muir, J. Am. Chem. Soc., **79**, 3921 (1957)

Penicillium sp. ATCC 12556

Dodson, R. M., A. H. Goldkamp and R. D. Muir, J. Am. Chem. Soc., **82**, 4026 (1960)

5α-Androstane-3, 17-dione

1α-Hydroxy-5α-androstane-3, 17-dione

Penicillium sp. ATCC 12556

Dodson, R. M., A. H. Goldkamp and R. D. Muir, J. Am. Chem. Soc., **82**, 4026 (1960)

11β, 21-Dihydroxy-16α, 17α-
isopropylidenedioxypregn-4-
ene-3, 20-dione

1α, 2α, 11β, 21-Tetrahydroxy-16α,
17α-isopropylidenedioxypregn-
4-ene-3, 20-dione

Nocardia corallina ATCC 999

Sax, K. J., C. E. Holmlund, L. I. Feldman, R. H. Evans, Jr., R. H. Blank, A. J. Shay, J. S. Schultz and M. Dann, Steroids, **5**, 345 (1965)

11-Deoxycortisol

1ξ, 17α, 21-Trihydroxypregn-
4-ene-3, 20-dione

Rhizoctonia ferrugena CBS

Greenspan, G., C. P. Schaffner, W. Charney, H. L.
Herzog and E. B. Hershberg, J. Am. Chem.
Soc., **79**, 3922 (1957)

9α-Fluorocortisol

9α-Fluoro-1ξ, 11β, 17α, 21-
tetrahydroxypregn-
4-ene-3, 20-dione

Mortierella sp.

Streptomyces sp. Merck collection No. MA
320

U. S. Pat. 2,962,423

McAleer, W. J., M. A. Kozlowski, T. H. Stoudt
and J. M. Chemerda, J. Org. Chem., **23**, 508
(1958)

9α-Fluoro-16α-hydroxy-
cortisol

9α-Fluoro-1ξ, 11β, 16α, 17α, 21-
pentahydroxypregn-4-
ene-3, 20-dione

Mortierella sp.

U. S. Pat. 2,962,423

(b) 2-Hydroxylation

19-Nortestosterone 17-acetate

1 or 2-Hydroxy-19-nor-
testosterone 17-acetate

Corynebacterium simplex ATCC 6946
(25%)

Kushinsky, S., J. Biol. Chem., **230**, 31 (1958)

9α-Fluoro-17α-methyl-11β, 17β-
dihydroxyandrost-4-en-3-one

9α-Fluoro-17α-methyl-1α, 2α, 17β-
trihydroxyandrost-4-ene-
3, 11-dione

Nocardia corallina ATCC 999 (18%)

Sax, K. J., C. E. Holmlund, L. I. Feldman, R. H.
Evans Jr., R. H. Blank, A. J. Shay, J. S. Schultz
and M. Dann, Steroids, 5, 345 (1965)

17α-Ethinyltestosterone

17α-Ethinyl-1α, 2α, 17β-
trihydroxyandrost-4-en-3-one

Nocardia corallina ATCC 999 (21%)

Sax, K. J., C. E. Holmlund, L. I. Feldman, R. H.
Evans, Jr., R. H. Blank, A. J. Shay, J. S. Schultz
and M. Dann, Steroids, 5, 345 (1965)

Androst-4-ene-3, 17-dione

Penicillium sp.

Penicillium sp. ATCC 12556

Streptomyces sp. DS-81-B

2β-Hydroxyandrost-4-ene-3, 17-dione

Dodson, R. M., A. H. Goldkamp and R. D. Muir, J. Am. Chem. Soc., **79**, 3921 (1957)

Dodson, R. M., A. H. Goldkamp and R. D. Muir, J. Am. Chem. Soc., **82**, 4026 (1960)

Herzog, H. L., M. J. Gentles, E. B. Hershberg, F. Carvajal, D. Sutter, W. Charney and C. P. Schaffner, J. Am. Chem. Soc., **79**, 3921 (1957)

Progesterone

Sclerotinia libertiana

2β, 15β-Dihydroxyprogesterone

Tanabe, K., R. Takasaki, R. Hayashi and M. Shirasaka, Chem. Pharm. Bull. (Japan), **7**, 804 (1959)

17α-Hydroxyprogesterone

Sclerotinia libertiana

2β, 17α-Dihydroxyprogesterone

Tanabe, K., R. Takasaki, R. Hayashi and M. Shirasaka, Chem. Pharm. Bull. (Japan), **7**, 804 (1959)

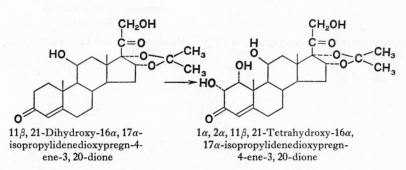

CH₂OH
C=O

11-Deoxycorticosterone

Sclerotinia libertiana

CH₂OH
C=O

HO

OH

2β, 15β, 21-Trihydroxypregn-
4-ene-3, 20-dione

Shirasaka, M., Chem. Pharm. Bull. (Japan), **9**, 54
(1961)

CH₂OAc
C=O

11-Deoxycorticosterone 21-
acetate

Sclerotinia sclerotiorum

CH₂OH
C=O

HO

OH

2β, 15β, 21-Trihydroxypregn-
4-ene-3, 20-dione

Japan Pat. 311,627

CH₂OH
C=O

HO

Corticosterone

Sclerotinia libertiana

CH₂OH
C=O

HO

HO

2β, 11β, 21-Trihydroxypregn-
4-ene-3, 20-dione

Shirasaka, M., Chem. Pharm. Bull. (Japan), **9**, 54
(1961)

CH₂OH
C=O

HO

O—C—CH₃
CH₃

11β, 21-Dihydroxy-16α, 17α-
isopropylidenedioxypregn-4-
ene-3, 20-dione

CH₂OH
C=O

H
O

OH

HO

O—C—CH₃
CH₃

1α, 2α, 11β, 21-Tetrahydroxy-16α,
17α-isopropylidenedioxypregn-
4-ene-3, 20-dione

— 13 —

Nocardia corallina ATCC 999

Sax, K. J., C. E. Holmlund, L. I. Feldman, R. H. Evans, Jr., R. H. Blank, A. J. Shay, J. S. Schultz and M. Dann, Steroids, **5**, 345 (1965)

11-Deoxycortisol	2β, 17α, 21-Trihydroxypregn-4-ene-3, 20-dione

Helminthosporium tritici-vulgaris H-25 (35%)

Kondo, E., J. Agr. Chem. Soc. (Japan), **34**, 762 (1960)

Rhizoctonia ferrugena CBS (3.2%)

Greenspan, G., C. P. Schaffner, W. Charney, H. L. Herzog and E. B. Hershberg, J. Am. Chem. Soc., **79**, 3922 (1957)

Rhizoctonia solani

U. S. Pat. 2,968,595

Sclerotinia libertiana

Tanabe, K., R. Takasaki, R. Hayashi and M. Shirasaka, Chem. Pharm. Bull. (Japan), **7**, 804 (1959)

Sclerotium oryzae

U. S. Pat. 2,968,595

Streptomyces sp. DS-81-B (5.7%)

Herzog, H.L., M. J. Gentles, E. B. Hershberg, F. Carvajal, D. Sutter, W. Charney and C. P. Schaffner, J. Am. Chem. Soc., **79**, 3921 (1957)

9α-Fluorocortisol	9α-Fluoro-2β, 11β, 16α, 17α, 21-pentahydroxypregn-4-ene-3, 20-dione

Streptomyces roseochromogenus ATCC 3347 (11%)

Goodman, J. J. and L. L. Smith, Appl. Microbiol., **9**, 372 (1961)

(c) 6-Hydroxylation

3β-Hydroxy-5α, 6α-oxido-
androstan-17-one

Nocardia restrictus No. 545

6α-Hydroxyandrost-4-ene-3, 17-dione

Lee, S. S. and C. J. Sih, Biochemistry, **3**, 1267 (1964)

11-Deoxycortisol

Curvularia lunata

6α, 14α, 17α, 21-Tetrahydroxypregn-
4-ene-3, 20-dione

Japan pat. 311,865

Estradiol 3-methylether

Fusarium moniliforme

Fusarium moniliforme ATCC 9851 (10%)
Fusarium moniliforme IH 4 (30%)

6β-Hydroxyestradiol 3-metylether

Crabbé, P. and C. Casas-Campillo, J. Org. Chem., **29**, 2731 (1964)

Casas-Campillo, C. and M. Bautista, Appl. Micro-biol., **13**, 977 (1965)

19-Nortestosterone

6β-Hydroxy-19-nortestosterone

Rhizopus nigricans ATCC 6227b (18.3%)

Rhizopus reflexus

Pederson, R. L., J. A. Campbell, J. C. Babcock, S. H. Eppstein, H. C. Murray, A. Weintraub, R. C. Meeks, P. D. Meister, L. M. Reineke and D. H. Peterson, J. Am. Chem. Soc., **78**, 1512 (1956)

U. S. Pat. 2,683,725

Testosterone

6β-Hydroxytestosterone

Fusarium roseum

Rhizopus nigricans

Rhizopus reflexus ATCC 1225

Rao, P. G., Indian J. Pharm., **25**, 131 (1963)

Tamm, Ch., Angew. Chem., **74**, 225 (1962)

Eppstein, S. H., P. D. Meister, H. M. Leigh, D. H. Peterson, H. C. Murray, L. M. Reineke and A. Weintraub, J. Am. Chem. Soc., **76**, 3174 (1954)

17α-Methyltestosterone

17α-Methyl-6β-hydroxytestosterone

Gibberella saubinetti (90%)

Rhizopus nigricans ATCC 6227b (4%)

Urech, J., E. Vischer and A. Wettstein, Helv. Chim. Acta, **43**, 1077 (1960)

Eppstein, S. H., P. D. Meister, H. M. Leigh, D. H. Peterson, H. C. Murray, L. M. Reineke and A. Weintraub, J. Am. Chem. Soc., **76**, 3174 (1954)

Androst-4-ene-3, 17-dione

6β-Hydroxyandrost-4-ene-3, 17-dione

Aspergillus niger

Fried, J., R. W. Thoma, D. Perlman, J. E. Herz and A. Borman, Recent Progr. Hormone Res., **11**, 149 (1955)

Rhizopus arrhizus ATCC 11145

Eppstein, S. H., P. D. Meister, H. M. Leigh, D. H. Peterson, H. C, Murray, L. M. Reineke and A. Weintraub, J. Am. Chem. Soc., **76**, 3174 (1954)

Gibberella saubinetti (13%)

Urech, J., E. Vischer and A. Wettstein, Helv. Chim. Acta, **43**, 1077 (1960)

Dehydroepiandrosterone

6β-Hydroxyandrost-4-ene-3, 17-dione

Bacillus pulvifaciens IAM N-19-2

Iizuka, H., A. Naito, and Y. Sato, J. Gen. Appl. Microbiol. (Japan), 7, 118 (1961)

A-Norprogesterone

6β-Hydroxy-A-norprogesterone

Aspergillus nidulans

Japan Pat. 408,385

Progesterone

6β-Hydroxyprogesterone

Actinomyces sp.

Vondrová, O. and A. Capek, Folia Microbiol., **8**, 117 (1963)

Streptomyces aureofaciens

Fried, J., R. W. Thoma, D. Perlman, J. E. Herz and A. Borman, Recent Progr. Hormone Res., **11**, 149 (1955)

11β, 21-Dihydroxy-cis-pregna-4, 17(20)-dien-3-one

6β, 21-Dihydroxy-cis-pregna-4, 17 (20)-diene-3,11-dione

Rhizopus arrhizus

Hanze, A. R., O. K. Sebek and H. C. Murray, J. Org. Chem., **25**, 1968 (1960)

Progesterone

6β, 11α-Dihydroxyprogesterone

Aspergillus niger (45%)

Dulaney, E. L., W. J. McAleer, M. Koslowski, E. O. Stapley and J. Jaglom, Appl. Microbiol., **3**, 336 (1955)

Aspergillus niger strain Wisc. 72-2 (20%)

Fried, J., R. W. Thoma, J. R. Gerke, J. E. Herz, M. N. Donin and D. Perlman, J. Am. Chem. Soc., **74**, 3962 (1952)

Aspergillus ochraceus

Dulaney, E. L., Mycologia, **47**, 464 (1955)

— 18 —

Aspergillus ochraceus, conidia

Schleg, M. C. and S. G. Knight, Mycologia, **54**, 317 (1962)

Aspergillus saitoi IAM R-1216

Iizuka, H., A. Naito and M. Hattori, J. Gen. Appl. Microbiol. (Japan), **4**, 67 (1958)

Aspergillus terreus (41%)

Dulaney, E. L., W. J. McAleer, M. Koslowski, E. O. Stapley and J. Jaglom, Appl. Microbiol., **3**, 336 (1955)

Boletus luteus H-11

Dermoloma sp. F-27

Schuytema, E. C., M. P. Hargie, D. J. Siehr, I. Merits, J. R. Schenck, M. S. Smith and E. L. Varner, Appl. Microbiol., **11**, 256 (1963)

Gloeosporium kaki

Shirasaka, M. and M. Tsuruta, Chem. Pharm. Bull. (Japan), **9**, 159 (1961)

Hygrophorus conicus C-219

Leucopaxillus paradoxus F-55

Schuytema, E. C., M. P. Hargie, D. J. Siehr, I. Merits, J. R. Schenck, M. S, Smith and E. L. Varner, Appl. Microbiol., **11**, 256 (1963)

Rhizopus arrhizus ATCC 11145 (5~15%)

Peterson, D. H., H. C. Murray, S. H. Eppstein, L. M. Reineke, A. Weintraub, P. D. Meister and H. M. Leigh, J. Am. Chem. Soc., **74**, 5933 (1952)

Rhizopus cambodjae (30%)

Camerino, B., C. G. Alberti, A. Vercellone and F. Ammannati, Gazz. Chim. Ital., **84**, 301, (1954)

Rhizopus nigricans ATCC 6227b (2%)

Peterson, D. H., H. C. Murray, S. H. Eppstein, L. M. Reineke, A. Weintraub, P. D. Meister and H. M. Leigh, J. Am. Chem. Soc., **74**, 5933 (1952)

Sclerotium hydrophilum

Shirasaka, M. and M. Tsuruta, Chem. Pharm. Bull. (Japan), **9**, 196 (1961)

Streptomyces fradiae

Vondrová, O. et al., Folia Microbiol., **8**, 176 (1963)

Streptomyces sp.

Shirasaka, M. and M. Tsuruta, J. Ferm. Assoc. (Japan), **19**, 389 (1961)

Progesterone   6β, 14α-Dihydroxyprogesterone

Achromobacter kashiwazakiensis IAM K-40-5

Tsuda, K., H. Iizuka, E. Ohki, Y. Sato, A. Naito and M. Hattori, J. Gen. Appl. Microbiol. (Japan), **5**, 7 (1959)

Bacillus cereus

Shirasaka, M., M. Ozaki and S. Sugawara, J. Gen. Appl. Microbiol. (Japan), **7**, 341 (1961)

Mucor corymbifer

Camerino, B., C. G. Alberti and A. Vercellone, Gazz. Chim. Ital., **83**, 684 (1953)

Progesterone

6β, 15α-Dihydroxyprogesterone

Fusarium lini

Gubler, A. and Ch. Tamm, Helv. Chim. Acta, **41**, 301 (1958)

Fusarium roseum

Rao, P. G., Indian J. Pharm., **25**, 131 (1963)

Gibberella saubinetti

Japan Pat. 313,770

Progesterone

6β, 17α-Dihydroxyprogesterone

Naucoria confragosa C-172

Schuytema, E. C., M. P. Hargie, D. J. Siehr, I. Merits, J. R. Schenck, M. S. Smith and E. L. Varner, Appl. Microbiol., **11**, 256 (1963)

Progesterone

6β-Hydroxyandrost-4-ene-3, 17-dione

Gliocladium catenulatum ATCC 10523

Peterson, D. H., S. H. Eppstein, P. D. Meister, H. C. Murray, H. M. Leigh, A. Weintraub and L. M. Reineke, J. Am. Chem. Soc., **75**, 5768 (1953)

16α-Hydroxyprogesterone

Aspergillus nidulans

6β, 16α-Dihydroxyprogesterone

Fried, J., R. W. Thoma, D. Perlman, J. E. Herz and A. Borman, Recent Progr. Hormone Res., 11, 149 (1955)

17α-Hydroxyprogesterone

Botrytis cinerea

Fusarium lycopersici
Gibberella saubinetti

Rhizopus arrhizus ATCC 11145 (45%)
Rhizopus nigricans ATCC 6227b (2%)

Sclerotium hydrophilum

6β, 17α-Dihydroxyprogesterone

Shirasaka, M., Chem. Pharm. Bull. (Japan), 9, 152 (1961)

Shirasaka, M. and M. Tsuruta, Chem. Pharm. Bull. (Japan), 9, 238 (1961)

Meister, P. D., D. H. Peterson, H. C. Murray, G. B. Spero, S. H. Eppstein, A. Weintraub, L. M. Reineke and H. M. Leigh, J. Am. Chem. Soc., 75, 416 (1953)

Shirasaka, M. and M. Tsuruta, Chem. Pharm. Bull. (Japan), 9, 196 (1961)

17α-Hydroxypregna-1, 4-diene-
3, 20-dione

6β, 17α-Dihydroxypregna-
1, 4-diene-3, 20-dione

Chaetomium funicola

Ger. Pat. 1,095,278

11-Deoxycorticosterone

6β, 21-Dihydroxypregn-
4-ene-3, 20-dione

Bacillus cereus

Shirasaka, M., M. Ozaki and S. Sugawara, J. Gen. Appl. Microbiol. (Japan), **7**, 341 (1961)

Botrytis cinerea

Shirasaka, M., Chem. Pharm. Bull. (Japan), **9**, 152 (1961)

Lenzites abietina (4.8%)

Meystre, Ch., E. Vischer and A. Wettstein, Helv. Chim. Acta, **38**, 381 (1955)

Rhizopus arrhizus ATCC 11145 (0.7%)

Eppstein, S. H., P. D. Meister, D. H. Peterson, H. C. Murray, H. M. Leigh, D. A. Lyttle, L. M. Reineke and A. Weintraub, J. Am. Chem. Soc., **75**, 408 (1953)

Sclerotinia sclerotiorum

Japan Pat. 311,629

Streptomyces fradiae

U. S. Pat. 2,649,401

Streptomyces sp.

Shirasaka, M. and M. Tsuruta, J. Ferm. Assoc. (Japan), **19**, 389 (1961)

Trichothecium roseum

Meystre, Ch., E. Vischer and A. Wettstein, Helv. Chim. Acta, **37**, 1548 (1954)

CH$_2$OH
C=O

11-Deoxycorticosterone

Sclerotium hydrophilum

Sclerotinia sclerotiorum

CH$_2$OH
C=O
HO

OH

6β, 11α, 21-Trihydroxypregn-
4-ene-3, 20-dione

Shirasaka, M. and M. Tsuruta, Chem. Pharm. Bull.
(Japan), **9** 196 (1961)

Japan Pat. 311,629

CH$_2$OH
C=O

11-Deoxycorticosterone

Cephalothecium roseum   ATCC 8685

CH$_2$OH
C=O
OH

OH

6β, 17α, 21-Trihydroxypregn-
4-ene-3, 20-dione

Meister, P. D., L. M. Reineke, R. C. Meeks, H. C.
Murray, S. H. Eppstein, H. M. Leigh, A. Weintraub and D. H. Peterson, J. Am. Chem. Soc.,
76, 4050 (1954)

CH$_2$OH
C=O
HO

Corticosterone

Sclerotium hydrophilum

CH$_2$OH
C=O
O

OH

6β, 21-Dihydroxypregn-
4-ene-3, 11, 20-trione

Shirasaka, M. and M. Tsuruta, Chem. Pharm. Bull.
(Japan), **9**, 196 (1961)

11-Deoxycortisol → 6β, 17α, 21-Trihydroxypregn-4-ene-3, 20-dione

Achromobacter kashiwazakiensis IAM K-40-5	Tsuda, K., H. Iizuka, E. Ohki, Y. Sato, A. Naito and M. Hattori, J. Gen. Appl. Microbiol. (Japan), **5**, 7 (1959)
Bacillus cereus IAM B-204-1	Sugawara, S., M. Tsuruta, M. Shirasaka and M. Nakamura, Arch. Biochem. Biophys, **80**, 383 (1959)
Botrytis cinerea	Shirasaka, M., Chem. Pharm. Bull. (Japan), **9**, 152 (1961)
Fusarium lycopersici	Shirasaka, M. and M. Tsuruta, Chem. Pharm Bull. (Japan), **9**, 238 (1961)
Fusarium roseum	Rao P. G., Indian J. Pharm, **25**, 131 (1963)
Gibberella saubinetti	Shirasaka, M. and M. Tsuruta, Chem. Pharm. Bull. (Japan), **9**, 238 (1961)
Gibberella saubinetti (26%)	Urech J., E. Vischer and A. Wettstein, Helv. Chim. Acta, **43**, 1077 (1960)
Helicostylum piriforme	U. S. Pat. 2,602,769
Helminthosporium leersii	Kòndo E., J. Agr. Chem. Soc. (Japan), **34**, 762 (1960)
Rhizopus arrhizus ATCC 11145 (20%)	Peterson, D. H., S. H. Eppstein, P. D. Meister, B. J. Magerlein, H. C. Murray, H. M. Leigh, A. Weintraub and L. M. Reineke, J. Am. Chem. Soc., **75**, 412 (1953)
Rhizopus nigricans ATCC 6227b	
Sclerotinia sclerotiorum	Japan Pat. 311,629
Sclerotium hydrophilum	Shirasaka, M. and M. Tsuruta, Chem. Pharm. Bull. (Japan), **9**, 196 (1961)
Streptomyces sp.	Shirasaka, M. and M. Tsuruta, J. Ferm. Assoc. (Japan), **19**, 389 (1961)

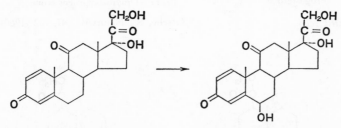

1-Dehydro-11-deoxycortisol

Chaetomium funicola

6β, 17α, 21-Trihydroxypregna-
1, 4-diene-3, 20-dione

Ger. Pat. 1,095,278

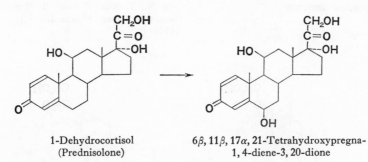

1-Dehydrocortisone (Prednisone)

Chaetomium funicola

6β, 17α, 21-Trihydroxypregna-
1, 4-diene-3, 11, 20-trione

Ger. Pat. 1,095,278

1-Dehydrocortisol
(Prednisolone)

Chaetomium funicola

6β, 11β, 17α, 21-Tetrahydroxypregna-
1, 4-diene-3, 20-dione

Ger. Pat. 1,095,278

(d) 7-Hydroxylation

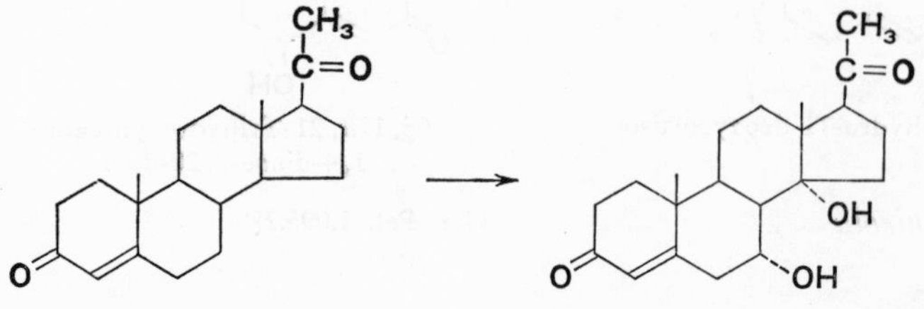

CH₃
C=O

Progesterone

Curvularia lunata

7α, 14α-Dihydroxyprogesterone

Zetsche, K., Naturwiss., **47**, 232 (1960)

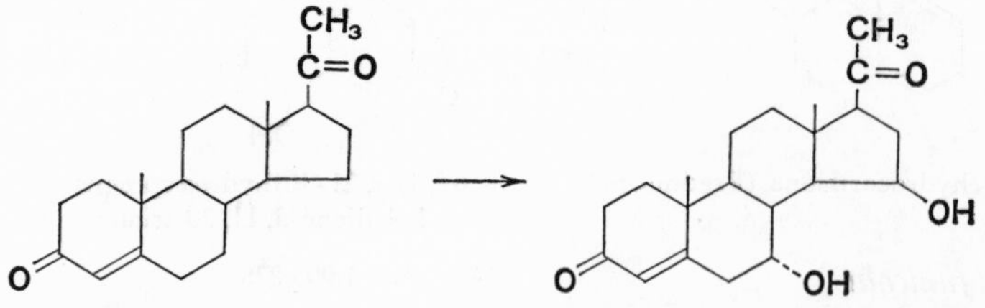

Progesterone

Helminthosporium sativum

7α, 15β-Dihydroxyprogesterone

Tsuda, K., T. Asai, Y. Sato, T. Tanaka and H. Hasegawa, Chem. Pharm. Bull. (Japan), **9**, 735 (1961)

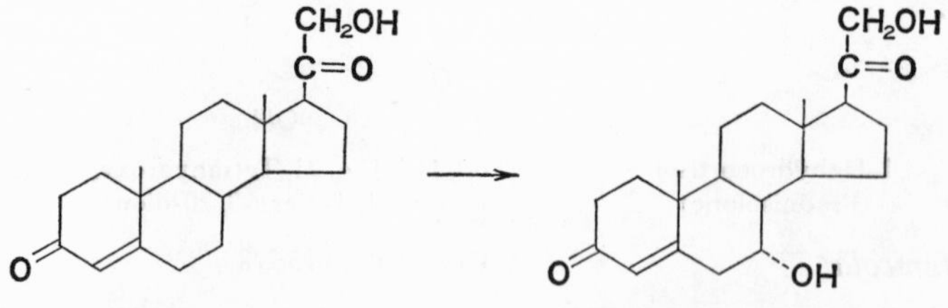

11-Deoxycorticosterone

Curvularia fallax (50~60%)
Curvularia pallescens (50~60%)
Peziza sp. ETH M-23 (50~60%)

7α, 21-Dihydroxypregn-4-ene-3, 20-dione

Meystre, Ch., E. Vischer and A. Wettstein, Helv. Chim. Acta, **38**, 381 (1955)

11-Deoxycortisol → 7α, 17α, 21-Trihydroxypregn-4-ene-3, 20-dione

Cephalosporium sp.   U. S. Pat. 2,962,512

Diplodia natalensis   U. S. Pat. 2,960,436

11-Deoxycortisol → 7α, 14α, 17α, 21-Tetrahydroxypregn-4-ene-3, 20-dione

Curvularia lunata   Shull G. M., Trans. N. Y. Acad. Sci., **19**, 147 (1956)

11-Deoxycortisol → 7α, 17α, 21-Trihydroxypregna-1, 4-diene-3, 20-dione

Diplodia natalensis   U. S. Pat. 2,960,436

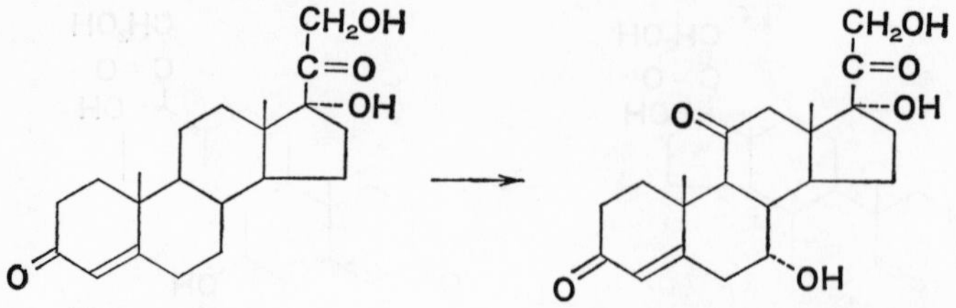

11-Deoxycortisol

7α, 17α, 21-Trihydroxypregn-
4-ene-3, 11, 20-trione

Diplodia natalensis

U. S. Pat. 2,960,436

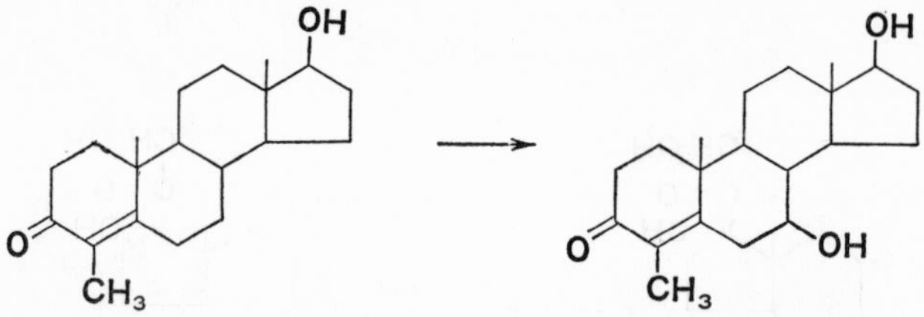

4-Methyltestosterone

4-Methyl-7β-hydroxytestosterone

Rhizopus nigricans

Tamm Ch., Angew. Chem., **74**, 225 (1962)

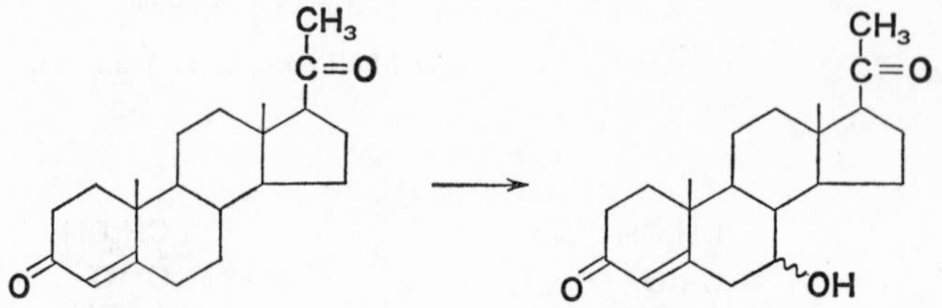

Progesterone

7ξ-Hydroxyprogesterone

Phycomyces blakesleeanus

Fried, J., R. W. Thoma, D. Perlman, J. E. Herz
and A. Borman, Recent Progr. Hormone Res.,
11, 149 (1955)

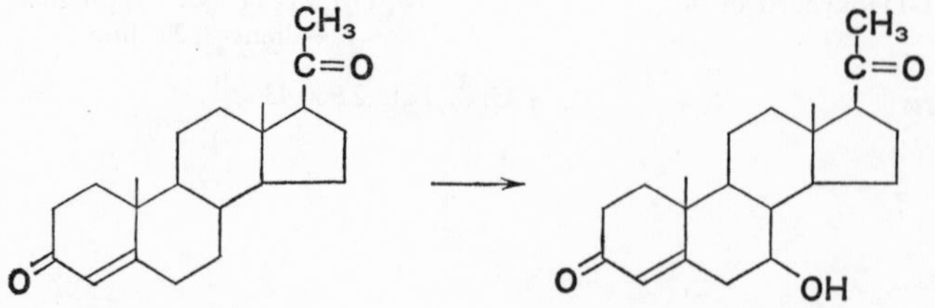

Progesterone

7β-Hydroxyprogesterone

Diplodia tubericola

Tsuda, K., T. Asai, Y. Sato, T. Tanaka and M.
Kato, J. Gen. Appl. Microbiol. (Japan), **5**, 1
(1959)

Progesterone   7ξ, 11α-Dihydroxyprogesterone

Absidia sp. (80%)

Rhizopus arrhizus (38%)

Ger. (East) Pat. 19,651

U. S. Pat. 2,602,769

Progesterone   7β, 15β-Dihydroxyprogesterone

Helminthosporium sativum

Tsuda, K., T. Asai, Y. Sato, T. Tanaka and H. Hasegawa, Chem. Pharm. Bull. (Japan), **9**, 735 (1961)

Diplodia tubericola

Syncephalastrum racemosum

Tsuda, K., T. Asai, Y. Sato, T. Tanaka, T. Matsuhisa and H. Hasegawa, Chem. Pharm. Bull. (Japan), **8**, 626 (1960)

Progesterone

7β, 14α, 15β-Trihydroxypregn-4-ene-3, 20-dione

Syncephalastrum racemosum

Tsuda, K., T. Asai, Y. Sato, T. Tanaka, T. Matsuhisa and H. Hasegawa, Chem. Pharm. Bull. (Japan), **8**, 626 (1960)

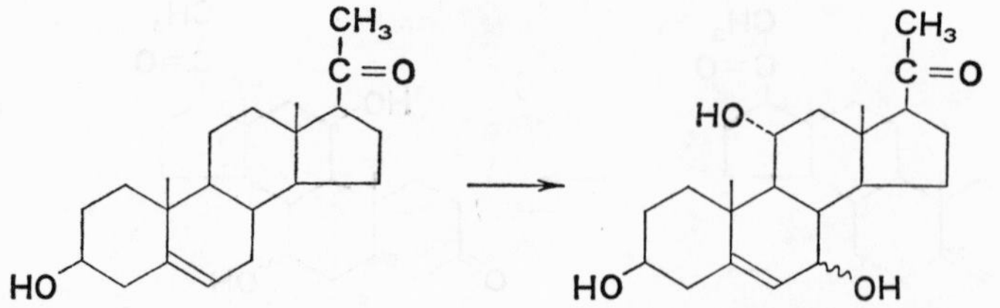

Pregnenolone

3β, 7ξ, 11α-Trihydroxypregn-
5-en-20-one

Rhizopus arrhizus (17%)

Can. Pat. 506,689

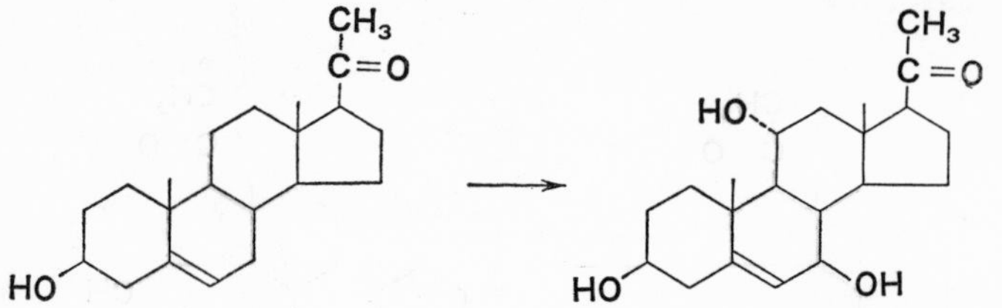

Pregnenolone

3β, 7β, 11α-Trihydroxypregn-
5-en-20-one

Rhizopus arrhizus

Eppstein, S. H., P. D. Meister, H. C. Murray and
D. H. Peterson, Vitamines and Hormones, **14**,
359 (1956)

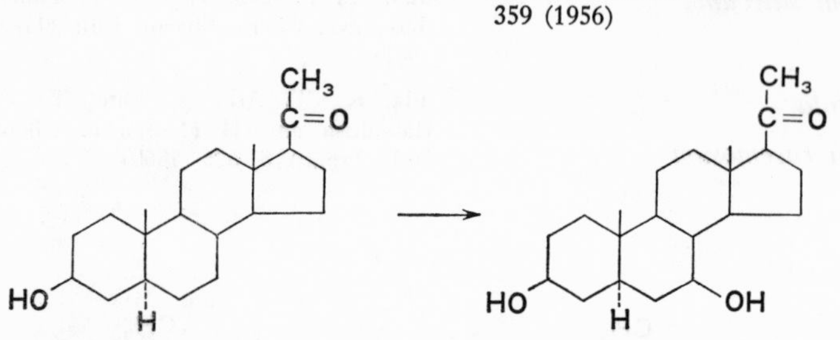

3β-Hydroxy-5α-pregnan-20-one

3β, 7β-Dihydroxy-5α-pregnan-20-one

Rhizopus arrhizus (5.2%)

U. S. Pat 2,602,769

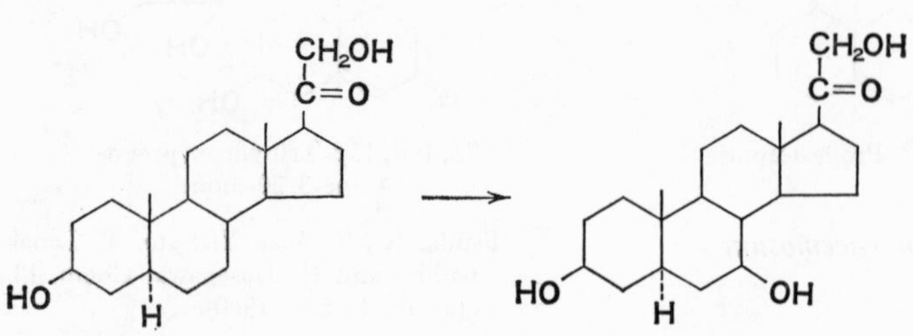

3β, 21-Dihydroxy-5α-pregnan-20-one

3β, 7β, 21-Trihydroxy-5α-pregnan-20-one

Rhizopus sp.

Kahnt, F. W., Ch. Meystre, R. Neher, E. Vischer
and A. Wettstein, Experientia, **8**, 422 (1952)

(e) 8-Hydroxylation

Progesterone → 8 (or 9)-Hydroxyprogesterone

Streptomyces aureofaciens

Fried, J., R. W. Thoma, D. Perlman, J. E. Herz and A. Borman, Recent Progr. Hormone Res., **11**, 149 (1955)

11-Deoxycorticosterone → 8β, 21-Dihydroxypregn-4-ene-3, 20-dione

Curvularia pallescens

Vischer, E., Ch. Meystre and A. Wettstein, Experientia, **11**, 465 (1955)

Helicostylum piriforme

Eppstein S. H., P. D. Meister, H. C. Murray and D. H. Peterson, Vitamines and Hormones, **14**, 359 (1956)

Mucor parasiticus
Neurospora crassa No. 74-A

Stone, D., M. Hayano, R. I. Dorfman, O. Hechter, C. R. Robinson and C. Djerassi, J. Am. Chem. Soc., **77**, 3926 (1955)

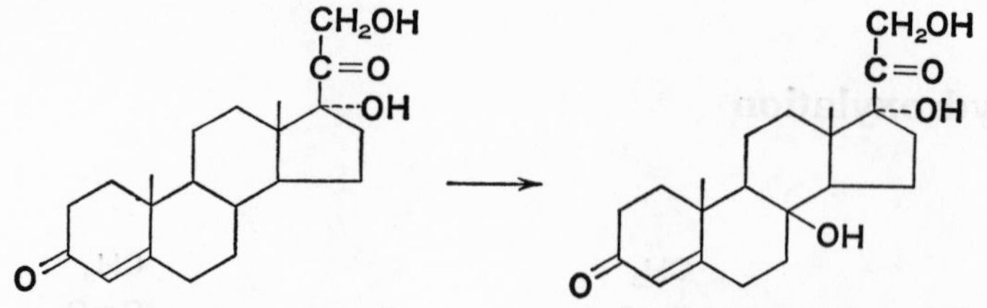

11-Deoxycortisol

8β, 17α, 21-Trihydroxypregn-
4-ene-3, 20-dione

Helicostylum piriforme

Eppstein, S. H., P. D. Meister, H. C. Murray and
D. H. Peterson, Vitamines and Hormones, **14**,
359 (1956)

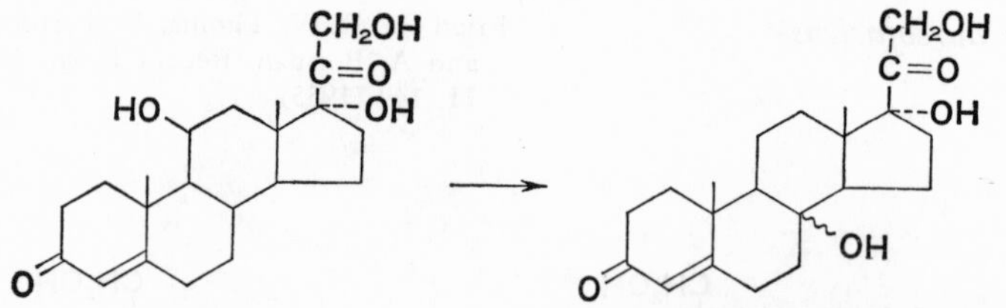

Cortisol

8ξ, 17α, 21-Trihydroxypregn-
4-ene-3, 20-dione

Helicostylum piriforme (8%)

U. S. Pat. 2,602,769

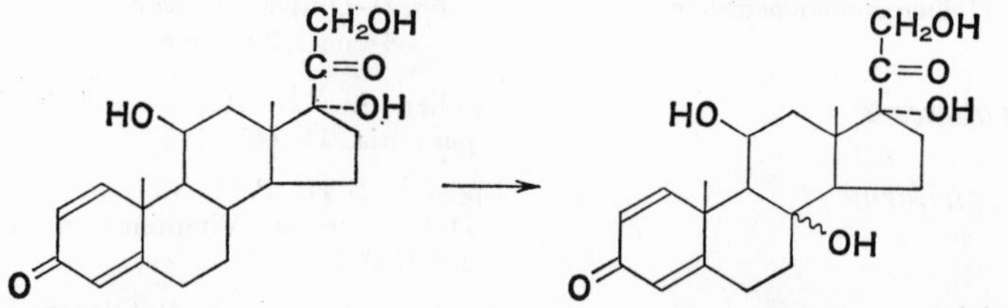

1-Dehydrocortisol
(Prednisolone)

8ξ, 11β, 17α, 21-Tetrahydroxypregna-
1, 4-diene-3, 20-dione

Helicostylum piriforme

Brit. Pat. 835,700

(f) 9-Hydroxylation

Androst-4-ene-3, 17-dione

9α-Hydroxyandrost-4-ene-3, 17-dione

Nocardia corallina

Nocardia restrictus

Brit. Pat. 862,701

Sih, C. J., Biochem. Biophys. Res. Comm., **7**, 87 (1962)

Androst-4-ene-3, 17-dione

9α, 12α-Dihydroxyandrost-4-ene-3, 17-dione

Cercospora melonis [*Corynespora melonis*]

Kondo, E. and K. Tori, J. Am. Chem. Soc., **86**, 736 (1964)

Androst-4-ene-3, 17-dione

9α, 14α-Dihydroxyandrost-4-ene-3, 17-dione

Cercospora melonis

Kondo, E. and K. Tori, J. Am. Chem. Soc., **86**. 736 (1964)

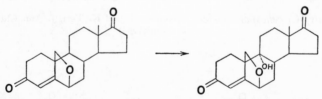

Androst-4-ene-3, 17-dione

9α, 15β-Dihydroxyandrost-
4-ene-3, 17-dione

Cercospora melonis

Kondo, E. and K. Tori, J. Am. Chem. Soc., **86**,
736 (1964)

Androst-4-ene-3, 17-dione

9α, 18-Dihydroxyandrost-
4-ene-3, 17-dione

Cercospora melonis

Kondo, E. and K. Tori, J. Am. Chem. Soc., **86**,
736 (1964)

6β, 19-Oxido-androst-4-ene-3, 17-dione

9α-Hydroxy-6β, 19-oxido-androst-
4-ene-3, 17-dione

Nocardia restrictus ATCC 14887

Sih, C. J., S. S. Lee, Y. Y. Tsong and K. C. Wang,
J. Am. Chem. Soc., **87**, 1385 (1965)

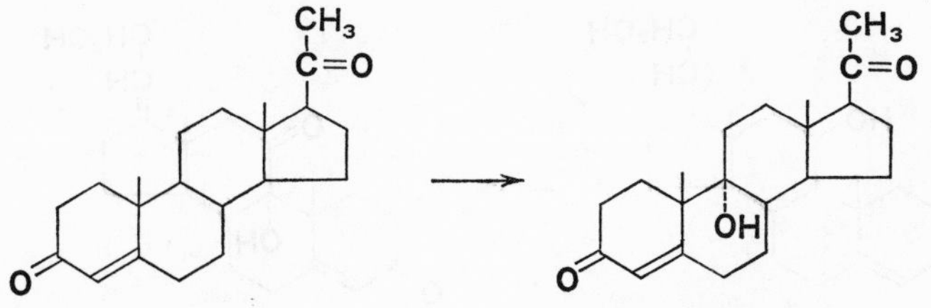

Progesterone

9α-Hydroxyprogesterone

Nocardia corallina
Nocardia restrictus

Brit. Pat. 862,701

U. S. Pat. 3,080,298

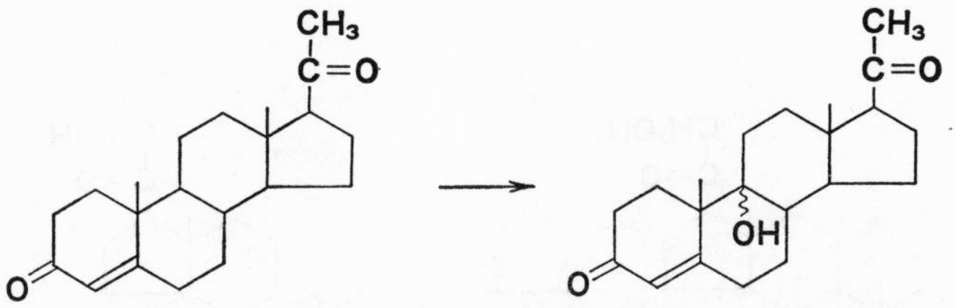

Progesterone

8 (or 9)-Hydroxyprogesterone

Streptomyces aureofaciens

Fried, J., R. W. Thoma, D. Perlman, J. E. Herz
and A. Borman, Recent Progr. Hormone Res.,
11, 149 (1955)

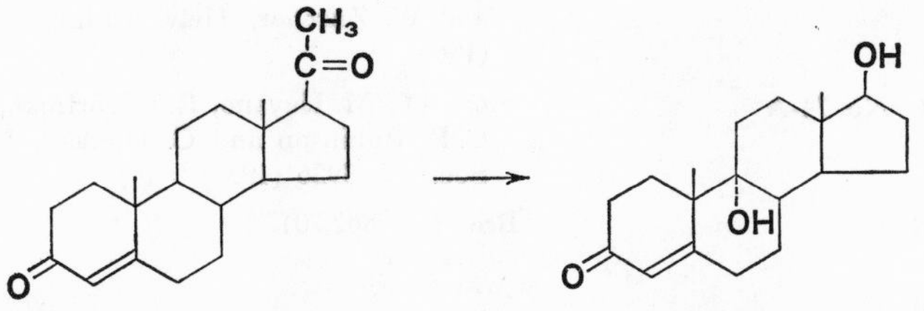

Progesterone

9α-Hydroxytestosterone

Nocardia corallina

Brit. Pat. 862,701

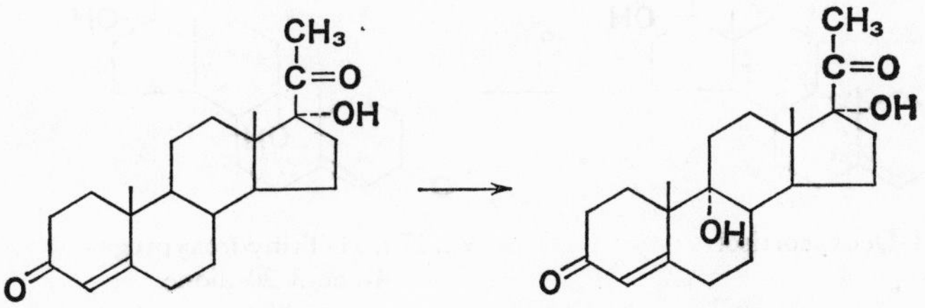

17α-Hydroxyprogesterone

9α, 17α-Dihydroxyprogesterone

Nocardia corallina

Brit. Pat. 862,701

CH₂OH $\quad\quad$ CH₂OH

11β, 21-Dihydroxy-cis-pregna-
4, 17(20)-dien-3-one

9α, 21-Dihydroxy-cis-pregna-
4, 17(20)-diene-3, 11-dione

Helicostylum piriforme

Cunninghamella blakesleeana

Hanze, A. R., O. K. Sebek and H. C. Murray, J.
Org. Chem., **25**, 1968 (1960)

11-Deoxycorticosterone

9α, 21-Dihydroxypregn-
4-ene-3, 20-dione

Mucor parasiticus

Tamm, Ch., A. Gubler, G. Juhasz, E. Weiss-Berg
and W. Zürcher, Helv. Chim. Acta., **46**, 889
(1963)

Neurospora crassa No 74-A

Stone D., M. Hayano, R. I. Dorfman, O. Hechter,
C. R. Robinson and C. Djerassi, J. Am. Chem.
Soc., **77**, 3926 (1955)

Nocardia corallina

Brit. Pat. 862,701

11-Deoxycortisol

9α, 17α, 21-Trihydroxypregn-
4-ene-3, 20-dione

Curvularia lunata (64%)

Japan Pat. 417,538

Nocardia corallina

Brit. Pat. 862,701

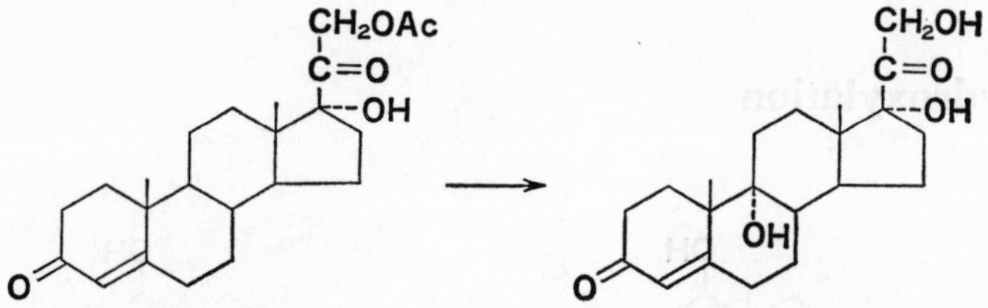

11-Deoxycortisol 21-acetate

9α, 17α, 21-Trihydroxypregn-
4-ene-3, 20-dione

Helminthosporium sigmoideum

Japan Pat. 417,540

(g) 10-Hydroxylation

19-Nortestosterone   10ξ-Hydroxy-19-nortestosterone

Rhizopus nigricans ATCC 6227b (1.2%)

Pederson, R. L., J. A. Campbell, J. C. Babcock, S. H. Eppstein, H. C. Murray, A. Weintraub, R. C. Meeks, P. D. Meister, L. M. Reineke and D. H. Peterson, J. Am. Chem. Soc., **78**, 1512 (1956)

(h) 11-Hydroxylation

| 19-Nortestosterone | 11α-Hydroxy-19-nortestosterone |

Rhizopus nigricans ATCC 6227b (4.2%)

Pederson, R. L., J. A. Campbell, J. C. Babcock, S. H. Eppstein, H. C. Murray, A. Weintraub, R. C. Meeks, P. D. Meister, L. M. Reineke and D. H. Peterson, J. Am. Chem. Soc., **78**, 1512 (1956)

Rhizopus reflexus

U. S. Pat. 2,683,725

| Testosterone | 11α-Hydroxytestosterone |

Aspergillus ochraceus NRRL 405, conidia

Vézina, C., S. N. Sehgal and K. Singh, Appl. Microbiol., **11**, 50 (1963)

Rhizopus nigricans

Tamm, Ch., Angew. Chem., **74**, 225 (1962)

Rhizopus reflexus ATCC 1225 (43%)

Eppstein, S. H., P. D. Meister, H. M. Leigh, D. H. Peterson, H. C. Murray, L. M. Reineke and A. Weintraub, J. Am. Chem. Soc., **76**, 3174 (1954)

| 17α-Methyltestosterone | 17α-Methyl-11α-hydroxytestosterone |

Aspergillus ochraceus

Brit. Pat. 921,424

Rhizopus nigricans ATCC 6227b (47.5%)

Eppstein, S. H., P. D. Meister, H. M. Leigh, D. H. Peterson, H. C. Murray, L. M. Reineke and A. Weintraub, J. Am. Chem. Soc., **76**, 3174 (1954)

Androst-4-ene-3, 17-dione

Rhizopus arrhizus ATCC 11145

Rhizopus arrhizus (24%)
Rhizopus nigricans (24%)

11α-Hydroxyandrost-4-ene-3, 17-dione

Eppstein, S. H., P. D. Meister, H. M. Leigh, D. H. Peterson, H. C. Murray, L. M. Reineke and A. Weintraub, J. Am. Chem. Soc., **76**, 3174 (1954)

U. S. Pat. 2,602,769

19-Norprogesterone

Rhizopus nigricans ATCC 6227b

11α-Hydroxy-19-norprogesterone

Bowers, A., C. Casas-Campillo and C. Djerassi, Tetrahedron, **2**, 165 (1958)

Progesterone

Aspergillus awamori IAM K-0625 (46%)

Aspergillus itaconicus

Aspergillus niger strain Wisc. 72-2 (35%)

Aspergillus ochraceus (87%)

Aspergillus ochraceus (64%)

Aspergillus ochraceus, conidia

11α-Hydroxyprogesterone

Iizuka, H., A. Naito and M. Hattori, J. Gen. Appl. Microbiol. (Japan), **4**, 67 (1958)

U. S. Pat. 2,649,402

Fried, J., R. W. Thoma, J. R. Gerke, J. E. Herz, M. N. Donin and D. Perlman, J. Am. Chem. Soc., **74**, 3962 (1952)

Dulaney, E. L., Mycologia, **47**, 464 (1955)

Brit. Pat. 912,274

Schleg, M. C. and S. G. Knight, Mycologia, **54**, 317 (1962)

Aspergillus ochraceus NRRL 405, conidia	Vézina, C., S. N. Sehgal and K. Singh, Appl. Microbiol, **11**, 50 (1963)
Aspergillus saitoi IAM R-1216 (70%)	Iizuka, H., A. Naito and M. Hattori, J. Gen. Appl. Microbiol. (Japan), **4**, 67 (1958)
Aspergillus sp.	Weisz, E., G. Wix and M. Bodánszky, Naturwiss., **43**, 39 (1956)
Aspergillus usamii U. V. mutant IAM 59-1 (18%)	Iizuka, H., A. Naito and M. Hattori, J. Gen. Appl. Microbiol. (Japan), **4**, 67 (1958)
Aspergillus usamii mut. *shirousamii* IAM B-407 (59%)	
Aspergillus wentii	U. S. Pat. 2,649,402
Bacillus cereus MB 717, NRRL B-1666	McAleer, W. J., T. A. Jacob, L. B. Turnbull, E. F. Schoenewaldt and T. H. Stoudt, Arch. Biochem. Biophys., **73**, 127 (1958)
Bacillus cereus var. *mycoides* MB 718	
Cnninghamella echinulata	U. S. Pat. 2,812,286
Dactylium dendroides (30%)	Dulaney, E. L., W. J. McAleer, H. R. Barkemeyer and C. Hlavac, Appl. Microbiol., **3**, 372 (1955)
Eurotium chevalieri (15%)	Brit. Pat. 740,858
Gloeosporium kaki	Shirasaka, M. and M. Tsuruta, Chem. Pharm. Bull. (Japan), **9**, 159 (1961)
Penicillium corylophilum	Dulaney, E. L., W. J. McAleer, M. Koslowski, E. O. Stapley and J. Jaglom, Appl. Microbiol., **3**, 336 (1955)
Penicillium lilacinum	
Penicillium tardum	
Pestalotia foedans (25%)	Can. Pat. 507,009
Pestalotia royenae	
Rhizopus arrhizus RH-176 (10%)	Peterson, D. H. and H. C. Murray, J. Am. Chem. Soc., **74**, 1871 (1952)
Rhizopus chinensis 10-10	Asai, T., K. Tsuda, K. Aida, E. Ohki, T. Tanaka, M. Hattori and H. Machida, J. Gen. Appl. Microbiol. (Japan), **4**, 63 (1958)
Rhizopus nigricans (80%)	U. S. Pat. 2,602,769
Rhizopus nigricans R-5-4	Asai, T., K. Tsuda, K. Aida, E. Ohki, T. Tanaka, M. Hattori and H. Machida, J. Gen. Appl. Microbiol. (Japan), **4**, 63 (1958)
Rhizopus sp. strain SY-152 (45%)	Mancera, O., A. Zaffaroni, B. A. Rubin, F. Sondheimer, G. Rosenkranz and C. Djerassi, J. Am. Chem. Soc., **74**, 3711 (1952)
Streptomyces fradiae	Vondrová, O. et al., Folia Microbiol (Prague), **8**, 176 (1963)
Streptomyces sp.	Shirasaka, M. and M. Tsuruta, J. Ferm. Assoc. (Japan), **19**, 389 (1961)

Progesterone	6β, 11α-Dihydroxyprogesterone
Aspergillus niger (45%)	Dulaney, E. L., W. J. McAleer, M. Koslowski, E. O. Stapley and J. Jaglom, Appl. Microbiol., **3**, 336 (1955)
Aspergillus niger strain Wisc. 72-2	Fried, J., R. W. Thoma, J. R. Gerke, J. E. Herz, M. N. Donin and D. Perlman, J. Am. Chem. Soc., **74**, 3962 (1952)
Aspergillus ochraceus	Dulaney, E. L., Mycologia, **47**, 464 (1955)
Aspergillus ochraceus, conidia	Schleg, M. C. and S. G. Knight, Mycologia, **54**, 317 (1962)
Aspergillus saitoi IAM R-1216	Iizuka, H., A. Naito and M. Hattori, J. Gen. Appl. Microbiol. (Japan), **4**, 67 (1958)
Aspergillus terreus (41%)	Dulaney, E. L., W. J. McAleer, M. Koslowski, E. O. Stapley and J. Jaglom, Appl. Microbiol., **3**, 336 (1955)
Aspergillus usamii U. V. mutant IAM 59-1	Iizuka, H., A. Naito and M. Hattori, J. Gen. Appl. Microbiol. (Japan), **4**, 67 (1958)
Boletus luteus H-11	Schuytema, E. C., M. P. Hargie, D. J. Siehr, I. Merits, J. R. Schenck, M. S. Smith and E. L. Varner, Appl. Microbiol., **11**, 256 (1963)
Dermoloma sp. F-27	
Gloeosporium kaki	Shirasaka, M. and M. Tsuruta, Chem. Pharm. Bull. (Japan), **9**, 159 (1961)
Hygrophorus conicus C-219	Schuytema, E. C., M. P. Hargie, D. J. Siehr, I. Merits, J. R. Schenck, M. S. Smith and E. L. Varner, Appl. Microbiol., **11**, 256 (1963)
Leucopaxillus paradoxus F-55	
Rhizopus arrhizus ATCC 11145	Peterson, D. H., H. C. Murray, S. H. Eppstein, L. M. Reineke, A. Weintraub, P. D. Meister and H. M. Leigh, J. Am. Chem. Soc., **74**, 5933 (1952)
Rhizopus cambodjae	Camerino, B., C. G. Alberti, A. Vercellone and F. Ammannati, Gazz. Chim. Ital., **84**, 301, (1954)
Rhizopus nigricans ATCC 6227b	Peterson, D. H., H. C. Murray, S. H. Eppstein, L. M. Reineke, A. Weintraub, P. D. Meister and H. M. Leigh, J. Am. Chem. Soc., **74**, 5933 (1952)
Sclerotium hydrophilum	Shirasaka, M. and M. Tsuruta, Chem. Pharm. Bull. (Japan), **9**, 196 (1961)

Streptomyces fradiae

Vondrová, O. et al., Folia Microbiol. (Prague), **8**, 176 (1963)

Streptomyces sp.

Shirasaka, M. and M. Tsuruta, J. Ferm. Assoc. (Japan), **19**, 389 (1961)

CH₃
C=O

Progesterone

HO
O
OH

7ξ, 11α-Dihydroxyprogesterone

Absidia sp. (80%)

Ger. (East) Pat. 19,651

Rhizopus arrhizus (38%)

U. S. Pat. 2,602,769

CH₃
C=O

Progesterone

CH₃
C=O
HO OH

11α, 17α-Dihydroxyprogesterone

Cephalothecium roseum ATCC 8685

Meister, P. D., L. M. Reineke, R. C. Meeks, H. C. Murray, S. H. Eppstein, H. M. Leigh, A. Weintraub and D. H. Peterson, J. Am. Chem. Soc., **76**, 4050 (1954)

Dactylium dendroides (15.4%)

Dulaney, E. L., W. J. McAleer, H. R. Barkemeyer and C. Hlavac, Appl. Microbiol, **3**, 372 (1955)

CH₃
C=O

Progesterone

CH₂OH
C=O
HO

11α, 21-Dihydroxyprogesterone
(11-Epicorticosterone)

Aspergillus sp.

Weisz, E., G. Wix and M. Bodánszky, Naturwiss., **43**, 39 (1956)

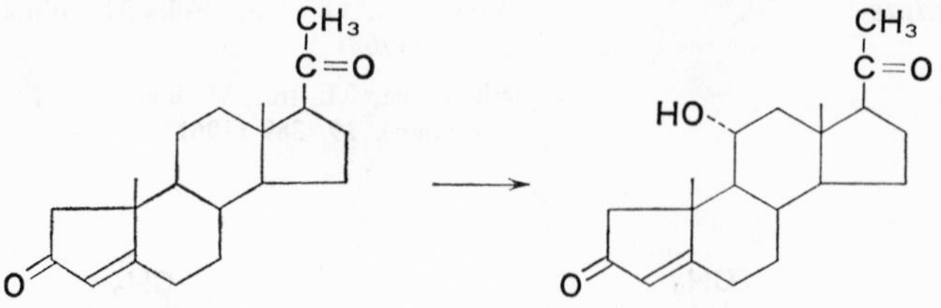

A-Norprogesterone

Aspergillus nidulans

Aspergillus nidulans

11α-Hydroxy-A-norprogesterone

U. S. Pat. 3,005,028

Japan Pat. 408,385

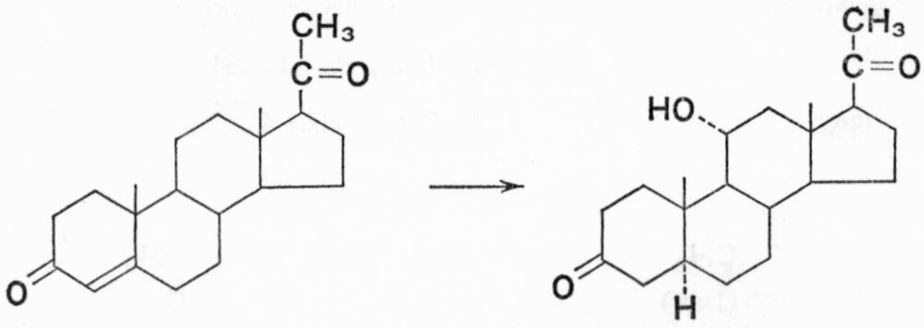

Progesterone

Rhizopus nigricans ATCC 6227b (0.5~ 4.0%)

11α-Hydroxy-5α-pregnane-3, 20-dione

Peterson, D. H., H. C. Murray, S. H. Eppstein, L. M. Reineke, A. Weintraub, P. D. Meister and H. M. Leigh, J. Am. Chem. Soc., **74**, 5933 (1952)

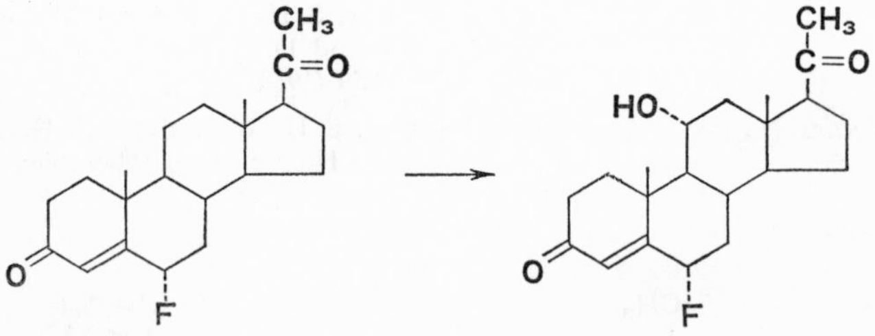

6α-Fluoroprogesterone

Aspergillus nidulans

Aspergillus ochraceus, conidia

6α-Fluoro-11α-hydroxyprogesterone

U. S. Pat. 3,004,047

Vézina, C., S. N. Sehgal and K. Singh, Appl. Microbiol., **11**, 50 (1963)

16α-Hydroxyprogesterone   11α, 16α-Dihydroxyprogesterone

Aspergillus nidulans (45%)

Fried, J., R. W. Thoma, D. Perlman, J. E. Herz and A. Borman, Recent Progr. Hormone. Res., **11**, 149 (1955)

17α-Hydroxyprogesterone   11α, 17α-Dihydroxyprogesterone

Absidia regnieri

Shirasaka, M., Chem. Pharm. Bull. (Japan), **9**, 59 (1961)

Aspergillus niger strain Wisc. 72-2 (15%)

Fried, J., R. W. Thoma, J. R. Gerke, J. E. Herz M. N. Donin and D. Perlman, J. Am. Chem. Soc., **74**, 3962 (1952)

Aspergillus ochraceus

Dulaney, E. L., Mycologia, **47**, 464 (1955)

Aspergillus ochraceus, conidia

Vézina, C., S. N. Sehgal and K. Singh, Appl. Microbiol., **11**, 50 (1963)

Cunninghamella echinulata

U. S. Pat. 2,812,286

Dactylium dendroides (27%)

Dulaney, E. L., W. J. McAleer, H. R. Barkemeyer and C. Hlavac, Appl. Microbiol., **3**, 372 (1955)

Gloeosporium kaki

Shirasaka, M. and M. Tsuruta, Chem. Pharm. Bull. (Japan), **9**, 159 (1961)

Rhizopus arrhizus ATCC 11145 (2%)
Rhizopus nigricans ATCC 6227b (17%)

Meister, P. D., D. H. Peterson, H. C. Murray, G. B. Spero, S. H. Eppstein, A. Weintraub, L. M. Reineke and H. M. Leigh, J. Am. Chem. Soc., **75**, 416 (1953)

Sclerotinia libertiana

Shirasaka, M., Chem. Pharm. Bull. (Japan), **9**, 54 (1961)

Sclerotium hydrophilum

Shirasaka, M. and M. Tsuruta, Chem. Pharm. Bull. (Japan), 9, 196 (1961)

17α-Bromoprogesterone

17α-Bromo-11α-hydroxyprogesterone

Aspergillus ochraceus, conidia

Vézina, C., S. N. Sehgal and K. Singh, Appl. Microbiol., **11**, 50 (1963)

17α-Methylprogesterone

17α-Methyl-11α-hydroxyprogesterone

Aspergillus ochraceus, conidia

Vézina, C., S. N. Sehgal and K. Singh, Appl. Microbiol., **11**, 50 (1963)

6-Dehydroprogesterone

11α-Hydroxypregna-4, 6-diene-3,20-dione

Rhizopus nigricans (50~60%)

Peterson, D. H., A. H. Nathan, P. D. Meister, S. H. Eppstein, H. C. Murray, A. Weintraub, L. M. Reineke and H. M. Leigh, J. Am. Chem. Soc., **75**, 419 (1953)

16-Dehydroprogesterone

11α-Hydroxy-17α-progesterone

Aspergillus niger

U. S. Pat. 2,649,402

Rhizopus nigricans

U. S. Pat. 2,602,769

Rhizopus nigricans ATCC 6227b

Meister, P. D., D. H. Peterson, H. C. Murray, S. H. Eppstein, L. M. Reineke, A. Weintraub and H. M. Leigh, J. Am. Chem. Soc., **75**, 55 (1953)

16-Dehydroprogesterone   11α-Hydroxyandrost-4-ene-3, 17-dione

Aspergillus ochraceus, conidia

Vézina, C., S. N. Sehgal and K. Singh, Appl. Microbiol., **11**, 50 (1963)

16α, 17α-Oxidoprogesterone   11α-Hydroxy-16α, 17α-oxidoprogesterone

Rhizopus nigricans (80%)

Ercoli, A., P. De Ruggieri and D. D. Morte, Gazz. Chim. Ital., **85**, 628 (1955)

pregnenolone   3β, 11α-Dihydroxypregn-5-ene-7, 20-dione

Rhizopus arrhizus (17.5%)

Can. Pat. 506,689

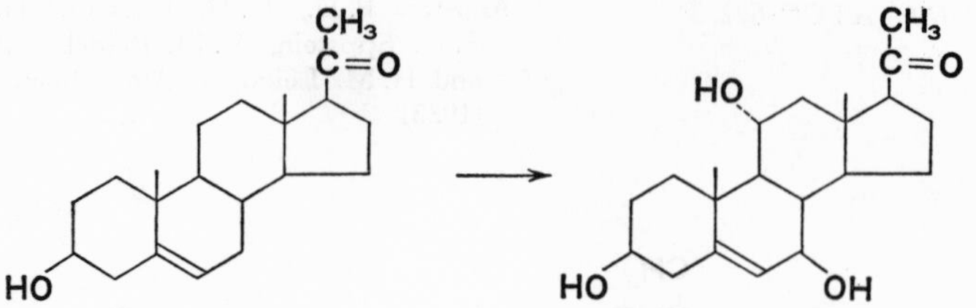

Pregnenolone

$3\beta, 7\beta, 11\alpha$-Trihydroxypregn-
5-en-20-one

Rhizopus arrhizus

U. S. Pat. 2,702,809

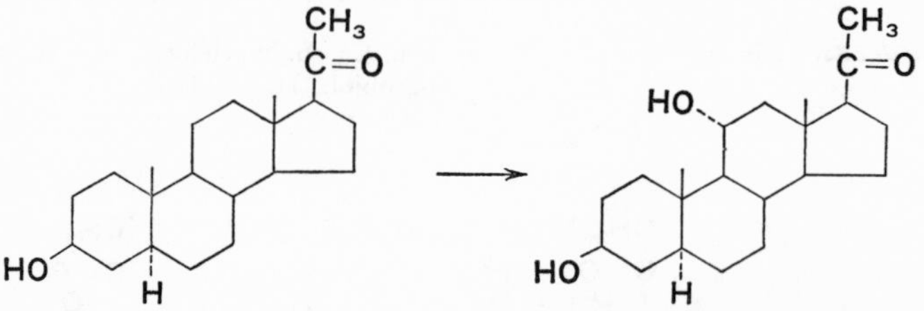

3β-Hydroxy-5α-pregnan-20-one

$3\beta, 11\alpha$-Dihydroxy-5α-pregnan-20-one

Rhizopus nigricans (23%)

U. S. Pat. 2,602,769

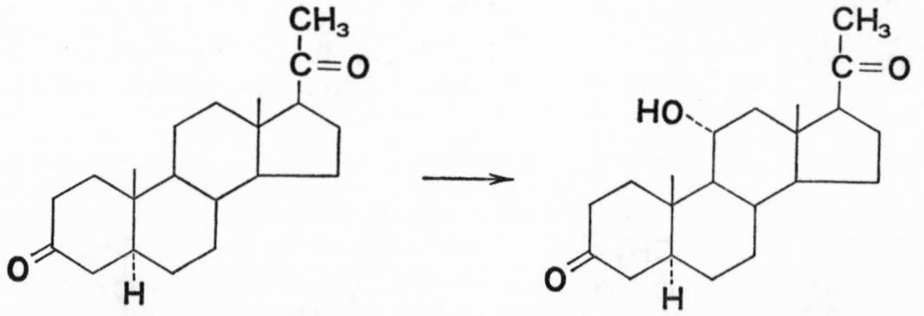

5α-Pregnane-3, 20-dione

11α-Hydroxy-5α-pregnane-3, 20-dione

Rhizopus nigricans ATCC 6227b (25%)

Eppstein, S. H., D. H. Peterson, H. M. Leigh,
H. C. Murray, A. Weintraub, L. M. Reineke
and P. D. Meister, J. Am. Chem. Soc., **75**, 421
(1953)

5β-Pregnane-3, 20-dione

11α-Hydroxy-5β-pregnane-3, 20-dione

Aspergillus niger

U. S. Pat. 2,649,402

Rhizopus nigricans ATCC 6227b (40%)

Eppstein, S. H., D. H. Peterson, H. M. Leigh, H. C. Murray, A. Weintraub, L. M. Reineke and P. D. Meister, J. Am. Chem. Soc., **75**, 421 (1953)

3α, 6α-Dihydroxy-5β-pregnan-20-one

3α, 6α, 11α-Trihydroxy-5β-pregnan-20-one

Calonectria decora

Ger. (East) Pat. 23,995

16α-Methyl-3α, 6α-dihydroxy-
5β-pregnan-20-one

16α-Methyl-3α, 6α, 11α-trihydroxy-
5β-pregnan-20-one

Calonectria decora

Ger. (East) Pat. 23,995

16α, 17α-Oxido-5β-pregnane-
3, 20-dione

11α-Hydroxy-16α, 17α-oxido-5β-pregnane-
3, 20-dione

Aspergillus ochraceus

U. S. Pat. 2,989,439

11-Deoxycorticosterone
(Cortexone)

11α, 21-Dihydroxypregn-4-ene-3, 20-
dione (11-Epicorticosterone)

Aspergillus niger   strain Wisc. 72-2 (67%)

Fried, J., R. W. Thoma, J. R. Gerke, J. E. Herz, M. N. Donin and D. Perlman, J. Am. Chem. Soc., **74**, 3962 (1952)

Aspergillus ochraceus (75%)

Dulaney, E. L., Mycologia, **47**, 464 (1955)

Aspergillus ochraceus NRRL 405, conidia

Vézina, C., S. N. Sehgal and K. Singh, Appl. Microbiol., **11**, 50 (1963)

Bacillus cereus

Shirasaka, M., M. Ozaki and S. Sugawara, J. Gen. Appl. Microbiol. (Japan), **7**, 341 (1961)

Cephalothecium roseum   ATCC 8685

Meister, P. D., L. M. Reineke, R. C. Meeks, H. C. Murray, S. H. Eppstein, H. M. Leigh, A. Weintraub and D. H. Peterson, J. Am. Chem. Soc., **76**, 4050 (1956)

Dactylium dendroides

Dulaney, E. L., W. J. McAleer, H. R. Barkemeyer and C. Hlavac, Appl. Microbiol., **3**, 372 (1955)

Glomerella lagenarium

Shirasaka, M. and M. Tsuruta, Chem. Pharm. Bull. (Japan), **9**, 159 (1961)

Rhizopus nigricans   ATCC 6227b (50~60%)

Eppstein, S. H., P. D. Meister, D. H. Peterson, H. C. Murray, H. M. Leigh, D. A. Lyttle, L. M. Reineke and A. Weintraub, J. Am. Chem. Soc., **75**, 408 (1953)

Sclerotinia sclerotiorum

Japan Pat. 311,629

Streptomyces sp.

Shirasaka, M. and M. Tsuruta, J. Ferm. Assoc. (Japan), **19**, 389 (1961)

11-Deoxycorticosterone

6β, 11α, 21-Trihydroxypregn-4-ene-3, 20-dione

Sclerotinia sclerotiorum

Japan Pat. 311,629

Sclerotium hydrophilum

Shirasaka, M. and M. Tsuruta, Chem. Pharm. Bull. (Japan), **9**, 196 (1961)

11-Deoxycorticosterone

11α, 17α, 21-Trihydroxypregn-
4-ene-3, 20-dione

Cephalothecium roseum ATCC 8685

Meister, P. D., L. M. Reineke, R. C. Meeks, H. C.
Murray, S. H. Eppstein, H. M. Leigh, A. Weintraub and D. H. Peterson, J. Am. Chem. Soc.,
76, 4050 (1954)

Scopulariopsis brevicaulis

Trichothecium roseum

U. S. Pat. 2,970,085

11-Deoxycorticosterone 21-acetate

11α, 21-Dihydroxypregn-
4-ene-3, 20-dione

Aspergillus clavatus

Aspergillus fischeri

Aspergillus nidulans (15.5%)

Aspergillus ustus

U. S. Pat. 2,649,402

Rhizopus nigricans

U. S. Pat. 2,602,769

11-Deoxycortisol

11α, 17α, 21-Trihydroxypregn-4-ene-
3, 20-dione (11-Epicortisol)

Absidia blakesleeana (18~50%)

Absidia glauca

Eroshin, V. K., Med. Prom. SSSR, **16**, 23 (1962)

Schmidt-Thomé, J., Angew. Chem., **69**, 238 (1957)

Absidia orchidis (43.9%)	Hanč, O., A. Čapek and B. Kakáč, Folia Microbiol., **6**, 392 (1961)
Absidia regnieri	Shirasaka, M., Chem. Pharm. Bull. (Japan), **9**, 59 (1961)
Aspergillus nidulans (70%)	Fried, J., R. W. Thoma, D. Perlman, J. E. Herz and A. Borman, Rec. Progr. Hormone Res., **11**, 149 (1955)
Aspergillus niger strain Wisc. 72-2 (25%)	Fried, J., R. W. Thoma, J. R. Gerke, J. E. Herz, M. N. Donin and D. Perlman, J. Am. Chem. Soc., **74**, 3962 (1952)
Aspergillus ochraceus (50%)	Dulaney, E. L., Mycologia, **47**, 464 (1955)
Aspergillus ochraceus NRRL 405, conidia	Vézina, C., S. N. Sehgal and K. Singh, Appl. Microbiol., **11**, 50 (1963)
Bacillus cereus IAM B-204-1	Sugawara, S., M. Tsuruta, M. Shirasaka and M. Nakamura, Arch. Biochem. Biophys., **80**, 383 (1959)
Beauveria sp. spore	U. S. Pat. 3,013,945
Cercospora melongenae (70%)	Kondo, E., K. Morihara, Y. Nozaki and E. Masuo, J. Agr. Chem. Soc. (Japan), **34**, 844 (1960)
Cercospora scirpicola	
Cercospora zinniae	
Cunninghamella echinulata	U. S. Pat. 2,812,286
Dactylium dendroides (16%)	Dulaney, E. L., W. J. McAleer, H. R. Barkemeyer and C. Hlavac, Appl. Microbiol., **3**, 372 (1955)
Delacroixia coronata (61%)	Brit. Pat. 848,914
Didymella lycopersici ATCC 11847 (30%)	Sehgal, S. N., K. Singh and C. Vézina, Steroids, **2**, 93 (1963)
Didymella lycopersici, conidia	Vézina, C., S. N. Sehgal and K. Singh, Appl. Microbiol., **11**, 50 (1963)
Gloeosporium foliicolum	Kondo, E. and E. Masuo, J. Agr. Chem. Soc. (Japan), **34**, 759 (1960)
Glomerella cingulata	
Glomerella lagenarium	Shirasaka, M. and M. Tsuruta, Chem. Pharm. Bull. (Japan), **9**, 159 (1961)
Glomerella mume	Kondo, E. and E. Masuo, J. Agr. Chem. Soc. (Japan), **34**, 759 (1960)
Helicostylum piriforme H-37, H-39	U. S. Pat. 2,602,769
Helminthosporium sigmoideum (70%)	Kondo, E., J. Agr. Chem. Soc. (Japan), **34**, 762 (1960)
Lichtheimia corymbifera (18~50%)	Eroshin, V. K., Med. Prom. SSSR, **16**, 23 (1962)
Lichtheimia ramosa (18~50%)	
Mycocladus hyalinus (73~80%)	
Penicillium expansum	Dan. Pat. 91,515
Rhizopus nigricans (8%)	U. S. Pat. 2,602,769

Sclerotinia sclerotiorum

Sclerotium hydrophilum

Streptomyces sp.

Tieghemella coerulea (23~24%)

Tieghemella cylindrospora (73~80%)

Tieghemella hyalospora (73~80%)

Tieghemella orchidis (18~22%)

Tieghemella repens (73~80%)

Tieghemella spinosa (18~50%)

Tieghemella tiegemii (18~50%)

Japan Pat. 311,629

Shirasaka, M. and M. Tsuruta, Chem. Pharm. Bull. (Japan), **9**, 196 (1961)

Shirasaka, M. and M. Ozaki, J. Ferm. Assoc. (Japan), **19**, 389 (1961)

Eroshin, V. K., Med. Prom. SSSR, **16**, 23 (1962)

11-Deoxycortisol 21-acetate

11α, 17α, 21-Trihydroxypregn-4-ene-3, 20-dione (11-Epicortisol)

Dactylium dendroides

Dan. Pat. 94,041

6α-Fluoro-11-deoxycortisol

6α-Fluoro-11α, 17α, 21-trihydroxypregn-4-ene-3, 20-dione

Aspergillus nidulans

U. S. Pat. 3,004,047

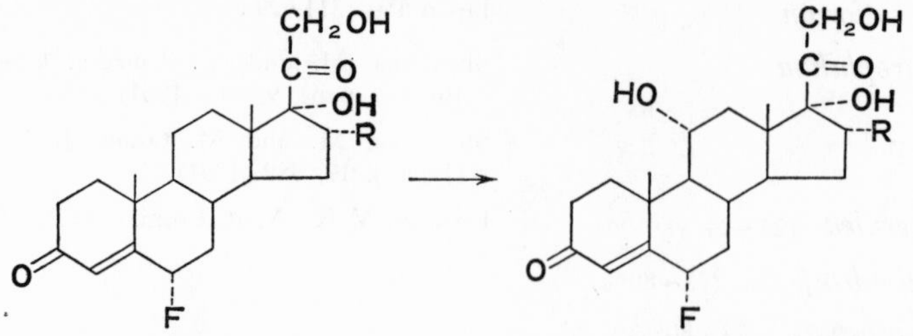

6α-Fluoro-16α-alkyl-11-deoxycortisol

Aspergillus ochraceus

6α-Fluoro-16α-alkyl-11α, 17α, 21-
trihydroxypregn-4-ene-3, 20-dione

U. S. Pat. 3,033,759

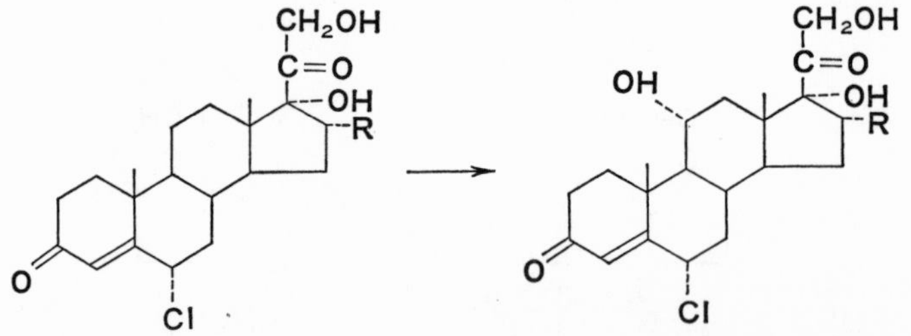

6α-Chloro-16α-alkyl-11-deoxycortisol

Aspergillus ochraceus

6α-Chloro-16α-alkyl-11α, 17α, 21-
trihydroxypregn-4-ene-3, 20-dione

U. S. Pat. 3,033,759

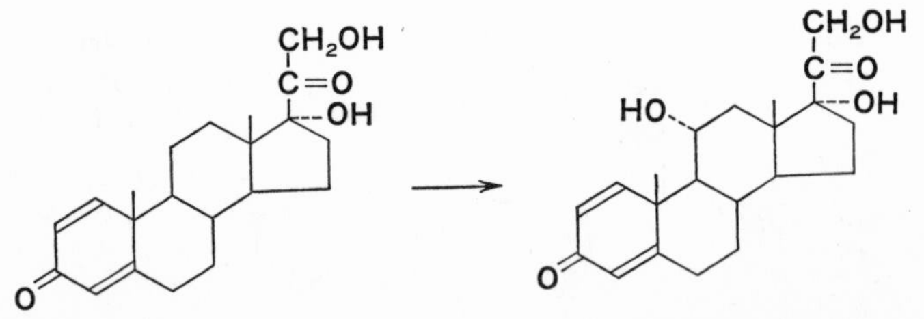

1-Dehydro-11-deoxycortisol

Aspergillus ochraceus NRRL 405, conidia

11α, 17α, 21-Trihydroxypregna-
1, 4-diene-3, 20-dione

Vézina, C., S. N. Sehgal and K. Singh, Appl
Microbiol., **11**, 50, (1963)

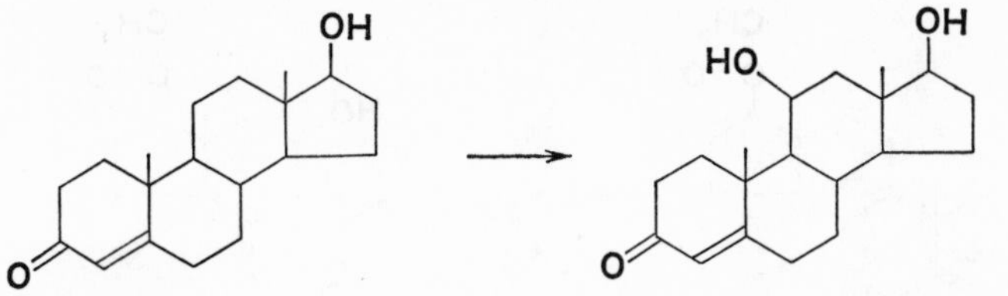

Testosterone

Aspergillus tamarii (25%)

11β-Hydroxytestosterone

Brannon, D. R., J. Martin, A. C. Oehlschlager, N. N. Durham and L. H. Zalkow, J. Org. Chem., **30**, 760 (1965)

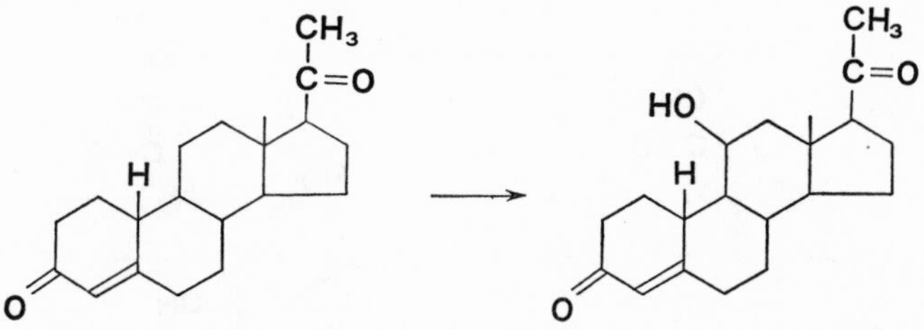

19-Norprogesterone

Curvularia lunata strain Syntex 192

11β-Hydroxy-19-norprogesterone

Bowers, A., C. Casas-Campillo and C. Djerassi, Tetrahedron, **2**, 165 (1958)

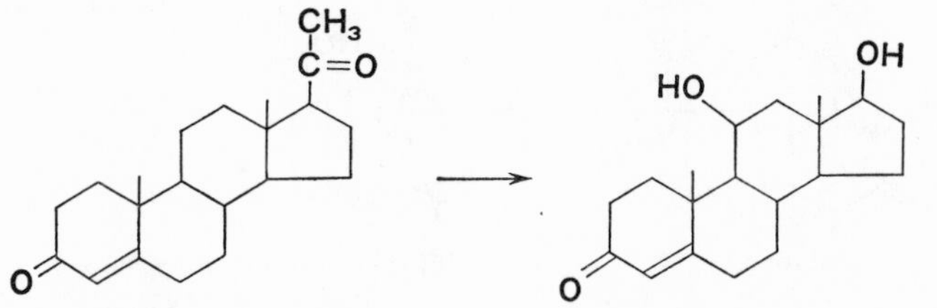

Progesterone

Aspergillus tamarii (14%)

11β-Hydroxytestosterone

Brannon, D. R., J. Martin, A. C. Oehlschlager, N. N. Durham and L. H. Zalkow, J. Org. Chem., **30**, 760 (1965)

Progesterone

11β-Hydroxyprogesterone

Cunninghamella blakesleeana

Eppstein, S. H., P. D. Meister, H. C. Murray and D. H. Peterson, Vitamins and Hormones, **14**, 359 (1956)

Curvularia lunata NRRL 2380

Shull, G. M. and D. A. Kita, J. Am. Chem. Soc., **77**, 763 (1955)

Progesterone

11β, 14α-Dihydroxyprogesterone

Curvularia lunata

Zetsche, K., Naturwiss., **47**, 232 (1960)

Progesterone

11β, 21-Dihydroxyprogesterone (Corticosterone)

Curvularia lunata

Rubin, B. A. et al., Bact. Proc., **56**, 33 (1956)

17α-Hydroxyprogesterone

11β, 17α-Dihydroxyprogesterone

Curvularia lunata NRRL 2380 (34%)

Shull, G. M. and D. A. Kita, J. Am. Chem. Soc., **77**, 763 (1955)

17α-Hydroxyprogesterone

Curvularia lunata NRRL 2380 (20%)

11β, 14α, 17α-Trihydroxyprogesterone

Shull, G. M. and D. A. Kita, J. Am. Chem. Soc., **77**, 763 (1955)

11β-Hydroxy-3, 20-dioxopregn-
4-en-18-oic acid-18, 11-lactone

Fusarium solani

11β-Hydroxy-18-norandrosta-
1, 4-diene-3, 17-dione

Urech, J., E. Vischer and A. Wettstein, Paper,
Meeting Swiss Chem. Soc., September, 1961

11β-Hydroxy-3, 20-dioxopregn-
4-en-18-oic acid-18, 11-lactone

Fusarium solani

11β-Hydroxy-18-nor-18-isoandrosta-
1, 4-diene-3, 17-dione

Urech, J., E. Vischer and A. Wettstein, Paper,
Meeting Swiss Chem. Soc., September, 1961

11-Deoxycorticosterone

11β, 21-Dihydroxypregn-4-ene-
3, 20-dione (Corticosterone)

Aspergillus fumigatus (2%)

U. S. Pat. 2,649,401

Cunninghamella blakesleeana H-334

Mann, K. M., F. R. Hanson and P. W. O'Connell,
Federation Proc., **14**, 251 (1955)

Curvularia lunata NRRL 2380 (28%)

Shull, G. M. and D. A. Kita, J. Am. Chem. Soc.,
77, 763 (1955)

Penicillium chrysogenum (2%)

U. S. Pat. 2,649,401

Saccharomyces pastorianus (2%)

Stachylidium bicolor

Shirasaka, M., Chem. Pharm. Bull. (Japan), **9**, 203
(1961)

Streptomyces fradiae strain Waksman
3535 (6%)

Colingsworth, D. R., M. P. Brunner and W. J.
Haines, J. Am. Chem. Soc., **74**, 2381 (1952)

Streptomyces sp. (2%)

U. S. Pat. 2,649,401

11-Deoxycortisol

11β, 17α, 21-Trihydroxypregn-4-ene-
3, 20-dione (Cortisol)

Absidia blakesleeana (0∼38%)

Eroshin, V. K., Med. Prom. SSSR, **16**, 23 (1962)

Absidia glauca

Schmidt-Thomé, J., Angew. Chem., **69**, 238 (1957)

Absidia orchidis (48.9%)

Hanč, O., A. Capek and B. Kakáč, Folia Microbiol., **6**, 392 (1961)

Botrytis cinerea

U. S. Pat. 2,789,940

Cephalothecium roseum

U. S. Pat. 2,765,258

Cercospora zinniae

Kondo, E., K. Morihara, Y. Nozaki and E. Masuo,
J. Agr. Chem. Soc. (Japan), **34**, 844 (1960)

Colletotrichum phomoides

Brit. Pat. 749,414

Colletotrichum pisi

Coniothyrium helliborine *Coniothyrium* sp.	Eppstein, S. H., P. D. Meister, H. C. Murray and D. H. Peterson, Vitamines and Hormones, **14**, 359 (1956)
Corticium microsclerotia *Corticium praticola* *Corticium sasakii* IFO 5254	Hasegawa, T., T. Takahashi, M. Nishikawa and H. Hagiwara, Bull. Agr. Chem. Soc. (Japan), **21**, 390 (1957)
Corticium vagum	Japan Pat. 276,077
Cunninghamella blakesleeana H-334 (19%)	Mann, K. M., F. R. Hanson, P. W. O'Connell, H. V. Anderson, M. P. Brunner and J. N. Karnemaat, Appl. Microbiol., **3**, 14 (1955)
Curvularia falcata	U. S. Pat. 2,765,258
Curvularia lunata NRRL 2380 (40%)	Shull, G. M. and D. A. Kita, J. Am. Chem. Soc., **77**, 763 (1955)
Curvularia pallescens	U. S. Pat. 2,658,023
Dothichiza sp.	Shull, G. M., Trans. N. Y. Acad. Sci., **19**, 147 (1957)
Helminthosporium sativum	Japan Pat. 305,739
Helminthosporium sigmoideum H-40	Kondo, E., J. Agr. Chem. Soc. (Japan), **34**, 762 (1960)
Lichtheimia corymbifera (0~38%) *Lichtheimia ramosa* (0~38%) *Mycocladus hyalinus* (2~6%)	Eroshin, V. K., Med. Prom. SSSR, **16**, 23 (1962)
Pseudomonas fluorescens	Brit. Pat. 859,694
Pycnosporium sp.	Brit. Pat. 769,999
Rhodoseptoria sp.	Shull, G. M., Trans. N. Y. Acad. Sci., **19**, 147 (1957)
Stachylidium bicolor	Shirasaka, M., Chem. Pharm. Bull. (Japan), **9**, 203 (1961)
Streptomyces fradiae strain Waksman 3535 (6%)	Colingsworth, D. R., M. P. Brunner and W. J. Haines, J. Am. Chem. Soc., **74**, 2381 (1952)
Tieghemella coerulea (42~45%) *Tieghemella cylindrospora* (2~6%) *Tieghemella hyalospora* (2~6%) *Tieghemella orchidis* (51~63%) *Tieghemella repens* (2~6%) *Tieghemella spinosa* (0~38%) *Tieghemella tiegemii* (0~38%)	Eroshin, V.K., Med. Prom. SSSR, **16**, 23 (1962)
Trichothecium roseum	Brit. Pat. 749,414

11-Deoxycortisol

11β, 14α, 17α, 21-Tetrahydroxypregn-
4-ene-3, 20-dione
(14α-Hydroxycortisol)

Curvularia lunata NRRL 2380

Agnello, E. J., B. L. Bloom and G. D. Laubach, J.,
Am. Chem. Soc., **77**, 4684 (1955)

11-Deoxycortisol

11β, 17α, 21-Trihydroxypregna-1, 4-
diene-3, 20-dione (Prednisolone)

Absidia orchidis

Hung. Pat. 150,009

Mixed culture of *Corticium sasakii* and
Pseudomonas boreopolis

Japan Pat. 303,584

The actions of *Helminthosporium sativum*
and *Bacillus pulvifaciens* IAM N-19-2
in one and the same fermentation vessel in
sequence

U. S. Pat. 2,993,839

16α-Methyl-11-deoxycortisol

16α-Methyl-11β, 17α, 21-trihydroxy-
pregn-4-ene-3, 20-dione

Curvularia lunata

Ger. Pat. 1,147,226

14-Dehydro-11-deoxycortisol

Curvularia lunata

11β, 17α, 21-Trihydroxy-14α, 15α-
oxidopregn-4-ene-3, 20-dione

Shull, G. M., Trans. N. Y. Acad. Sci., **19**, 147
(1956)

14α, 15α-Oxido-11-deoxycortisol

Curvularia lunata

11β, 17α, 21-Trihydroxy-14α, 15α-
oxidopregn-4-ene-3, 20-dione

Shull, G. M., Trans. N. Y. Acad. Sci., **19**, 147
(1956)

(i) 12-Hydroxylation

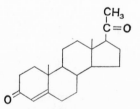

Androst-4-ene-3, 17-dione

9α, 12α-Dihydroxyandrost-
4-ene-3, 17-dione

Cercospora melonis

Kondo, E. and K. Tori, J. Am. Chem. Soc., **86**,
736 (1964)

Progesterone

12β, 15α-Dihydroxyprogesterone

Calonectria decora

Ger. Pat. 1,067,020

Progesterone

12β, 15β-Dihydroxyprogesterone

Calonectria decora (80%)

Schubert, A., G. Langbein and R. Siebert, Chem.
Ber., **90**, 2576 (1957)

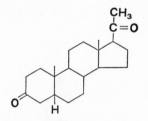

11α-Hydroxyprogesterone

Calonectria decora

11α, 12β-Dihydroxyprogesterone

Schubert, A., G. Langbein and R. Siebert, Chem. Ber., **90**, 2576 (1957)

5α-Pregnane-3, 20-dione

Calonectria decora

12β, 15α-Dihydroxy-5α-pregnane-3, 20-dione

Ger. Pat. 1,067,020

5β-Pregnane-3, 20-dione

Calonectria decora

12β, 15α-Dihydroxy-5β-pregnane-3, 20-dione

Ger. Pat. 1,067,020

(j) 14-Hydroxylation

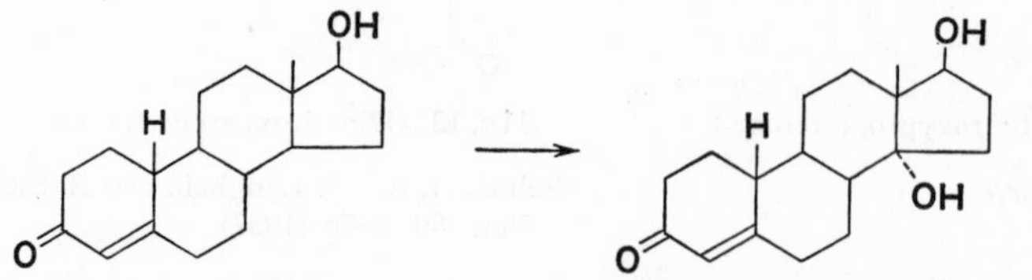

19-Nortestosterone

Mucor griseocyanus

14α-Hydroxy-19-nortestosterone

U. S. Pat. 2,662,089

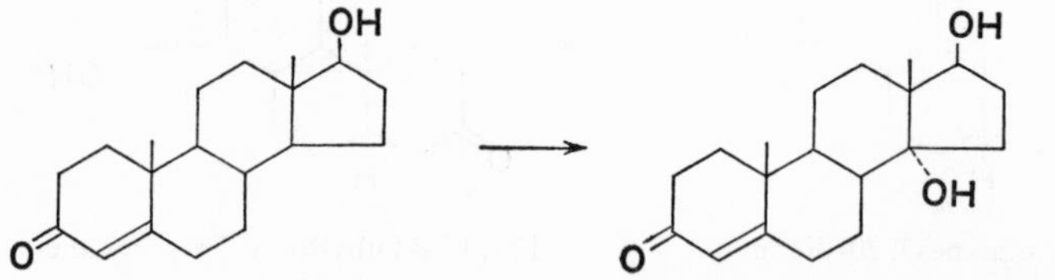

Testosterone

Mucor griseocyanus (ca. 100%)

Mucor sp. (35%)

14α-Hydroxytestosterone

Meister, P. D., S. H. Eppstein, D. H. Peterson, H. C. Murray, H. M. Leigh, A. Weintraub and L. M. Reineke, Abstr. paper 123rd Meeting Am. Chem. Soc., Los Angeles, March, 1953 p. 5c

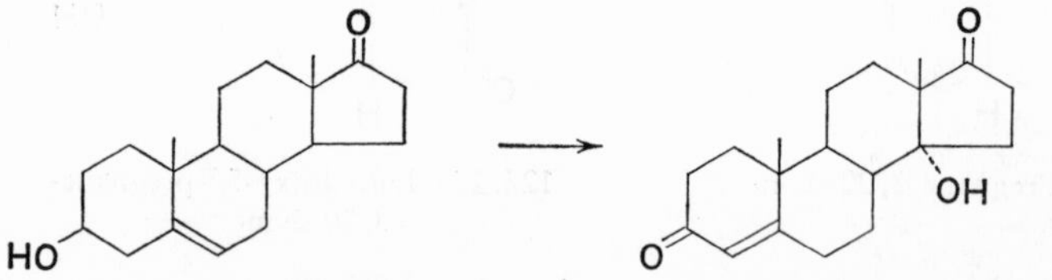

Dehydroepiandrosterone

Bacillus pulvifaciens IAM N-19-2

14α-Hydroxyandrost-4-ene-3, 17-dione

Iizuka H., A. Naito and Y. Sato, J. Gen. Appl. Microbiol. (Japan), 7, 118 (1961)

Dehydroepiandrosterone

14α-Hydroxyandrosta-1, 4-
diene-3, 17-dione

Bacillus pulvifaciens IAM N-19-2

Iizuka, H., A. Naito and Y. Sato, J. Gen. Appl.
Microbiol. (Japan), **7**, 118 (1961)

Androst-4-ene-3, 17-dione

9α, 14α-Dihydroxyandrost-
4-ene-3, 17-dione

Cercospora melonis

Kondo, E. and K. Tori, J. Am. Chem. Soc., **86**,
736 (1964)

Progesterone

14α-Hydroxyprogesterone

Absidia regnieri

Shirasaka, M., Chem. Pharm. Bull. (Japan), **9**, 59
(1961)

Bacillus cereus

Eppstein, S. H., P. D. Meister, H. C. Murray and
D. H. Peterson, Vitamins and Hormones, **14**,
359 (1956)

Helicostylum piriforme

U. S. Pat. 2,670,358

Mucor griseocyanus (15%)

Mucor griseocyanus, sporangiospore

Vézina, C., S. N. Sehgal and K. Singh, Appl.
Microbiol., **11**, 50 (1963)

Mucor parasiticus (15%)

U. S. Pat. 2,670,358

Stachylidium theobromae, conidia

Vézina, C., S. N. Sehgal and K. Singh, Appl.
Microbiol., **11**, 50 (1963)

Progesterone

6β, 14α-Dihydroxyprogesterone

Achromobacter kashiwazakiensis IAM K-40-5

Tsuda, K., H. Iizuka, E. Ohki, Y. Sato, A. Naito and M. Hattori, J. Gen. Appl. Microbiol. (Japan), **5**, 7 (1959)

Bacillus cereus

Shirasaka, M., M. Ozaki and S. Sugawara, J. Gem. Appl. Microbiol. (Japan), **7**, 341 (1961)

Mucor corymbifer

Camerino, B., C. G. Alberti and A. Vercellone, Gazz. Chim. Ital, **83**, 684 (1953)

Progesterone

7α, 14α-Dihydroxyprogesterone

Curvularia lunata

Zetsche, K., Naturwiss., **47**, 232 (1960)

Progesterone

7β, 14α, 15β-Trihydroxyprogesterone

Syncephalastrum racemosum

Tsuda, K., T. Asai, Y. Sato, T. Tanaka, T. Matsuhisa and H. Hasegawa, Chem. Pharm. Bull. (Japan), **8**, 626 (1960)

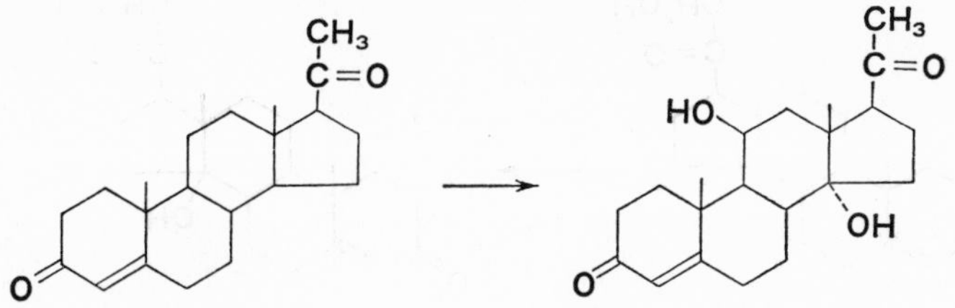

Progesterone

Curvularia lunata

11β, 14α-Dihydroxyprogesterone

Zetsche, K., Naturwiss., **47**, 232 (1960)

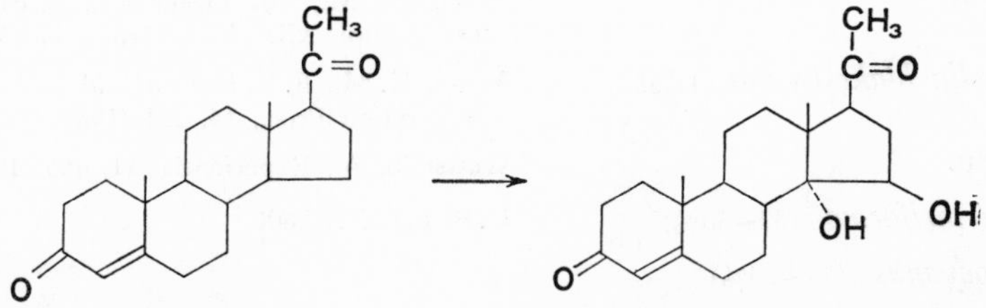

Progesterone

Helminthosporium sativum

14α, 15β-Dihydroxyprogesterone

Tsuda, K., T. Asai, Y. Sato, T. Tanaka and H. Hasegawa, Chem. Pharm. Bull. (Japan), **9**, 735 (1961)

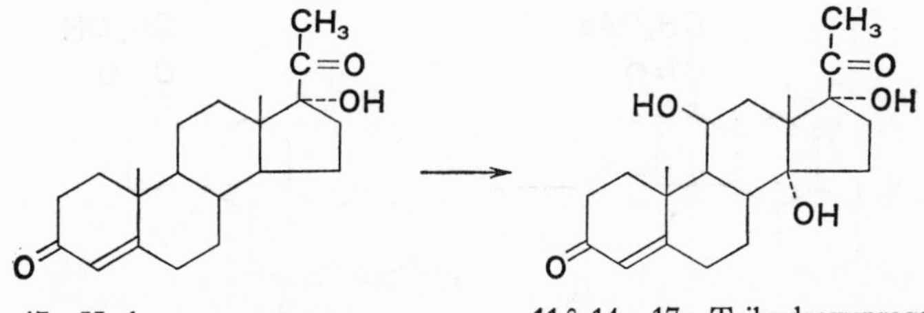

17α-Hydroxyprogesterone

Curvularia lunata NRRL 2380 (20%)

11β, 14α, 17α-Trihydroxyprogesterone

Shull, G. M. and D. A. Kita, J. Am. Chem. Soc., **77**, 763 (1955)

11-Deoxycorticosterone

14α, 21-Dihydroxypregn-4-
ene-3, 20-dione

Absidia regnieri

Shirasaka, M., Chem. Pharm. Bull. (Japan), **9**, 59 (1961)

Bacillus cereus

Shirasaka, M., M. Ozaki and S. Sugawara, J. Gen. Appl. Microbiol. (Japan), **7**, 341 (1961)

Cunninghamella blakesleeana H-334

Mann, K. M., F. R. Hanson and P. W. O'Connell, Federation Proc., **14**, 251 (1955)

Curvularia sp.

Wettstein, A., Experientia, **11**, 465 (1955)

Helicostylum piriforme (30~50%)

U. S. Pat. 2,703,806

Mucor griseocyanus (30~50%)

Mucor parasiticus

Tamm, Ch., A. Gubler, G. Juhasz, E. Weiss-Berg and W. Zürcher, Helv. Chim. Acta., **46**, 889 (1963)

Stachylidium bicolor

Shirasaka, M., Chem. Pharm. Bull. (Japan), **9**, 203 (1961)

11-Deoxycorticosterone 21-acetate

14α, 21-Dihydroxypregn-4-
ene-3, 20-dione

Mucor griseocyanus (25%)

Meister, P. D., S. H. Eppstein, D. H. Peterson, H. C. Murray, H. M. Leigh, A. Weintraub and L. M. Reineke, Abstr. 123rd Meeting Am. Chem. Soc., Los Angeles, March, 1953 p. 5c

Corticosterone → 14α, 21-Dihydroxypregn-4-ene-3, 11, 20-trione

Absidia regnieri Shirasaka, M., Chem. Pharm. Bull. (Japan), **9**, 59 (1961)

Bacillus cereus Shirasaka, M., M. Ozaki and S. Sugawara, J. Gen. Appl. Microbiol. (Japan), **7**, 341 (1961)

11-Deoxycortisol → 14α, 17α, 21-Trihydroxypregn-4-ene-3, 20-dione

Absidia regnieri Shirasaka, M., Chem. Pharm. Bull. (Japan), **9**, 59 (1961)

Cunninghamella blakesleeana Eppstein, S. H., P. D. Meister, H. C. Murray and D. H. Peterson, Vitamins and Hormones, **14**, 359 (1956)
Helicostylum piriforme

Helminthosporium avenae H-9 Kondo, E., J. Agr. Chem. Soc. (Japan), **34**, 762 (1960)

11-Deoxycortisol → 7α, 14α, 17α, 21-Tetrahydroxypregn-4-ene-3, 20-dione

Curvularia lunata Shull, G. M., Trans. N. Y. Acad. Sci., **19**, 147 (1956)

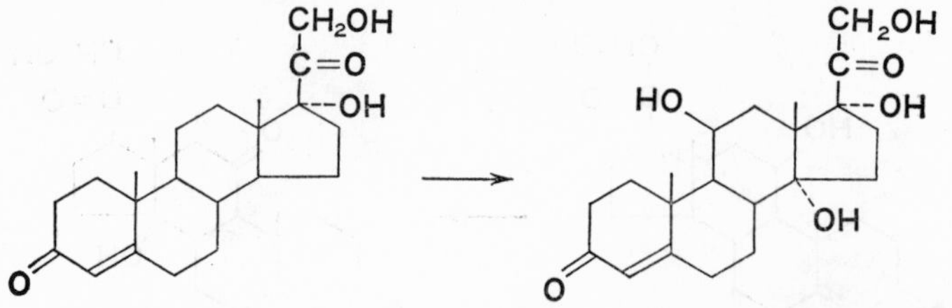

11-Deoxycortisol

11β, 14α, 17α, 21-Tetrahydroxypregn-
4-ene-3, 20-dione

Curvularia lunata NRRL 2380

Agnello, E. J., B. L. Bloom and G. D. Laubach,
J. Am. Chem. Soc., **77**, 4684 (1955)

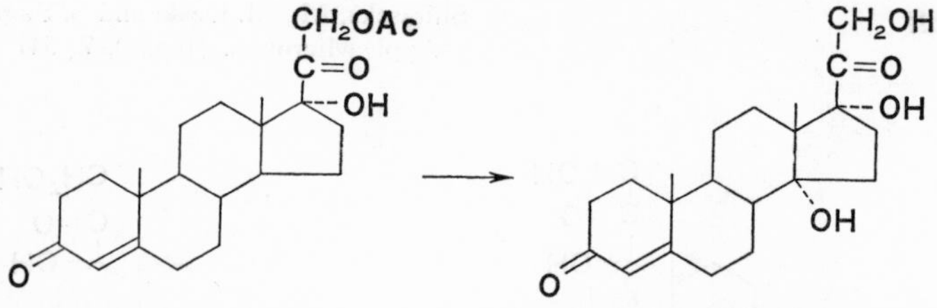

11-Deoxycortisol 21-acetate

14α, 17α, 21-Trihydroxypregn-
4-ene-3, 20-dione

Mycobacterium lacticola
Mycobacterium smegmatis

Belg. Pat. 538,327

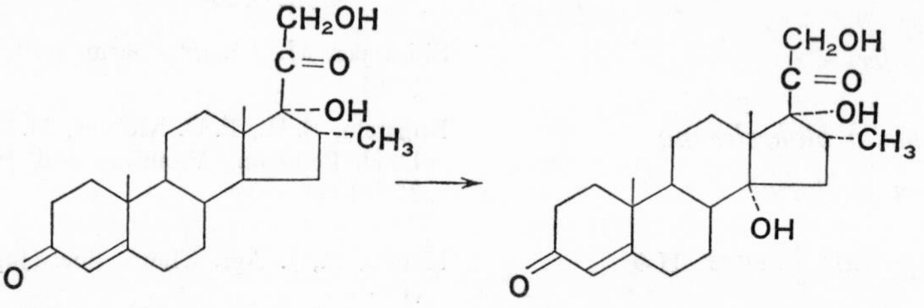

16α-Methyl-11-deoxycortisol

16α-Methyl-14α, 17α, 21-trihydroxy-
pregn-4-ene-3, 20-dione

Curvularia lunata

Ger. Pat. 1,147,226

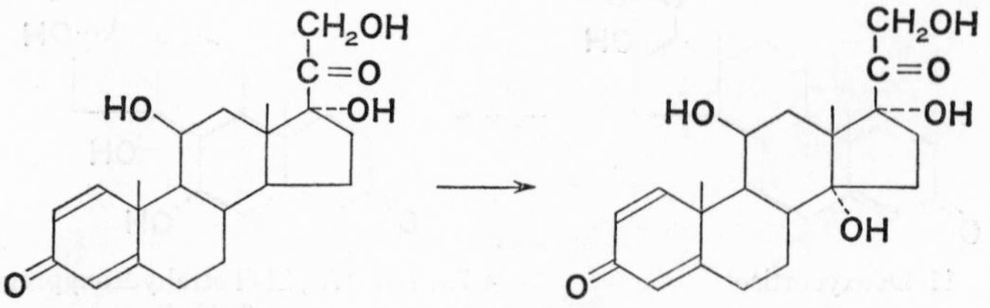

1-Dehydrocortisol
(Prednisolone)

11β, 14α, 17α, 21-Tetrahydroxy-
pregna-1, 4-diene-3, 20-dione

Helicostylum piriforme

Brit. Pat. 835,700

(k) 15-Hydroxylation

Estrone → 15α-Hydroxyestrone

Fusarium moniliforme

Fusarium moniliforme ATCC 9851 (20%)

Fusarium moniliforme ATCC 11161 (10%)

Fusarium moniliforme IH 4 (53.5%)

Crabbé, P. and C. Casas-Campillo, J. Org. Chem. **29**, 2731 (1964)

Casas-Campillo, C. and M. Bautista, Appl. Micro-biol., **13**, 977, (1965)

Estradiol → 15α-Hydroxyestradiol

Fusarium moniliforme

Fusarium moniliforme ATCC 9851 (29%)

Fusarium moniliforme IH 4 (42.5%)

Crabbé, P. and C. Casas-Campillo, J. Org. Chem., **29**, 2731 (1964)

Casas-Campillo, C. and M. Bautista, Appl. Micro-biol., **13**, 977 (1965)

Testosterone → 15α-Hydroxytestosterone

Fusarium lini

Fusarium roseum

Gibberella saubinetti

Tamm, Ch., A. Gubler, G. Juhasz, E. Weiss-Berg and W. Zürcher, Helv. Chim. Acta, **46**, 889, (1963)

Rao, P. G., Indian J. Pharm., **25**, 131 (1963)

Japan Pat. 313,770

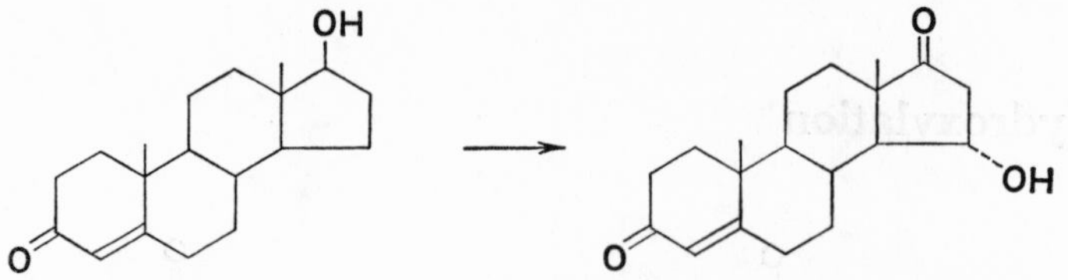

Testosterone

15α-Hydroxyandrost-4-ene-3, 17-dione

Fusarium sp.

Peterson, D. H., Record Chem. Progr., **17**, 211 (1956)

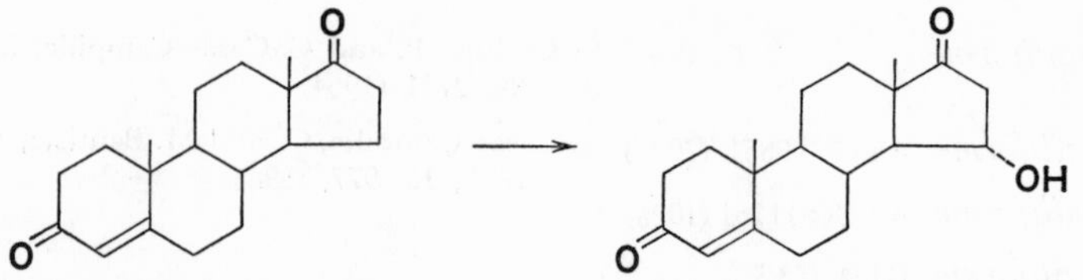

Androst-4-ene-3, 17-dione

15α-Hydroxyandrost-
4-ene-3, 17-dione

Fusarium lini

Tamm, Ch., A. Gubler, G. Juhasz, E. Weiss-Berg and W. Zürcher, Helv. Chim. Acta., **46**, 889, (1963)

Gibberella saubinetti (21%)

Urech, J., E. Vischer and A. Wettstein, Helv. Chim. Acta, **43**, 1077 (1960)

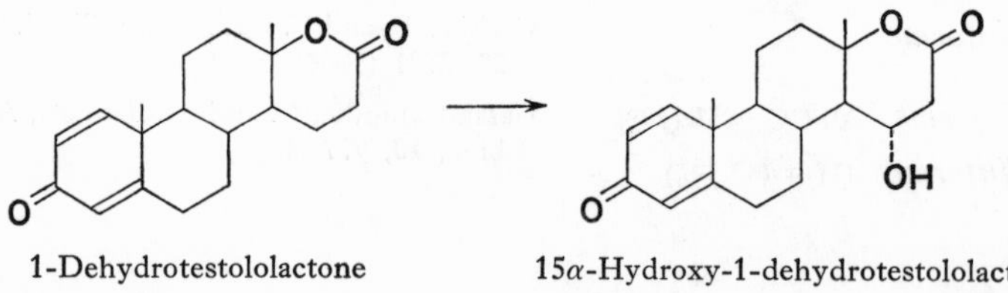

1-Dehydrotestololactone

15α-Hydroxy-1-dehydrotestololactone

Penicillium sp. ATCC 11598

Neidleman, S. L., P. A. Diassi, B. Junta. R. M. Palmere, S. C. Pan, Tetrahedron Letter No. 44 5337 (1966)

| | Progesterone | 15α-Hydroxyprogesterone |

Progesterone → 15α-Hydroxyprogesterone

Colletotrichum antirrhini

Eppstein, S. H., P. D. Meister, H. C. Murray and D. H. Peterson, Vitamins and Hormones, **14**, 359 (1956)

Fusarium culmorum

Klüger, B., R. Siebert and A. Schubert, Naturwiss, **44**, 40 (1957)

Fusarium lini

Tamm, Ch., A. Gubler, G. Juhasz, E. Weiss-Berg and W. Zürcher, Helv. Chim. Acta, **46**, 889 (1963)

Fusarium lycopersici

Shirasaka, M. and M. Tsuruta, Chem. Pharm. Bull. (Japan), **9**, 238 (1961)

Fusarium lycopersici

Klüger, B., R. Siebert and A. Schubert, Naturwiss, **44**, 40 (1957)

Fusarium roseum

Rao, P. G., Indian J. Pharm., **25**, 131 (1962)

Fusarium solani

Klüger, B., R. Siebert and A. Schubert, Naturwiss., **44**, 40 (1957)

Gibberella saubinetti

Shirasaka, M. and M. Tsuruta, Chem. Pharm. Bull. (Japan), **9**, 238 (1961)

Helminthosporium sativum

Tsuda, K., T. Asai, Y. Sato, T. Tanaka and H. Hasegawa, Chem. Pharm. Bull. (Japan), **9**, 735 (1961)

Nigrospora oryzae

U. S. Pat. 2,793,163

Penicillium notatum

Camerino, B., R. Modelli and C. Spalla, Gazz. Chim. Ital., **86**, 1226 (1956)

Penicillium urticae

Eppstein, S. H., P. D. Meiter, H. C. Murray and D. H. Peterson, Vitamins and Hormones, **14**, 359 (1956)

Streptomyces aureus

U. S. Pat. 2,753,290

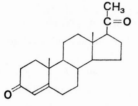

Progesterone

6β, 15α-Dihydroxyprogesterone

Fusarium lini

Tamm, Ch., A. Gubler, G. Juhasz, E. Weiss-Berg and W. Zürcher, Helv. Chim. Acta, **46**, 889 (1963)

Fusarium roseum

Rao, P. G., Indian J. Pharm, **25**, 131 (1962)

Gibberella saubinetti

Japan Pat. 313,770

Progesterone

11α, 15α-Dihydroxyprogesterone

Nigrospora oryzae

U. S. Pat. 2,793,163

Progesterone

12β, 15α-Dihydroxyprogesterone

Calonectria decora

Ger. Pat. 1,067,020

11α-Hydroxyprogesterone

11α, 15α-Dihydroxyprogesterone

Calonectria decora

Ger. Pat. 1,067,020

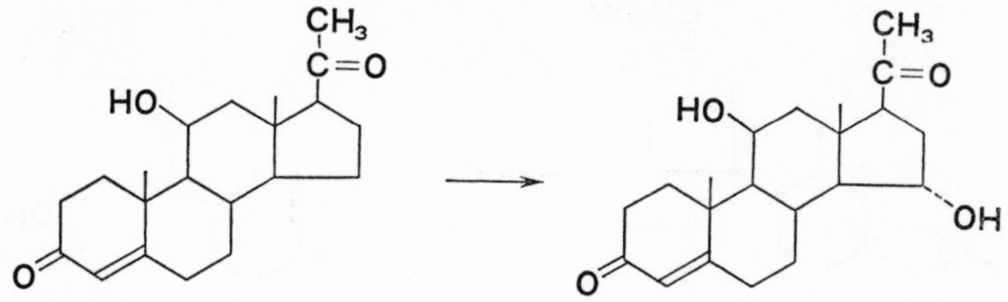

11β-Hydroxyprogesterone

Calonectria decora

11β, 15α-Dihydroxyprogesterone

Ger. Pat. 1,067,020

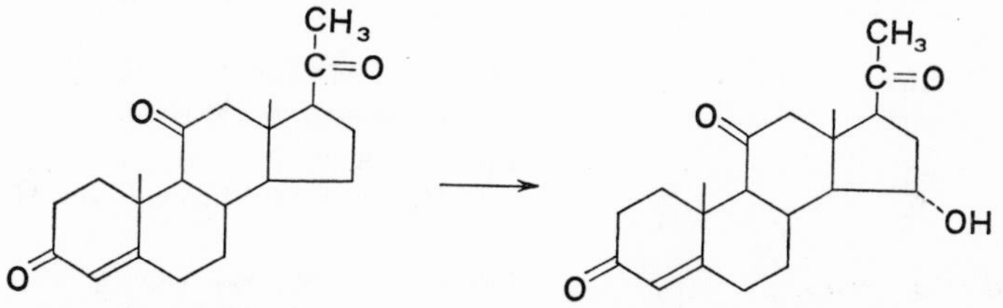

11-Oxoprogesterone

Calonectria decora

15α-Hydroxy-11-oxoprogesterone
(15α-Hydroxypregn-4-ene-3, 11, 20-trione)

Ger. Pat. 1,067,020

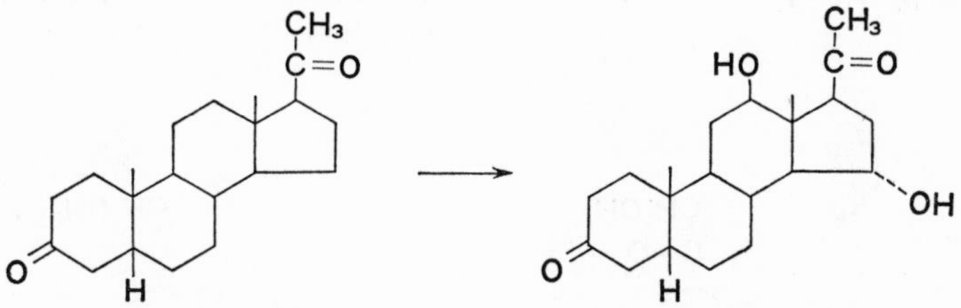

5α-Pregnane-3, 20-dione

Calonectria decora

12β, 15α-Dihydroxy-5α-pregnane-
3, 20-dione

Ger. Pat. 1,067,020

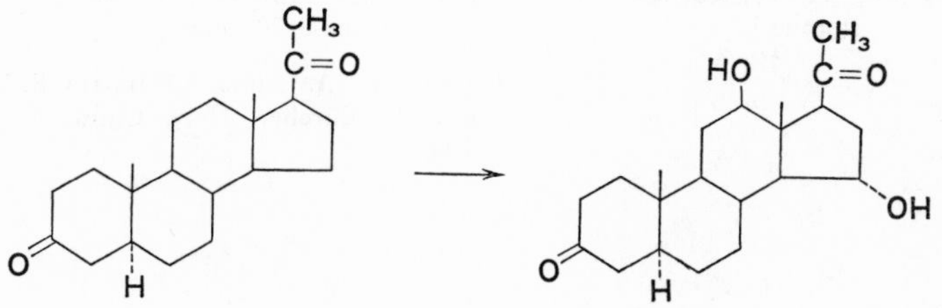

5β-Pregnane-3, 20-dione

Calonectria decora

12β, 15α-Dihydroxy-5β-pregnane-
3, 20-dione

Ger. Pat. 1,067,020

11-Deoxycorticosterone → 15α, 21-Dihydroxypregn-4-ene-3, 20-dione

Fusarium lini

Tamm, Ch., A. Gubler, G. Juhasz, E. Weiss-Berg and W. Zürcher, Helv. Chim. Acta, **46**, 889, 1166 (1963)

Fusarium lycopersici

Shirasaka, M. and M. Tsuruta, Chem. Pharm. Bull. (Japan), **9**, 238 (1961)

Fusarium sp.

Eppstein, S. H., P. D. Meister, H. C. Murray and D. H. Peterson, Vitamins and Hormones, **14**, 359 (1956)

Gibberella baccata (70%)

Urech, J., E. Vischer and A. Wettstein, Helv. Chim. Acta, **43**, 1077 (1960)

Gibberella saubinetti

Shirasaka, M. and M. Tsuruta, Chem. Pharm. Bull. (Japan), **9**, 238 (1961)

Gibberella saubinetti (50%)

Urech, J., E. Vischer and A. Wettstein, Helv. Chim. Acta, **43**, 1077 (1960)

Lenzites abietina (19%)

Meystre, Ch., E. Vischer and A. Wettstein, Helv. Chim. Acta, **38**, 381 (1955)

14α-Hydroxy-11-deoxycortico-sterone → 14α, 15α, 21-Trihydroxypregn-4-ene-3, 20-dione

Fusarium lini

Tamm, Ch., A. Gubler, G. Juhasz, E. Weiss-Berg and W. Zürcher, Helv. Chim. Acta, **46**, 889 (1963)

CH₂OAc
C=O

$\longrightarrow$

CH₂OH
C=O
OH

11-Deoxycorticosterone 21-acetate

Calonectria decora

Nigrospora oryzae

15α, 21-Dihydroxypregn-4-ene-3, 20-dione

Ger. Pat. 1,067,020

U. S. Pat. 2,793,163

CH₂OH
C=O
--OH

$\longrightarrow$

CH₂OH
C=O
--OH
OH

11-Deoxycortisol

15α, 17α, 21-Trihydroxypregn-4-ene-3, 20-dione

Fusarium lini

Tamm, Ch., A. Gubler, G. Juhasz, E. Weiss-Berg and W. Zürcher, Helv. Chim. Acta, **46**, 889 (1963)

Fusarium roseum

Rao, P. G., Indian J. Pharm., **25**, 131 (1963)

Gibberella baccata (2~4%)

Gibberella saubinetti (5%)

Urech, J., E. Vischer and A. Wettstein, Helv. Chim. Acta, **43**, 1077 (1960)

Helminthosporium sativum (42%)

Tsuda, K., T. Asai, Y. Sato and T. Tanaka, Chem. Pharm. Bull. (Japan), **7**, 534 (1959)

Hormodendrum olivaceum

U. S. Pat. 3,010,877

Hormodendrum viride strain Lederle No. Z-10

Bernstein, S., L. I. Feldman, W. S. Allen, R. H. Blank and C. E. Linden, Chem. & Ind. 111 (1956)

O

$\longrightarrow$

O
OH
OH

Androst-4-ene-3, 17-dione

9α, 15β-Dihydroxyandrost-4-ene-3, 17-dione

Cercospora melonis

Kondo, E. and K. Tori, J. Am. Chem. Soc., **86**, 736 (1964)

Progesterone

15β-Hydroxyprogesterone

Bacillus megaterium NRRL B-938

McAleer, W. J., T. A. Jacob, L. B. Turnbull, E. F. Schoenewaldt and T. H. Stoudt, Arch. Biochem. Biophys., **73**, 127 (1958)

Helminthosporium sativum

Tsuda, K., T. Asai, Y. Sato, T. Tanaka and H. Hasegawa, Chem. Pharm, Bull. (Japan), **9**, 735 (1961)

Phycomyces blakesleeana

Eppstein, S. H., P. D., Meister, H. C. Murray and D. H. Peterson, Vitamins and Hormones, **14**, 359 (1956)

Progesterone

7α, 15β-Dihydroxyprogesterone

Helminthosporium sativum

Tsuda, K., T. Asai, Y. Sato, T. Tanaka and H. Hasegawa, Chem. Pharm. Bull (Japan), **9**, 735 (1961)

Progesterone

7β, 15β-Dihydroxyprogesterone

Diplodia tubericola

Tsuda, K., T. Asai, Y. Sato, T. Tanaka, T. Matsuhisa and H. Hasegawa, Chem. Pharm. Bull. (Japan), **8**, 626 (1960)

Helminthosporium sativum

Tsuda, K., T. Asai, Y. Sato, T. Tanaka and H. Hasegawa, Chem. Pharm. Bull. (Japan), **9**, 375 (1961)

Syncephalastrum racemosum

Tsuda, K., T. Asai, Y. Sato, T. Tanaka, and T. Matsuhisa and H. Hasegawa, Chem. Pharm. Bull. (Japan), **8**, 626 (1960)

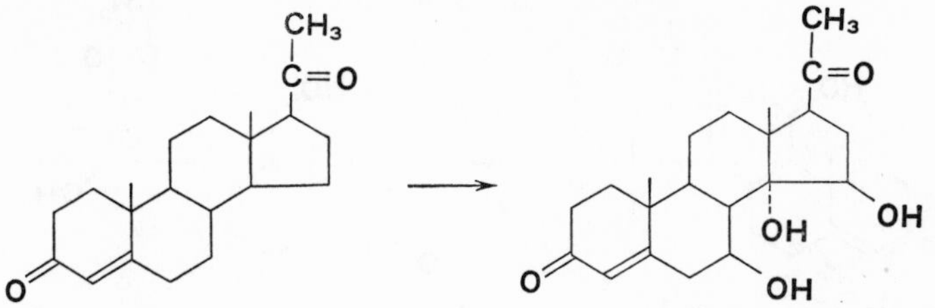

Progesterone

Syncephalastrum racemosum

7β, 14α, 15β-Trihydroxyprogesterone

Tsuda, K., T. Asai, Y. Sato, T. Tanaka, T. Matsuhisa and H. Hasegawa, Chem. Pharm. Bull. (Japan), **8**, 626 (1960)

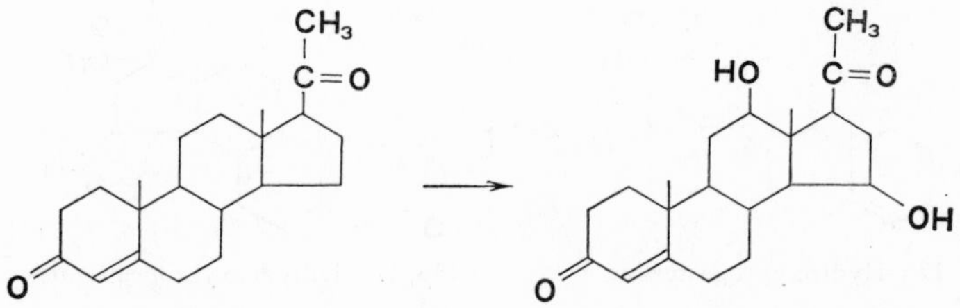

Progesterone

Calonectria decora (80%)

12β, 15β-Dihydroxyprogesterone

Schubert, A., G. Langbein and R. Siebert, Chem. Ber., **90**, 2576 (1957)

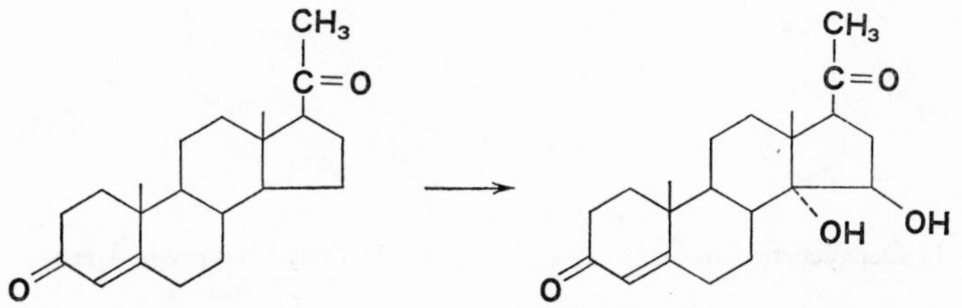

Progesterone

Helminthosporium sativum

14α, 15β-Dihydroxyprogesterone

Tsuda, K., T. Asai, Y. Sato, T. Tanaka and H. Hasegawa, Chem. Pharm. Bull. (Japan), **9**, 735 (1961)

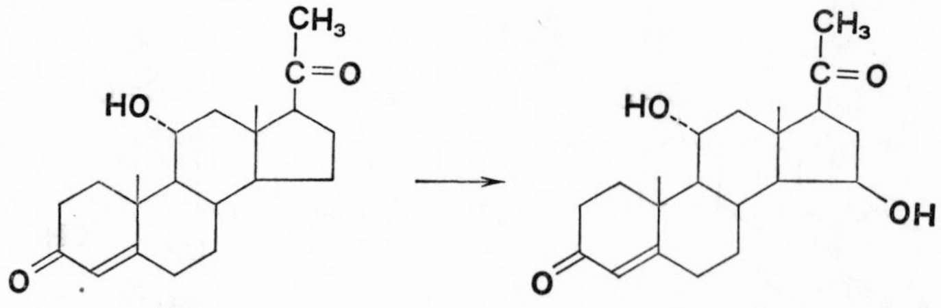

11α-Hydroxyprogesterone

Calonectria decora

11α, 15β-Dihydroxyprogesterone

Schubert, A., G. Langbein and R. Siebert, Chem. Ber., **90**, 2576 (1957)

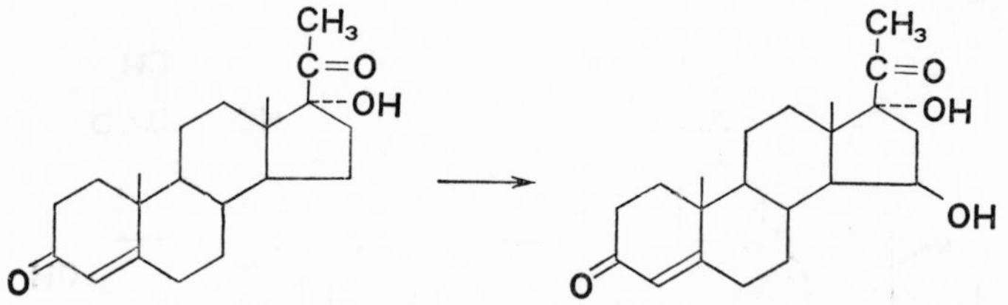

17α-Hydroxyprogesterone

Nigrospora oryzae

15β, 17α-Dihydroxyprogesterone

U. S. Pat. 2,793,163

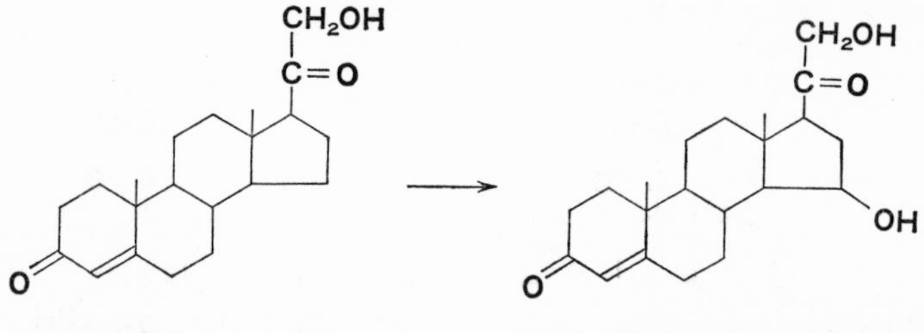

11-Deoxycorticosterone

Fusarium sp.

Gibberella baccata (20~60%)

15β, 21-Dihydroxypregn-4-ene-3, 20-dione

Eppstein, S. H., P. D. Meister, H. C. Murray and D. H. Peterson, Vitamins and Hormones, **14**, 359 (1956)

Meystre, Ch., E. Vischer and A. Wettstein, Helv. Chim. Acta, **38**, 381 (1955)

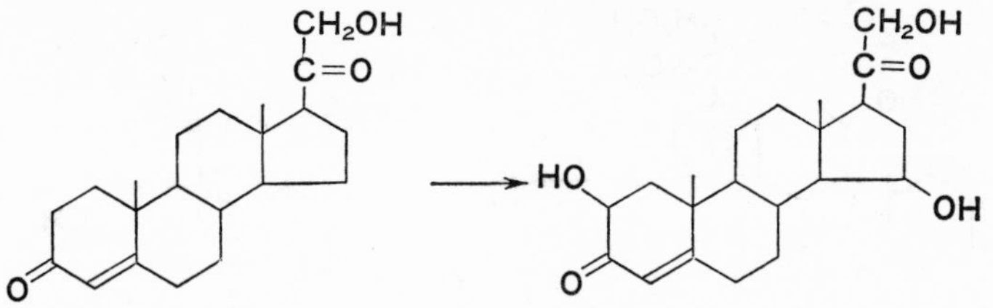

11-Deoxycorticosterone

2β, 15β, 21-Trihydroxypregn-
4-ene-3, 20-dione

Sclerotinia libertiana

Shirasaka, M., Chem. Pharm. Bull. (Japan), **9**, 54
(1961)

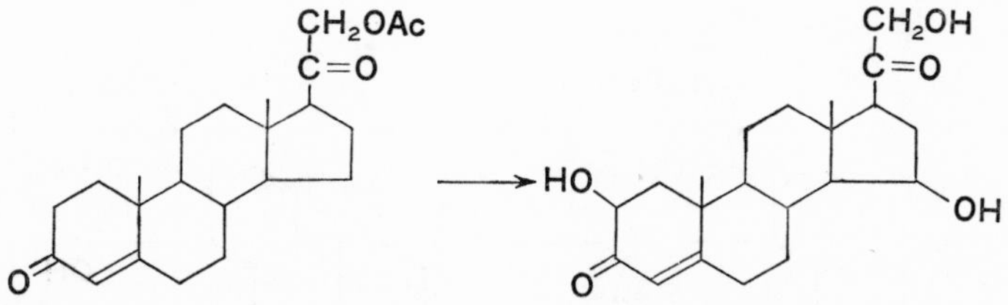

11-Deoxycorticosterone 21-acetate

2β, 15β, 21-Trihydroxypregn-
4-ene-3, 20-dione

Sclerotinia sclerotiorum

Japan Pat. 311,627

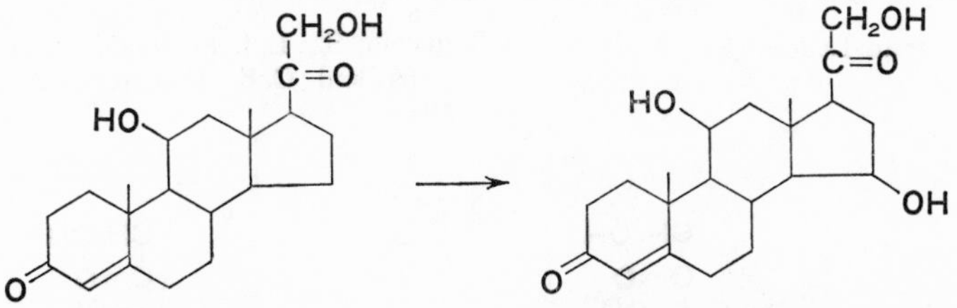

Corticosterone

11β, 15β, 21-Trihydroxypregn-
4-ene-3, 20-dione

Botrytis cinerea

Shirasaka, M., Chem. Pharm. Bull. (Japan), **9**, 152
(1961)

Sclerotinia libertiana

Shirasaka, M., Chem. Pharm. Bull. (Japan), **9**, 54
(1961)

Sclerotinia sclerotiorum

Japan Pat. 311,627

Corticosterone

15β, 21-Dihydroxypregn-4-ene-3, 11, 20-trione

Botrytis cinerea

Shirasaka, M., Chem. Pharm. Bull. (Japan), **9**, 152 (1961)

Sclerotium hydrophilum

Shirasaka, M. and M. Tsuruta, Chem. Pharm. Bull. (Japan), **9**, 196 (1961)

11-Deoxycortisol

15β, 17α, 21-Trihydroxypregn-4-ene-3, 20-dione

Bacillus megaterium

U. S. Pat. 2,958,631

Spicaria simplicissima

U. S. Pat. 3,010,877

Spicaria sp. strain Lederle No. Z-118

Bernstein, S., L. I. Feldman, W. S. Allen, R. H. Blank and C. E. Linden, Chem. & Ind., 111 (1956)

6α-Fluoro-11-deoxycortisol

6α-Fluoro-15β, 17α, 21-trihydroxypregn-4-ene-3, 20-dione

Aspergillus nidulans

U. S. Pat. 3,004,047

(1) 16-Hydroxylation

Estrone → 16α-Hydroxyestrone

Streptomyces halstedii ATCC 13499, NRRL B-2138

Streptomyces mediocidicus ATCC 13278

Kita, D. A., J. L. Sardinas and G. M. Shull, Nature, **190**, 627 (1961)

Estradiol → 16α-Hydroxyestradiol (Estriol)

Streptomyces halstedii ATCC 13499, NRRL B-2138

Streptomyces mediocidicus ATCC 13278

Kita, D. A., J. L. Sardinas and G. M. Shull, Nature, **190**, 627 (1961)

Testosterone → 16α-Hydroxytestosterone

Pestalotia funera

Thoma, R. W. et al., 69th Meeting N. Y. C. Branch of Soc. Am. Bact. N. Y. (1955)

Staurophoma sp.

U. S. Pat. 3,071,516

Streptomyces roseochromogenus

Eppstein, S. H., P. D. Meister, H. C. Murray and D. H. Peterson, Vitamins and Hormones, **14**, 359 (1956)

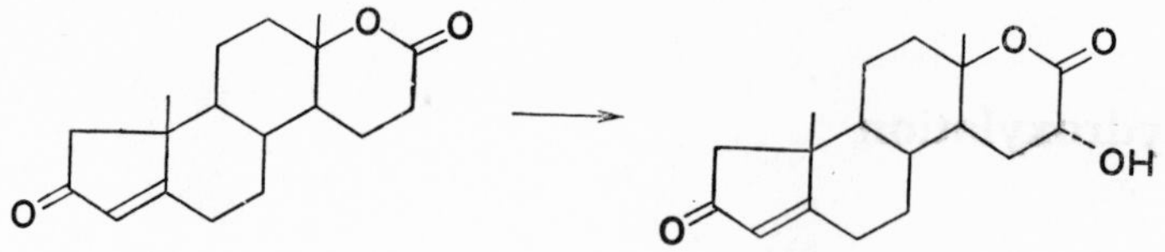

A-Nortestololactone

Streptomyces roseochromogenus

16α-Hydroxy-A-nortestololactone

U. S. Pat. 3,098,079

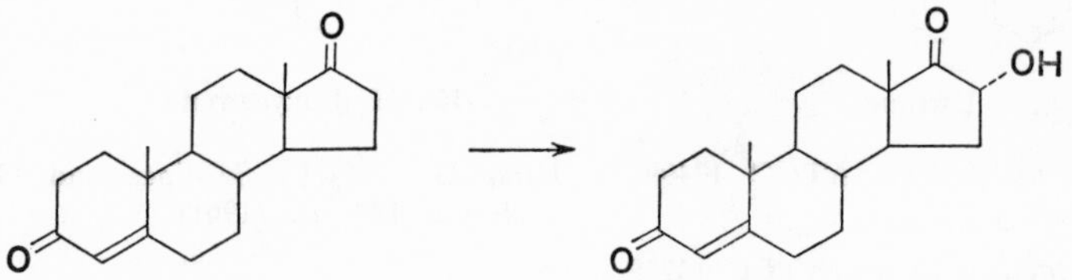

Androst-4-ene-3, 17-dione

Staurophoma sp.

Streptomyces roseochromogenus

16α-Hydroxyandrost-4-ene-3, 17-dione

U. S. Pat. 3,071,516

Eppstein, S. H., P. D. Meister, H. C. Murray and D. H. Peterson, Vitamins and Hormones, **14**, 359 (1956)

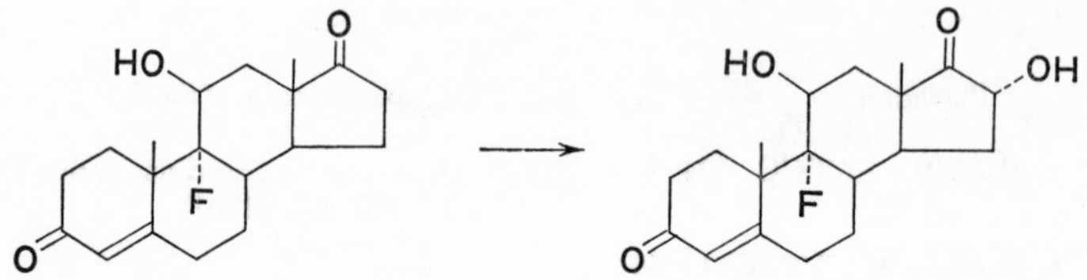

9α-Fluoro-11β-hydroxyandrost-
4-ene-3, 17-dione

Streptomyces roseochromogenus strain
Lederle AE-409

9α-Fluoro-11β, 16α-dihydroxyandrost-
4-ene-3, 17-dione

Bernstein, S., R. H. Lenhard, N. E. Rigler and M. A. Darken, J. Org. Chem., **25**, 297 (1960)

Progesterone

16α-Hydroxyprogesterone

Actinomyces sp. ATCC 11009

Perlman, D., E. Titus and J. Fried, J. Am. Chem. Soc., **74**, 2126 (1952)

Actinomycetes

Vondrová, O. and A. Čapek, Folia Microbiol, **8**, 117 (1963)

Staurophoma sp.

U. S. Pat. 3,071,516

Streptomyces sp. (30~40%)

Perlman, D., E. O'Brien, A. P. Bayan and R. B. Greenfield, J. Bacteriol, **69**, 347 (1955)

Streptomyces sp.

Shirasaka, M. and M. Ozaki, J. Ferm. Assoc. (Japan), **19**, 389 (1961)

12α-Fluoro-11β-hydroxy-progesterone

12α-Fluoro-11β, 16α-dihydroxy-progesterone

Streptomyces roseochromogenus

Brit. Pat. 916,790

11-Deoxycorticosterone

16α, 21-Dihydroxypregn-4-ene-3, 20-dione

Didymella vodakii

Wettstein, A., Experientia, **11**, 465 (1955)

Streptomyces roseochromogenus

Eppstein, S. H., P. D. Meister, H. C. Murray and D. H. Peterson, Vitamins and Hormones, **14**, 359 (1956)

Streptomyces sp. (15%)

Vischer, E., J. Schmidlin and A. Wettstein, Helv. Chim. Acta, **37**, 321 (1954)

11-Deoxycortisol

16α, 17α, 21-Trihydroxypregn-
4-ene-3, 20-dione

Streptomyces roseochromogenus, conidia
Streptomyces viridis, conidia

Vézina, C., S. N. Sehgal and K. Singh, Appl.
Microbiol., **11**, 50 (1963)

Cortisol

11β, 16α, 17α, 21-Tetrahydroxypregn-
4-ene-3, 20-dione

Nocardia italica

Belg. Pat. 620,272

9α-Fluorocortisol

9α-Fluoro-11β, 16α, 17α, 21-
tetrahydroxypregn-4-
ene-3, 20-dione

Nocardia italica

Belg. Pat. 620,272

Streptomyces halstedii

U. S. Pat. 2,991,230

Streptomyces roseochromogenus strain
Waksman No. 3689 (50%)

Thoma, R. W., J. Fried, S. Bonanno and P.
Grabowich, J. Am. Chem. Soc., **79**, 4818 (1957)

Streptomyces roseochromogenus, spore

U. S. Pat. 2,982,693

9α-Fluorocortisol

9α-Fluoro-2β, 11β, 16α, 17α, 21-
pentahydroxypregn-4-
ene-3, 20-dione

Streptomyces roseochromogenus   ATCC
3347 (71%)

Streptomyces roseochromogenus   strain
Waksman No. 3689 (75%)

Goodman, J. J. and L. L. Smith, Appl. Microbiol.,
9, 372 (1961)

12α-Fluorocortisol

12α-Fluoro-11β, 16α, 17α, 21-
tetrahydroxypregn-4-
ene-3, 20-dione

Streptomyces roseochromogenus

Brit. Pat. 916,790

9α-Fluoroprednisolone

9α-Fluoro-11β, 16α, 17α, 21-
tetrahydroxypregna-1, 4-
diene-3, 20-dione

Nocardia italica

Streptomyces roseochromogenus   strain
Waksman No. 3689 (20%)

Belg. Pat. 620,272

Thoma, R. W., J. Fried, S. Bonanno and P.
Grabowich, J. Am. Chem. Soc., **79**, 4818 (1957)

(m) 17-Hydroxylation

Progesterone → 17α-Hydroxyprogesterone

Cephalothecium roseum

Meister, P. D., L. M. Reineke, R. C. Meeks, H. C. Murray, S. H. Eppstein, H. M. Leigh, A. Weintraub and D. H. Peterson, J. Am. Chem. Soc., **76**, 4050 (1954)

Sporormia minima

U. S. Pat. 2,813,060

Trichoderma album (15%)

Japan Pat. 228,171

Trichoderma koningi (10~15%)

Trichoderma sp. (10~15%)

Trichoderma sp. (*Trichoderma ligno-rum*)

Brit. Pat. 759,731

Progesterone → 6β, 17α-Dihydroxyprogesterone

Naucoria confragosa C-172

Schuytema, E. C., M. P. Hargie, D. J. Siehr, I. Merits, J. R. Schenck, M. S. Smith and E. L. Varner, Appl. Microbiol., **11**, 256 (1963)

Progesterone

Cephalothecium roseum ATCC 8685

Dactylium dendroides

11α, 17α-Dihydroxyprogesterone

Meister, P. D., L. M. Reineke, R. C. Meeks, H. C. Murray, S. H. Eppstein, H. M. Leigh, A. Weintraub and D. H. Peterson, J. Am. Chem. Soc., **76**, 4050 (1954)

Dulaney, E. L., W. J. McAleer, H. R. Barkemeyer and C. Hlavac, Appl. Microbiol., **3**, 372 (1955)

11α-Hydroxyprogesterone

Dactylium dendroides

Sepedonium ampullosporum

11α, 17α-Dihydroxyprogesterone

Dulaney, E. L., W. J. McAleer, H. R. Barkemeyer and C. Hlavac, Appl. Microbiol., **3**, 372 (1955)

U. S. Pat. 3,011,951

11β-Hydroxyprogesterone

Sporormia minima

Trichoderma viride (8~10%)

11β, 17α-Dihydroxyprogesterone

U. S. Pat. 2,813,060

Japan Pat. 228,171

11-Deoxycorticosterone → 17α, 21-Dihydroxypregn-4-ene-3, 20-dione (11-Deoxycortisol)

Sporormia minima

U. S. Pat. 2,813,060

Trichothecium roseum

Meystre Ch., E. Vischer and A. Wettstein, Helv. Chim. Acta, **37**, 1548 (1954)

Trichoderma viride (8~10%)

Japan Pat. 228,171

11-Deoxycorticosterone → 6β, 17α, 21-Trihydroxypregn-4-ene-3, 20-dione

Cephalothecium roseum ATCC 8685

Meister, P.D., L. M. Reineke, R. C. Meeks, H. C. Murray, S. H., Eppstein, H. M. Leigh, A. Weintraub and D. H. Peterson, J. Am. Chem. Soc., **76**, 4050 (1954)

11-Deoxycorticosterone → 11α, 17α, 21-Trihydroxypregn-4-ene-3, 20-dione

Cephalothecium roseum ATCC 8685

Meister, P. D., L. M. Reineke, R. C. Meeks, H. C. Murray, S. H. Eppstein, H. M. Leigh, A. Weintraub and D. H. Peterson, J. Am. Chem. Soc., **76**, 4050 (1954)

Scopulariopsis brevicaulis

U. S. Pat. 2,970,085

Trichothecium roseum

CH₂OH / C=O structure

11-Deoxycorticosterone

17α, 21-Dihydroxypregn-4-ene-
3, 11, 20-trione (Cortisone)

Cephalothecium roseum ATCC 8685

Meister, P. D., L. M. Reineke, R. C. Meeks, H. C.
Murray, S. H. Eppstein, H. M. Leigh, A. Weintraub and D. H. Peterson, J. Am. Chem. Soc.,
76, 4050 (1954)

Corticosterone

17α, 21-Dihydroxypregn-4-ene-
3, 11, 20-trione (Cortisone)

Cephalothecium roseum ATCC 8685

Meister, P. D., L. M. Reineke, R. C. Meeks, H. C.
Murray, S. H. Eppstein, H. M. Leigh, A. Weintraub and D. H. Peterson, J. Am. Chem. Soc.,
76, 4050 (1954)

Trichothecium roseum

Meystre Ch., E. Vischer and A. Wettstein, Helv.
Chim. Acta, **37**, 1548 (1954)

Corticosterone

11β, 17α, 21-Trihydroxypregn-4-ene-
3, 20-dione (Cortisol)

Cephalothecium roseum ATCC 8685

Meister, P. D., L. M. Reineke, R. C. Meeks, H. C.
Murray, S. H. Eppstein, H. M. Leigh, A. Weintraub and D. H. Peterson, J. Am. Chem. Soc.,
76, 4050 (1954)

Sporormia minima

U. S. Pat. 2,813,060

Trichothecium roseum

Meystre, Ch., E. Vischer and A. Wettstein, Helv.
Chim. Acta, **37**, 1548 (1954)

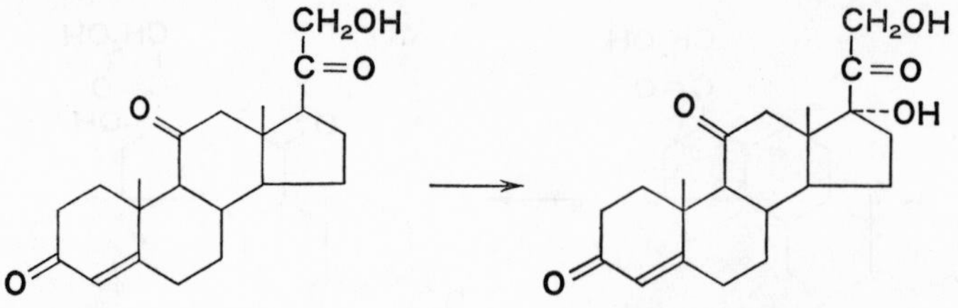

11-Dehydrocorticosterone

17α, 21-Dihydroxypregn-4-ene-
3, 11, 20-trione (Cortisone)

Trichothecium roseum

Meystre, Ch., E. Vischer and A. Wettstein, Helv.
Chim. Acta, **37**, 1548 (1954)

(n) 18-Hydroxylation

Androst-4-ene-3, 17-dione

9α, 18-Dihydroxyandrost-
4-ene-3, 17-dione

Cercospora melonis

Kondo, E. and K. Tori, J. Am. Chem. Soc., **86**, 736 (1964)

(o) 19-Hydroxylation

11-Deoxycortisol → 17α, 19, 21-Trihydroxypregn-4-ene-3, 20-dione

Corticium sasakii

Hasegawa, T. and T. Takahashi, Bull. Agr. Chem. Soc. (Japan), **22**, 212 (1958)

Corticium vagum

Japan Pat. 276,077

Pestalotia sp.

Japan Pat. 310,308

(p) 21-Hydroxylation

19-Norprogesterone

21-Hydroxy-19-norpregn-
4-ene-3, 20-dione

Aspergillus niger ATCC 9142

Zaffaroni, A., C. Casas-Campillo, F. Cordoba and
G. Rosenkranz, Experientia, **11**, 219 (1955)

Progesterone

21-Hydroxypregn-4-ene-3, 20-dione
(11-Deoxycorticosterone)

Aspergillus niger ATCC 9142

Zaffaroni, A., C. Casas-Campillo, F. Cordoba and
G. Rosenkranz, Experientia, **11**, 219 (1955)

Cercosporella herpotrichoides

U. S. Pat. 3,056,730

Hendersonia sp. (25~30%)

Japan Pat. 228,172

Kabatiella phoradendri

U. S. Pat. 2,977,286

Ophiobolus herbotrichus (60%)

Meystre, Ch., E. Vischer and A. Wettstein, Helv.
Chim. Acta, **37**, 1548 (1954)

Sclerotinia fructicola

U. S. Pat. 2,778,776

Wojnowicia graminis (35~45%)

McAleer, W. J. and E. L. Dulaney, Arch. Biochem.
Biophys., **62**, 109 (1956)

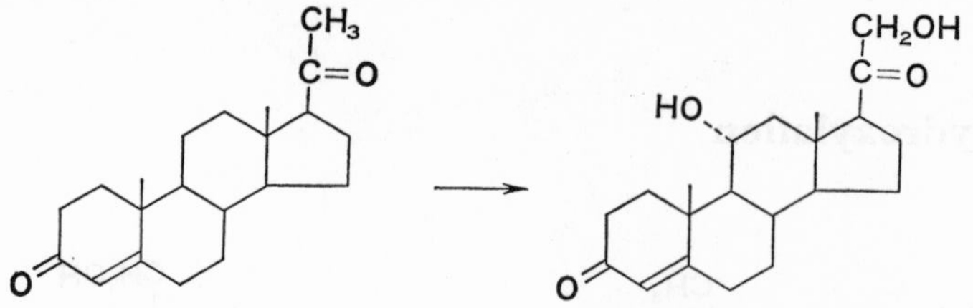

Progesterone

11α, 21-Dihydroxypregn-
4-ene-3, 20-dione

Aspergillus sp.

Weisz, E., G. Wix and M. Bodánszky, Naturwiss., **43**, 39 (1956)

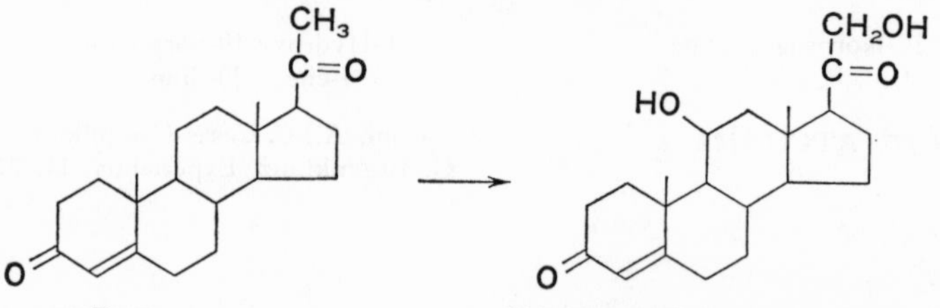

Progesterone

11β, 21-Dihydroxypregn-4-ene-
3, 20-dione (Corticosterone)

Curvularia lunata

Rubin, B. A. et al., Bact. Proc., **56**, 33 (1956)

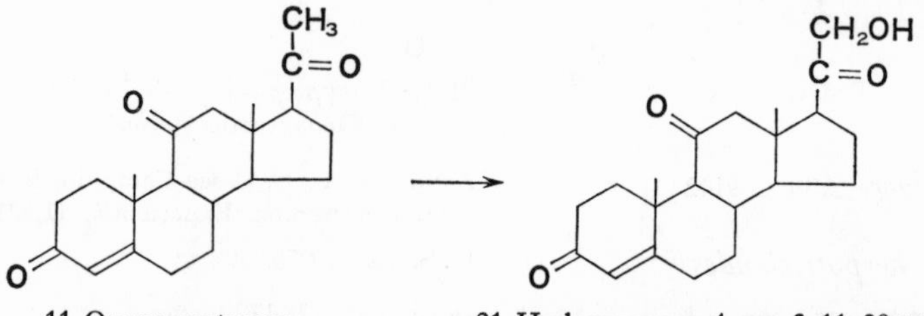

11-Oxoprogesterone

21-Hydroxypregn-4-ene-3, 11, 20-trione

Aspergillus niger ATCC 9142

Zaffaroni, A., C. Casas-Campillo, F. Cordoba and G. Rosenkranz, Experientia, **11**, 219 (1955)

Ophiobolus herbotrichus

Meystre, Ch., E. Vischer and A. Wettstein, Helv. Chim. Acta, **37**, 1548 (1954)

17α-Hydroxy-19-norprogesterone

17α, 21-Dihydroxy-19-norpregn-
4-ene-3, 20-dione

Ophiobolus herbotrichus

Zaffaroni, A., H. J. Ringold, G. Rosenkranz, F.
Sondheimer, G. H. Thomas and C. Djerassi, J.
Am. Chem. Soc., **76**, 6210 (1954)

6β-Hydroxyprogesterone

6β, 21-Dihydroxypregn-
4-ene-3, 20-dione

Aspergillus niger ATCC 9142

Zaffaroni, A., C. Casas-Campillo, F. Cordoba and
G. Rosenkranz, Experientia, **11**, 219 (1955)

11α-Hydroxyprogesterone

11α, 21-Dihydroxypregn-4-ene-3, 20-
dione (11-Epicorticosterone)

Aspergillus niger ATCC 9142

Hendersonia sp. (10%)

Zaffaroni, A., C. Casas-Campillo, F. Cordoba and
G. Rosenkranz, Experientia, **11**, 219 (1955)

Japan Pat. 228,172

11β-Hydroxyprogesterone

Aspergillus niger ATCC 9142

Hendersonia acicola (10~15%)

11β, 21-Dihydroxypregn-4-ene-
3, 20-dione (Corticosterone)

Zaffaroni, A., C. Casas-Campillo, F. Cordoba and
G. Rosenkranz, Experientia, **11**, 219 (1955)

Brit. Pat. 767,360

14α-Hydroxyprogesterone

Aspergillus niger ATCC 9142

14α, 21-Dihydroxypregn-
4-ene-3, 20-dione

Zaffaroni, A., C. Casas-Campillo, F. Cordoba and
G. Rosenkranz, Experientia, **11**, 219 (1955)

17α-Hydroxyprogesterone

Aspergillus niger (18%)
Ophiobolus herbotrichus

17α, 21-Dihydroxypregn-4-ene-
3, 20-dione (11-Deoxycortisol)

Brit. Pat. 749,943

Meystre, Ch., E. Vischer and A. Wettstein, Helv.
Chim. Acta, **37**, 1548 (1954)

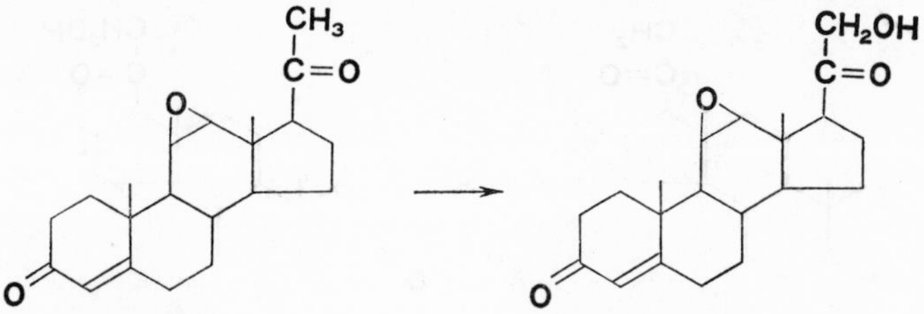

11β, 12β-Oxidoprogesterone

11β, 12β-Oxido-21-hydroxypregn-
4-ene-3, 20-dione

Cercosporella herpotrichoides

U. S. Pat. 3,056,730

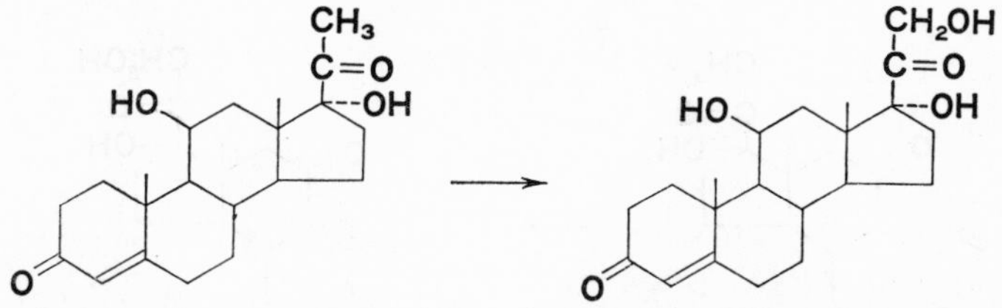

11β, 17α-Dihydroxyprogesterone

11β, 17α, 21-Trihydroxypregn-4-ene-
3, 20-dione (Cortisol)

Hendersonia herpotricia (5%)

Japan Pat. 228,172

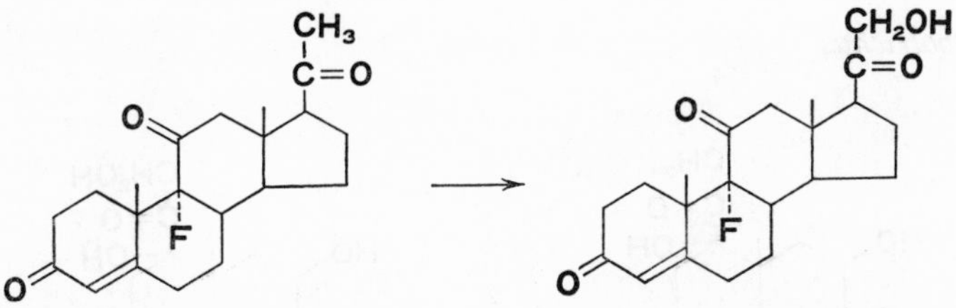

9α-Fluoro-11-oxoprogesterone

9α-Fluoro-21-hydroxypregn-
4-ene-3, 11, 20-trione

Cercosporella herpotrichoides

U. S. Pat. 3,056,730

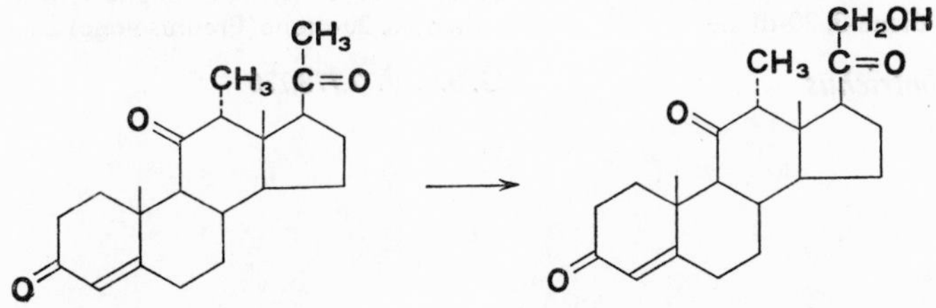

12α-Methyl-11-oxoprogesterone

12α-Methyl-21-hydroxypregn-4-
ene-3, 11, 20-trione

Cercosporella herpotrichoides
Kabatiella phoradendri

U. S. Pat. 3,056,730
U. S. Pat. 2,977,286

— 99 —

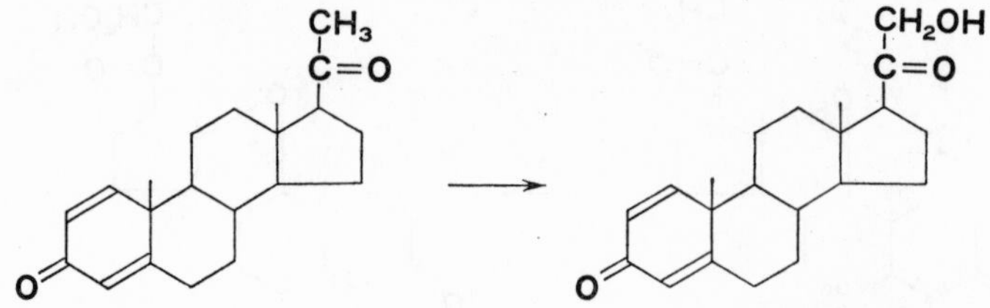

1-Dehydroprogesterone

Ophiobolus herbotrichus

21-Hydroxypregna-1, 4-
diene-3, 20-dione

U. S. Pat. 2,778,776

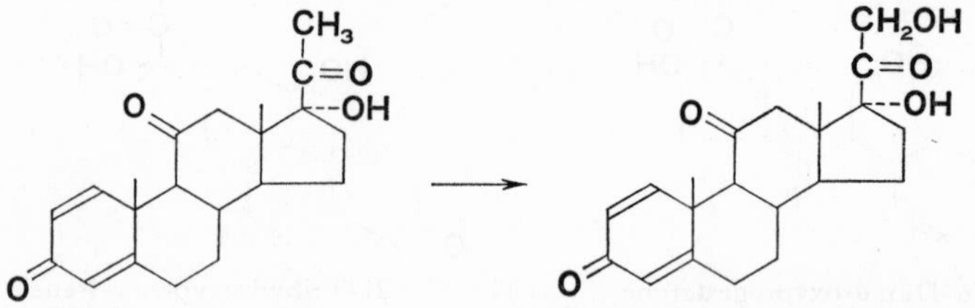

17α-Hydroxypregna-1, 4-
diene-3, 11, 20-trione

Sclerotinia fructicola
Ophiobolus herbotrichus

17α, 21-Dihydroxypregna-1, 4-diene-
3, 11, 20-trione (Prednisone)

U. S. Pat. 2,778,776

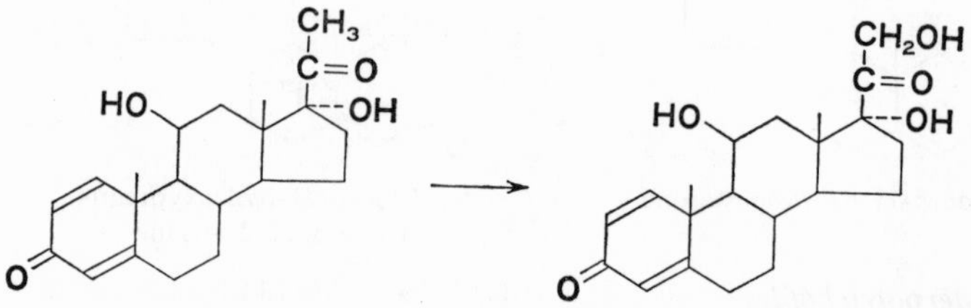

11β, 17α-Dihydroxypregna-1, 4-
diene-3, 20-dione

Ophiobolus herbotrichus

11β, 17α, 21-Trihydroxypregna-1, 4-
diene-3, 20-dione (Prednisolone)

U. S. Pat. 2,778,776

B. Dehydrogenation

(a) $\diagup CH{-}OH \longrightarrow \diagup C{=}O$

Estradiol → Estrone

Actinomycetes of the Albus group (100%)	Welsch, M. and C. Heusghem, Compt. Rend. Soc. Biol., **142**, 1074 (1948)
Flavobacterium dehydrogenans	Ercoli, A., Biochim. Terap. sper., **28**, 125 (1941)
Proactinomyces sp.	Turfitt, G. E., Biochem. J., **42**, 376 (1948)
Pseudodiphtheria bacilli	Zimmermann, W. and G. May, Zntr. Bakt. Parasitenk. I Abt, **151**, 462 (1944)
Pseudomonas testosteroni ATCC 11996	Hurlock, B. and P. Talalay, J. Biol. Chem., **233**, 886 (1958)
Streptomyces diastaticus, conidia	Vézina, C., S. N. Sehgal and K. Singh, Appl. Microbiol, **11**, 50 (1963)
Streptomyces rimosus, conidia	

Estradiol → 16α-Hydroxyestrone

Streptomyces halstedii ATCC 13499	Kita, D. A., J. L. Sardinas and G. M. Shull, Nature, **190**, 627 (1961)
Streptomyces mediocidicus ATCC 13278	

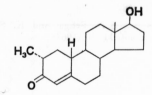

19-Nortestosterone → Estrone

Bacillus sphaericus ATCC 7055

Nocardia corallina

Gaul, C., R. I. Dorfman and S. R. Stitch, Biochem. Biophys. Acta, **49**, 387 (1961)

U. S. Pat. 3,087,864

19-Nortestosterone → 19-Norandrost-4-ene-3, 17-dione

Bacillus sphaericus ATCC 7055

Gaul, C., R. I. Dorfman and S. R. Stitch, Biochem. Biophys. Acta, **49**, 387 (1961)

2α-Methyl-19-nortestosterone → 2-Methylestrone

Septomyxa affinis ATCC 6737 (17%)

Peterson, D. H., L. M. Reineke, H. C. Murray and O. K. Sebek, Chem. & Ind., 1301 (1960)

4-Methyl-19-nortestosterone → 4-Methylestrone

Septomyxa affinis ATCC 6737 (17%)

Peterson, D. H., L. M. Reineke, H. C. Murray and O. K. Sebek, Chem. & Ind., 1301 (1960)

Testosterone

Androst-4-ene-3, 17-dione

Bacillus pulvifaciens IAM N-19-2

Iizuka, H., A. Naito and Y. Sato, J. Gen. Appl. Microbiol. (Japan), **7**, 118 (1961)

Pseudomonas chlororaphis IAM 1511

Naito, A., Y. Sato, H. Iizuka and K. Tsuda, Steroids, **3**, 327 (1964)

Pseudomonas testosteroni ATCC 11996

Marcus, P. I. and P. Talalay, J. Biol. Chem., **218**, 661 (1956)

Testosterone

Androst-1-ene-3, 17-dione

Nocardia corallina

U. S. Pat. 3,087,864

Testosterone

15α-Hydroxyandrost-4-ene-3, 17-dione

Fusarium sp.

Peterson, D. H., Record Chem. Progr., **17**, 211 (1956)

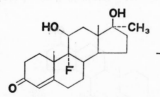

9α-Fluoro-17α-methyl-11β, 17β-dihydroxyandrost-4-en-3-one

9α-Fluoro-17α-methyl-1α, 2α, 17β-trihydroxyandrost-4-ene-3, 11-dione

Nocardia corallina ATCC 999 (18%)

Sax, K. J., C. E. Holmlund, L. I. Feldman, R. H. Evans, Jr., R. H. Blank, A. J. Shay, J. S. Schultz and M. Dann, Steroids, **5**, 345 (1965)

2α-Hydroxytestosterone 2α,
17β-diacetate

Nocardia corallina

2-Hydroxyandrost-1-ene-3,
17-dione

U. S. Pat. 3,087,864

2α-Hydroxytestosterone

Bacillus sphaericus ATCC 7055

2-Hydroxyandrosta-1, 4-diene-
3, 17-dione

Gaul, C., S. R. Stitch, M. Gut and R. I. Dorfman,
J. Org. Chem., **24**, 418 (1959)

3α-Hydroxyandrost-5-en-17-one

Aerobic bacteria (87%)

Flavobacterium carbonilicum

Flavobacterium dehydrogenans

Proactinomyces erythropolis

Androst-4-ene-3, 17-dione

Mamoli, L. and A. Vercellone Ber., **71B**, 1686
(1938)

Molina, L., A. Ercoli, Boll. ist sieroterap milanese,
23, 164 (1944)

Arnaudi, C., Boll. sez. ital., Soc. intern. Microbiol.,
11, 208 (1939)

Turfitt, G. E., Biochem. J, **40**, 79 (1946)

3α-Hydroxyandrost-5-en-17-one

Impoverished yeast
Oxidizing bacteria (81%)

Testosterone

U. S. Pat. 2,236,574

Mamoli, L., Ber., **71B**, 2278 (1938)

Androst-5-ene-3β, 17β-diol

Androst-4-ene-3, 17-dione

Flavobacterium androstenedionicum
Flavobacterium carbonilicum

Molina, L. and A. Ercoli, Boll. ist sieroterap milanese, **23**, 164 (1944)

Flavobacterium dehydrogenans (4%)
Proactinomyces erythropolis

Ercoli, A., Z. physiol. Chem., **270**, 266 (1941)

Turfitt, G. E., Biochem. J., **40**, 79 (1946)

Androst-5-ene-3β, 17β-diol

Testosterone

Flavobacterium carbonilicum

Molina, L. and A. Ercoli, Boll. ist sieroterap. milanese, **23**, 164 (1944)

Flavobacterium dehydrogenans (64%)

Ercoli, A., Z. Physiol. Chem., **270**, 266 (1941)

Pseudodiphtheria bacilli

Zimmermann, W. and G. May, Zentr. Bakt. Parasitenk. IAbt., **151**, 462 (1944)

Androst-5-ene-3β, 17β-diol

3β-Hydroxyandrost-5-en-17-one

Pseudomonas sp.

Talalay, P. and M. M. Dobson, J. Biol. Chem, **205**, 823 (1953)

Androst-5-ene-3β, 17α-diol

17α-Hydroxyandrost-4-
en-3-one
(Epitestosterone)

Yeast

U. S. Pat. 2,186,906

Dehydroepiandrosterone

Androst-4-ene-3, 17-dione

Alcaligenes faecalis (100%)

Hughes, H. B. and L. H. Schmidt, Proc. Soc. Expt. Biol. Med., **51**, 162 (1942)

Bacillus pulvifaciens IAM N-19-2

Iizuka, H., A. Naito and Y. Sato, J. Gen. Appl. Microbiol (Japan), **7**, 118 (1961)

Fusarium caucasicum
Fusarium solani

Vischer, E. and A. Wettstein, Experientia, **9**, 371 (1953)

Dehydroepiandrosterone

1α-Hydroxyandrost-4-ene-
3, 17-dione

Penicillium sp.

Dodson, R. M., A. H. Goldkamp and R. D. Muir, J. Am. Chem. Soc., **79**, 3921 (1957)

Dehydroepiandrosterone

Androst-5-ene-3, 17-dione

Pseudomonas testosteroni ATCC 11996

Talalay, P. and P. I. Marcus, J. Biol. Chem., **218**, 675 (1956)

17α-Methylandrost-5-ene-
3β, 17β-diol

17α-Methyltestosterone

Dehydrogenating bacteria (75%)

Mamoli, L., Gazz. Chim. Ital., **69**, 237 (1939)

17α-Ethinylandrost-5-ene-
3β, 17β-diol

17α-Ethinyltestosterone

Flavobacterium dehydrogenans

Ercoli, A., Biochim. Terap. sper., **28**, 125 (1941)

3β-Hydroxy-5α, 6α-oxido-
androstan-17-one

6α-Hydroxyandrost-4-ene-
3, 17-dione

Nocardia restrictus No. 545

Lee, S. S. and C. J. Sih, Biochemistry, **3**, 1267 (1964)

3β, 5α, 6β-Trihydroxy
androstan-17-one

Nocardia restrictus No. 545

6β-Hydroxyandrost-4-ene-
3, 17-dione

Lee, S. S. and C. J. Sih, Biochemistry, **3**, 1267 (1964)

3α-Hydroxy-5α-androstan-17-one

Pseudomonas sp.

5α-Androstane-3, 17-dione

Talalay, P. and P. I. Marcus, Nature, **173**, 1189 (1954)

5α-Androstane-3β, 17β-diol

Flavobacterium dehydrogenans
Pseudomonas testosteroni ATCC 11996

5α-Androstane-3, 17-dione

Arnaudi, C., Experientia, **7**, 81 (1951)

Talalay, P. and P. I. Marcus, J. Biol. Chem, **218**, 675 (1956)

Pregnenolone

Aspergillus niger
Bacillus pulvifaciens IAM N-19-2

Bacterial mixture

Progesterone

Perlman, D., Science, **115**, 529 (1952)

Iizuka, H., A. Naito and Y. Sato, J. Gen. Appl. Microbiol (Japan), **7**, 118 (1961)

Mamoli, L., Ber., **71 B**, 2701 (1938)

Flavobacterium dehydrogenans (82%)

Ercoli, A., Boll. Sci. Fac. Chim. Ind. Bologna, **279** (1940)

Phycomyces blakesleeanus

Perlman, D., Science, **115**, 529 (1952)

Streptomyces sp.

Pregnenolone

Androsta-1, 4-diene-3, 17-dione

Fusarium caucasicum

Fusarium solani

Vischer, E. and A. Wettstein, Experientia, **9**, 371 (1953)

Pycnodothis sp.

Shull, G. M., Trans. N.Y. Acad. Sci., **19**, 147 (1956)

3β-Hydroxy-5β-pregnan-20-one

Progesterone

Streptomyces sp.

Perlman, D., E. O'Brien, A. P. Bayan and R. B. Greenfield, Jr., J. Bacteriol, **69**, 347 (1955)

3β, 21-Dihydroxypregn-5-en-20-one 21-acetate

21-Hydroxypregn-4-ene-3, 20-dione
(11-Deoxycorticosterone)

Corynebacterium mediolanum (34%)

Mamoli, L., Ber., **72 B**, 1863 (1939)

Corticosterone

17α, 21-Dihydroxypregn-
4-ene-3, 11, 20-trione
(Cortisone)

Cephalothecium roseum

Meister, P. D., L. M. Reineke, R. C. Meeks, H. C.
Murray, S. H. Eppstein, H. M. Leigh, A.
Weintraub and D. H. Peterson, J. Am. Chem.
Soc., **76**, 4050 (1954)

Trichothecium roseum

Meystre, Ch. E. Vischer and A. Wettstein, Helv.
Chim. Acta, **37**, 1548 (1954)

Corticosterone

6β, 21-Dihydroxypregn-4-ene-
3, 11, 20-trione

Sclerotium hydrophilum

Shirasaka, M. and M. Tsuruta, Chem. Pharm.
Bull (Japan), **9**, 196 (1961)

Corticosterone

14α, 21-Dihydroxypregn-
4-ene-3, 11, 20-trione

Absidia regnieri

Shirasaka, M., Chem. Pharm. Bull. (Japan), **9**, 59
(1961)

Bacillus cereus

Shirasaka, M., M. Ozaki and S. Sugawara, J. Gen.
Appl. Microbiol. (Japan), **7**, 341 (1961)

Corticosterone

15β, 21-Dihydroxypregn-
4-ene-3, 11, 20-trione

Botrytis cinerea

Shirasaka, M., Chem. Pharm. Bull. (Japan), **9**, 152
(1961)

Sclerotium hydrophilum

Shirasaka, M. and M. Tsuruta, Chem. Pharm.
Bull. (Japan), **9**, 196 (1961)

11β, 21-Dihydroxy-cis-pregna-
4, 17(20)-dien-3-one

6β, 21-Dihydroxy-cis-pregna-
4, 17(20)-diene-3, 11-dione

Rhizopus arrhizus

Hanze, A. R., O. K. Sebek and H. C. Murray, J.
Org. Chem., **25**, 1968 (1960)

11β, 21-Dihydroxy-cis-pregna-
4, 17(20)-dien-3-one

9α, 21-Dihydroxy-cis-pregna-
4, 17(20)-diene-3, 11-dione

Helicostylum piriforme
Cunninghamella blakesleeana

Hanze, A. R., O. K. Sebek and H. C. Murray, J.
Org. Chem., **25**, 1968 (1960)

3β, 17α, 21-Trihydroxy-
pregn-5-en-20-one

Corynebacterium mediolanum

17α, 21-Dihydroxypregn-4-ene-
3, 20-dione
(11-Deoxycortisol)

U. S. Pat. 3,030,278

3α, 17α, 21-Trihydroxy-5α-
pregnane-11, 20-dione

Pseudomonas sp.

16α, 17α, 21-Trihydroxy-5α-
pregnane-3, 11, 20-trione

Talalay, P. and P. I. Marcus, Nature, **173**, **1189**
(1954)

11β, 21-Dihydroxy-16α, 17α-iso-
propylidenedioxypregn-4-ene-
3, 20-dione

Nocardia corallina ATCC 999

21-Hydroxy-16α, 17α-isopropyli-
denedioxypregna-1, 4-diene-
3, 11, 20-trione

Sax, K. J., C. E. Holmlund, L. I. Feldman, R. H.
Evans, Jr., R. H. Blank, A. J. Shay, J. S. Schultz
and M. Dann, Steroids, **5**, 345 (1965)

(b) $\rangle CH_2 \longrightarrow \rangle C=O$

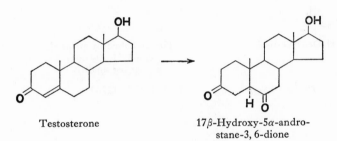

19-Nortestosterone

17β-Hydroxy-19-nor-5α-
androstane-3, 6-dione

Rhizopus reflexus

U. S. Pat. 2,692,273

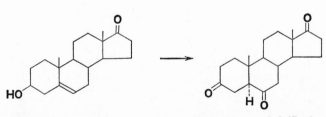

Testosterone

17β-Hydroxy-5α-andro-
stane-3, 6-dione

Rhizopus reflexus

U. S. Pat. 2,692,273

Dehydroepiandrosterone

5α-Androstane-3, 6, 17-trione

Bacillus pulvifaciens IAM N-19-2

Iizuka, H., A. Naito and Y. Sato, J. Gen. Appl.
Microbiol. (Japan), **7**, 118 (1961)

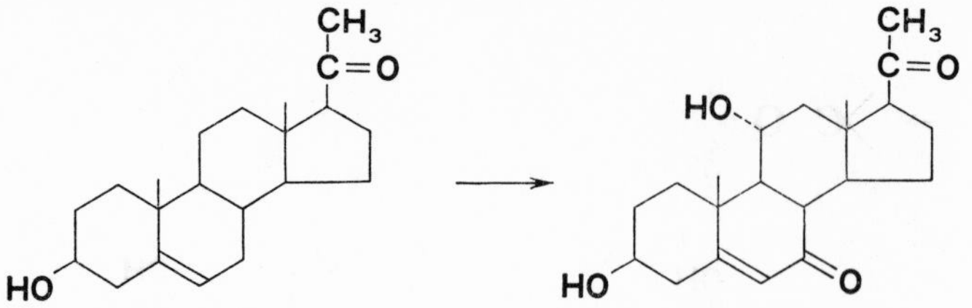

Pregnenolone

Rhizopus arrhizus (17.5%)

3β, 11α-Dihydroxypregn-5-
ene-7, 20-dione

Can. Pat. 506,689

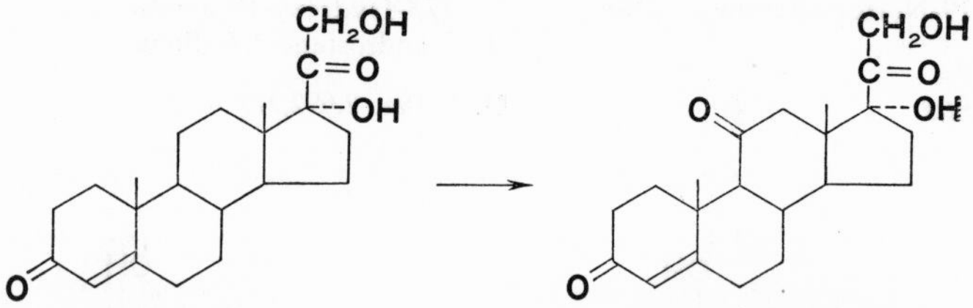

11-Deoxycortisol

Cunninghamella blakesleeana (9.5~ 13.0%)

17α, 21-Dihydroxypregn-4-
ene-3, 11, 20-trione
(Cortisone)

U. S. Pat. 2,602,769

(c) $-CH_2-CH_2- \longrightarrow -CH=CH-$

19-Nortestosterone

17β-Hydroxy-19-norandrosta-
1, 4-dien-3-one

Protaminobacter alboflavum
Protaminobacter rubrum

U. S. Pat. 2,776,927

Testosterone

1-Dehydrotestololactone

Cylindrocarpon radicicola (50%)

Fried, J., R. W. Thoma and A. Klingsberg, J. Am. Chem. Soc., **75**, 5764 (1953)

Testosterone

Androsta-1, 4-diene-3, 17-dione

Bacillus pulvifaciens IAM N-19-2

Iizuka, H., A. Naito and Y. Sato, J. Gen. Appl. Microbiol. (Japan), **7**, 118 (1961)

Pseudomonas chlororaphis IAM 1511

Naito, A., Y. Sato, H. Iizuka and K. Tsuda, Steroids, **3**, 327 (1964)

Pseudomonas testosteroni ATCC 11996

Levy, H. R. and P. Talalay, J. Am. Chem. Soc., **79**, 2658 (1957)

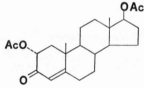

Testosterone

Androst-1-ene-3, 17-dione

Nocardia corallina

U. S. Pat. 3,087,864

2α-Hydroxytestosterone

2-Hydroxyandrosta-1, 4-diene-
3, 17-dione

Bacillus sphaericus ATCC 7055

Gaul, C., S. R. Stitch, M. Gut and R. I. Dorfman,
J. Org. Chem., 24, 418 (1959)

2α-Hydroxytestosterone
2α, 17β-diacetate

2-Hydroxyandrost-1-ene-
3, 17-dione

Nocardia corallina

U. S. Pat. 3,087,864

17α-Methyltestosterone

17α-Methyl-17β-hydroxyandrosta-
1, 4-dien-3-one

Bacterium aromaticus

Japan Pat. 289,328

Didymella lycopersici

Vischer, E., Ch. Meystre and A. Wettstein, Helv.
Chim. Acta., 38, 1502 (1955)

Flavobacterium aquatile

Japan Pat. 305,166

Fusarium solani   Brit. Pat. 917,081

Pseudomonas graveolens   Japan Pat. 413,161

Stereum fasciatum   Japan Pat. 307,724

9α-Fluoro-17α-methyl-11β-   9α-Fluoro-17α-methyl-11β, 17β-
hydroxytestosterone   dihydroxyandrosta-1, 4-
                                   dien-3-one

Nocardia corallina ATCC 999 (12%)   Sax, K. J., C. E. Holmlund, L. I. Feldman, R. H.
                                      Evans, Jr., R. H. Blank, A. J. Shay, J. S. Schultz
                                      and M. Dann, Steroids, **5**, 345 (1965)

17α-Ethinyltestosterone   17α-Ethinyl-17β-hydroxyandrosta-
                                   1, 4-dien-3-one

Didymella lycopersici   Vischer, E., Ch. Meystre and A. Wettstein, Helv.
                                   Chim. Acta., **38**, 1502 (1955)

Androst-4-ene-3, 17-dione   Androsta-1, 4-diene-3, 17-dione

Bacillus pulvifaciens IAM N-19-2   Iizuka, H., A. Naito and Y. Sato, J. Gen. Appl.
                                     Microbiol. (Japan), **7**, 118 (1961)

Bacillus sphaericus   Stoudt, T. H., W. J. McAleer, J. M. Chemerda,
                                   M. A. Kozlowski, R. F. Hirschmann, V. Marlatt
                                   and R. Miller, Arch. Biochem. Biophys, **59**, 304
                                   (1955)

Fusarium caucasicum   Ger. Pat. 1,135,455

Fusarium lateritium (80%)   Čapek, A., O. Hanč and M. Tadra, Folia Microbiol,
                                   8, 120 (1963)

Fusarium solani (100%)   Vischer, E. and A. Wettstein Experientia, **9**, 371 (1953)

Nocardia restrictus   Sih, C. J. Biochem. Biophys. Res. Comm., **7**, 87 (1962)

Protaminobacter alboflavum   U.S. Pat. 2,776,928

Protaminobacter rubrum

Pseudomonas testosteroni ATCC 11996   Levy, H. R. and P. Talalay, J. Am. Chem. Soc., **79**, 2658 (1957)

Androsta-4, 6-diene-3, 17-dione   Androsta-1, 4, 6-triene-3, 17-dione

Protaminobacter alboflavum   U.S. Pat. 2,776,927

Protaminobacter rubrum

Dehydroepiandrosterone   Androsta-1, 4-diene-3, 17-dione

Bacillus pulvifaciens IAM N-19-2   Iizuka, H., A. Naito and Y. Sato, J. Gen. Appl. Microbiol (Japan), **7**, 118 (1961)

Fusarium caucasicum   Vischer, E. and A. Wettstein, Experientia, **9**, 371 (1953)

Fusarium solani

5α-Androstane-3, 17-dione   Androsta-1, 4-diene-3, 17-dione

Mycobacterium smegmatis   Brit. Pat. 850,951

Pseudomonas testosteroni ATCC 11996   Levy, H. R. and P. Talalay, J. Am. Chem. Soc., **79**, 2658 (1957)

17β-Hydroxy-5β-androstan-3-one

Pseudomonas testosteroni ATCC 11996

Androsta-1, 4-diene-3, 17-dione

Levy, H. R. and P. Talalay, J. Am. Chem. Soc., **79**, 2658 (1957)

Progesterone

Pregna-1, 4-diene-3, 20-dione
(1-Dehydroprogesterone)

A Gram positive bacteria (90%)

Catroux, G. and H. Blachére, Ann. Inst. Pasteur, **105**, 162 (1963)

Bacillus sphaericus

Stoudt, T. H., W. J. McAller, J. M. Chemerda, M. A. Kozlowski, R. F. Hirschmann, V. Marlatt and R. Miller, Arch. Biochem. Biophys, **59**, 304 (1955)

Calonectria decora

Vischer, E., Ch. Meystre and A. Wettstein, Helv. Chim. Acta, **38**, 835 (1955)

Cylindrocarpon radicicola ATCC 11011

Peterson, G. E., R. W. Thoma, D. Perlman and J. Fried, J. Bacteriol, **74**, 684 (1957)

Didymella lycopersici

Vischer, E., Ch. Meystre and A. Wettstein, Helv. Chim. Acta, **38**, 1502 (1955)

Fusarium solani

Nishikawa, M., S. Noguchi and T. Hasegawa, Pharm. Bull. (Japan), **3**, 322 (1955)

Gloeosporium olivarum

Kondo, E. and E. Masuo, J. Agr. Chem. Soc. (Japan), **34**, 847 (1960)

Nocardia sp.

Sih, C. J. and R. E. Bennett, Biochem. Biophys. Acta, **38**, 378 (1960)

Septomyxa affinis ATCC 6737

Spero, G. B., J. L. Thompson, B. J. Magerlein, A. R. Hanze, H. C. Murray, O. K. Sebek and J. A. Hogg, J. Am. Chem. Soc., **78**, 6213 (1956)

Septomyxa affinis, conidia

Vézina, C., S. N. Sehgal and K. Singh, Appl. Microbiol., **11**, 50 (1963)

Streptomyces lavendulae

Peterson, G. E., R. W. Thoma, D. Perlman and J. Fried, J. Bacteriol., **74**, 684 (1957)

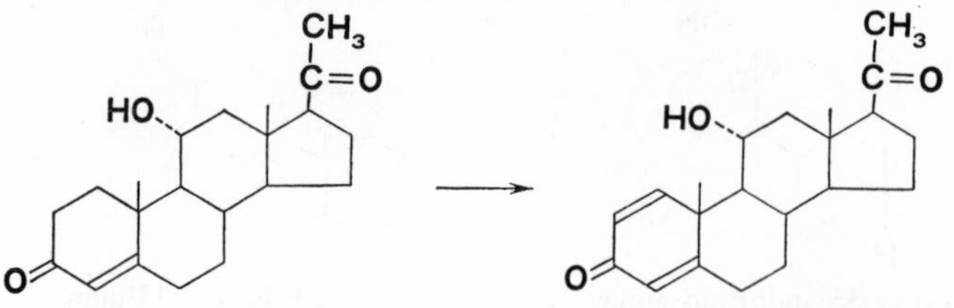

11α-Hydroxyprogesterone

Bacillus cyclooxydans

11α-Hydroxypregna-1, 4-
diene-3, 20-dione

U. S. Pat. 2,822,318

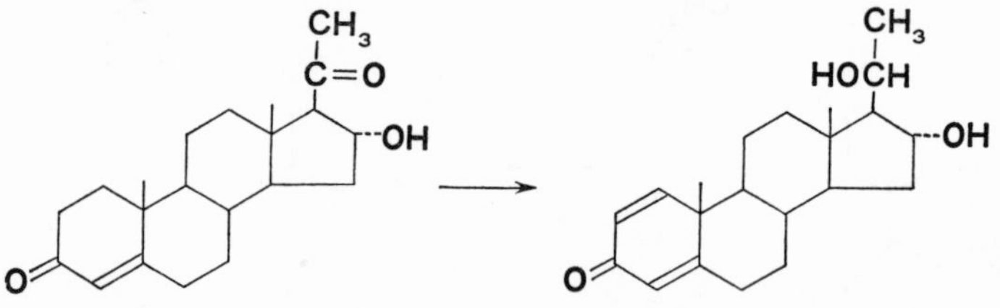

16α-Hydroxyprogesterone

Streptomyces lavendulae

16α, 20β-Dihydroxypregna-
1, 4-dien-3-one

Fried, J., R. W. Thoma, D. Perlman, J. E. Herz
and A. Borman, Recent Progr. Horm. Res., **11**
149 (1955)

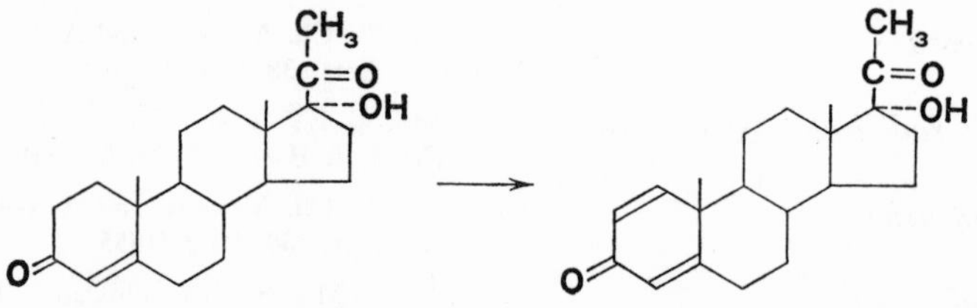

17α-Hydroxyprogesterone

Protaminobacter alboflavum
Protaminobacter rubrum

17α-Hydroxypregna-1, 4-diene-
3, 20-dione

U. S. Pat. 2,776,927

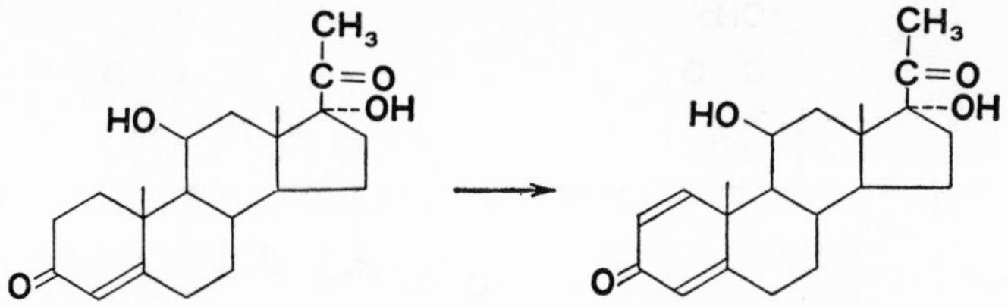

11β, 17α-Dihydroxyprogesterone

11β, 17α-Dihydroxypregna-1, 4-diene-3, 20-dione

U.S. Pat. 2,776,927

Protaminobacter alboflavum

Protaminobacter rubrum

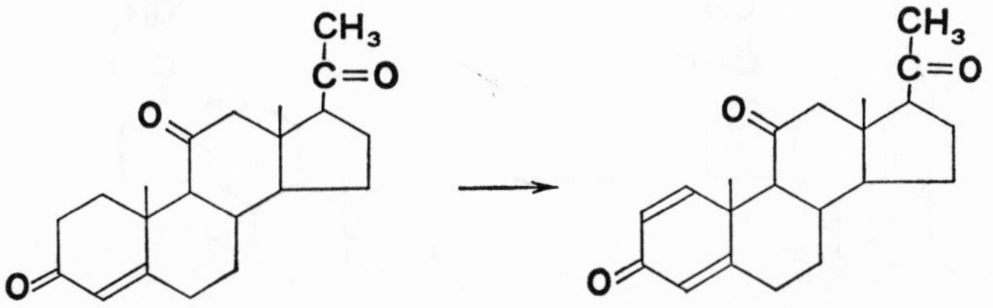

11-Oxoprogesterone

Pregna-1, 4-diene-3, 11, 20-trione

U. S. Pat. 2,776,927

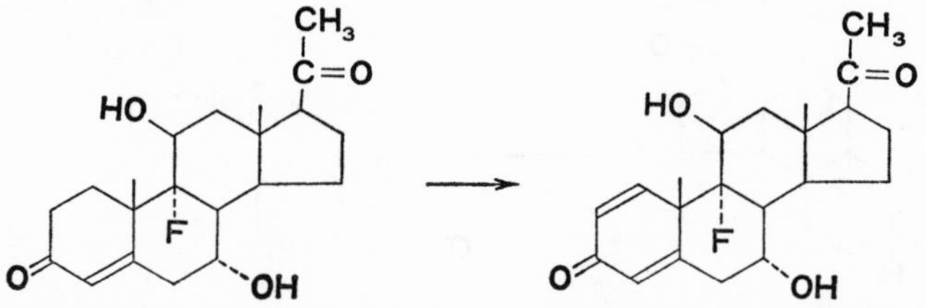

Protaminobacter alboflavum

Protaminobacter rubrum

9α-Fluoro-7α, 11β-dihydroxy-progesterone

9α-Fluoro-7α, 11β-dihydroxy-pregna-1, 4-diene-3, 20-dione

U. S. Pat. 2,962,512

Nocardia corallina

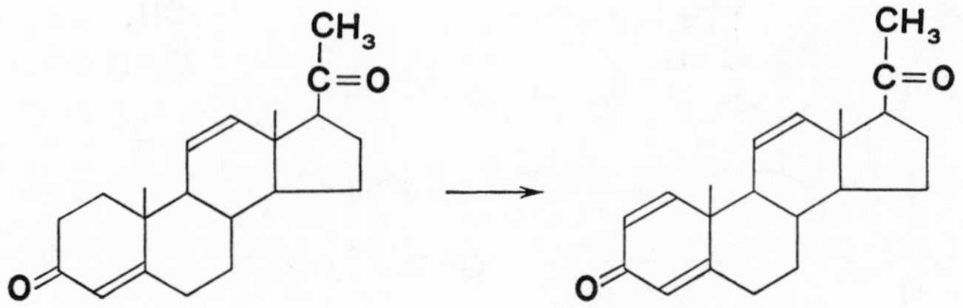

11-Dehydroprogesterone

Pregna-1, 4, 11-triene-3, 20-dione

Didymella lycopersici

Vischer, E., Ch. Meystre and A. Wettstein, Helv. Chim. Acta, **38**, 1502 (1955)

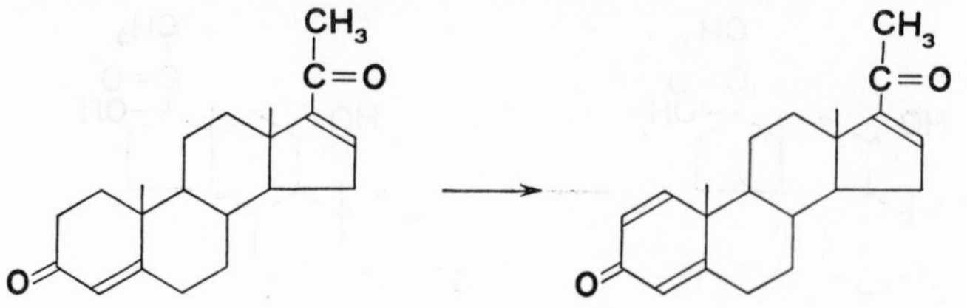

16-Dehydroprogesterone

Protaminobacter alboflavum

Protaminobacter rubrum

Pregna-1, 4, 16-triene-3, 20-dione

U. S. 2,776,927

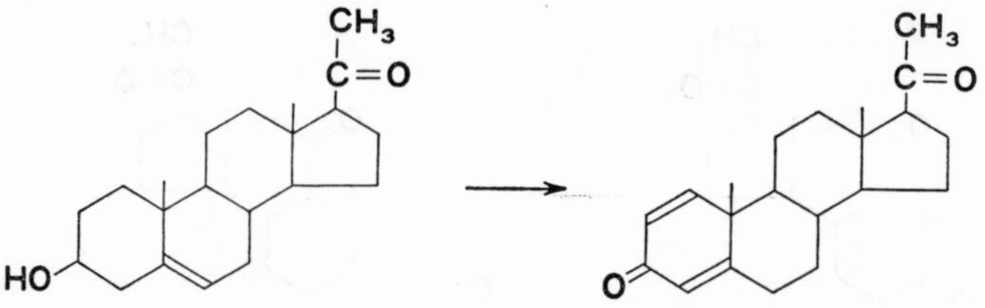

Pregnenolone

Bacillus pulvifaciens IAM N-19-2

Pregna-1, 4-diene-3, 20-dione

Iizuka, H., A. Naito and Y. Sato, J. Gen. Appl. Microbiol (Japan), **7**, 118 (1961)

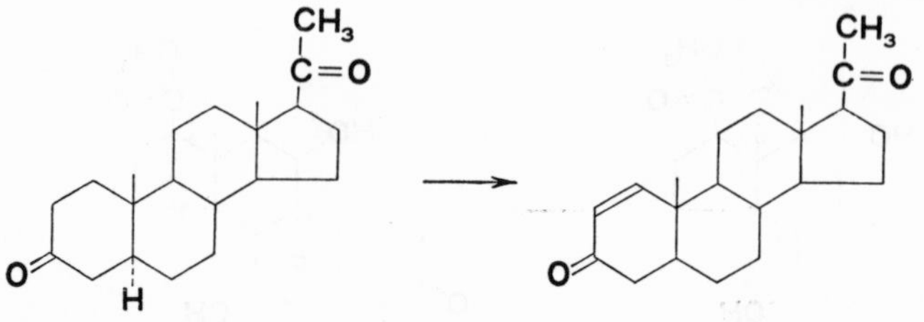

5α-Pregnane-3, 20-dione

Septomyxa affinis ATCC 6763

Pregn-1-ene-3, 20-dione

Fonken, G. S. and H. C. Murray, J. Org. Chem., **27**, 1102 (1962)

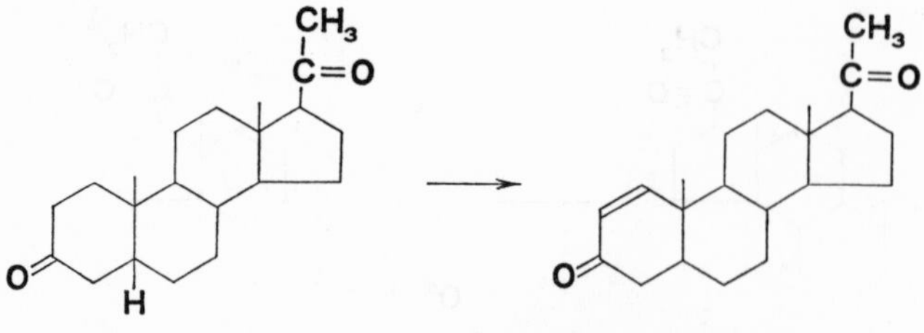

5β-Pregnane-3, 20-dione

Septomyxa affinis ATCC 6737

Pregn-1-ene-3, 20-dione

Fonken, G. S. and H. C. Murray, J. Org. Chem., **27**, 1102 (1962)

5α-Pregnane-3, 20-dione → Pregna-1, 4-diene-3, 20-dione

Nocardia sp.

Sih, C. J. and R. E. Bennett, Biochem. Biophys. Acta, **38**, 378 (1960)

5β-Pregnane-3, 20-dione → Pregna-1, 4-diene-3, 20-dione

Nocardia sp.

Sih, C. J. and R. E. Bennett, Biochem. Biophys. Acta, **38**, 378 (1960)

Progesterone → 17β-Hydroxyandrosta-1, 4-dien-3-one (1-Dehydrotestosterone)

Cylindrocarpon radicicola ATCC 11011

Fried, J., R. W. Thoma and A. Klingsberg, J. Am. Chem. Soc., **75**, 5764 (1953)

Fusarium solani

Nishikawa, M., S. Noguchi and T. Hasegawa, Pharm. Bull. (Japan), **3**, 322 (1955)

Streptomyces lavendulae strain Rutgers Univ. No. 3440-14 (12%)

Fried, J., R. W. Thoma and A. Klingsberg, J. Am. Chem. Soc., **75**, 5764 (1953)

Progesterone → Androsta-1, 4-diene-3, 17-dione

Calonectria decora

Vischer, E., Ch. Meystre and A. Wettstein, Helv. Chim. Acta, **38**, 835 (1955)

Cylindrocarpon radicicola ATCC **11011**

Peterson, G. E., R. W. Thoma, D. Perlman and J. Fried, J. Bacteriol, **74**, 684 (1957)

Fusarium caucasicum
Fusarium solani

Vischer, E. and A. Wettstein, Experientia, **9**, 371 (1953)

Fusarium solani

Nishikawa, M., S. Noguchi and T. Hasegawa, Pharm. Bull. (Japan), **3**, 322 (1955)

Streptomyces lavendulae strain Rutgers Univ. No. 3440-14 (7%)

Fried, J., R. W. Thoma and A. Klingsberg, J. Am. Chem. Soc., **75**, 5764 (1953)

Progesterone → 1-Dehydrotestololactone

Cylindrocarpon radicicola ATCC **11011** (50%)

Fried, J., R. W. Thoma and A. Klingsberg, J. Am. Chem. Soc., **75**, 5764 (1953)

Fusarium lateritium (40%)

Čapek, A., O. Hanč and M. Tadra, Folia Microbiol., **8**, 120 (1963)

Fusarium solani

Nishikawa, M., S. Noguchi and T. Hasegawa, Pharm. Bull. (Japan), **3**, 322 (1955)

Pregnenolone → Androsta-1, 4-diene-3, 17-dione

Fusarium caucasicum

Fusarium solani

Vischer, E. and A. Wettstein, Experientia, **9**, 371 (1953)

Pycnodothis sp.

Shull, G. M., Trans. N. Y. Acad. Sci., **19**, 147 (1956)

11-Deoxycorticosterone → 21-Hydroxypregna-1, 4-diene-3, 20-dione

Bacillus sphaericus

Stoudt, T. H., W. J. McAleer, J. M. Chemerda, M. A. Kozlowski, R. F. Hirschmann, V. Marlatt and R. Miller, Arch. Biochen. Biophys., **59**, 304 (1955)

Calonectria decora

Vischer, E., Ch. Meystre and A. Wettstein, Helv. Chim. Acta, **38**, 835 (1955)

Didymella lycopersici

Vischer, E., Ch. Meystre and A. Wettstein, Helv. Chim. Acta, **38**, 1502 (1955)

Gliocladium roseum

Helminthosporium turcicum

Ophiobolus heterostropus

Shirasaka, M. and M. Tsuruta, Chem. Pharm. Bull. (Japan), **9**, 207 (1961)

11-Deoxycorticosterone

Androsta-1, 4-diene-3, 17-dione

Fusarium caucasicum
Fusarium solani

Vischer, E. and A. Wettstein, Experientia, **9**, 371 (1953)

11-Deoxycorticosterone

1-Dehydrotestololactone

Fusarium sp.

Shull, G. M., Trans. N. Y. Acad. Sci., **19**, 147 (1956)

16α-Methyl-11-deoxycorticosterone

16α-Methyl-21-hydroxypregna-1, 4-diene-3, 20-dione

Arthrobacter simplex
Bacillus lentus

Belg. Pat. 614,196

21-Hydroxypregna-4, 6-diene-3, 20-dione 21-acetate

21-Hydroxypregna-1, 4, 6-triene-3, 20-dione

Didymella lycopersici

Vischer, E., Ch. Meystre and A. Wettstein, Helv. Chim. Acta, **38**, 1502 (1955)

17α-Methyl-21-hydroxypregn-
4-ene-3, 11, 20-trione 21-acetate

Didymella lycopersici

17α-Methyl-21-hydroxypregna-
1, 4-diene-3, 11, 20-trione

Vischer, E., Ch. Meystre and A. Wettstein, Helv.
Chim. Acta, **38**, 1502 (1955)

Corticosterone

11β, 21-Dihydroxypregna-
1, 4-diene-3, 20-dione

Bacillus pulvifaciens IAM N-19-2

Iizuka, H., A. Naito and Y. Sato, J. Gen. Appl.
Microbiol. (Japan), **7**, 118 (1961)

Bacillus sphaericus

Stoudt, T. H., W. J. McAleer, J. M. Chemerda,
M. A. Kozlowski, R. F. Hirschmann, V. Marlatt
and R. Miller, Arch. Biochem. Biophys, **59**, 304
(1955)

Calonectria decora

Vischer, E., Ch. Meystre and A. Wettstein, Helv.
Chim. Acta, **38**, 835 (1955)

Didymella lycopersici

Vischer, E., Ch. Meystre and A. Wettstein, Helv.
Chim. Acta, **38**, 1502 (1955)

Gliocladium roseum
Helminthosporium turcicum
Ophiobolus heterostropus

Shirasaka, M. and M. Tsuruta, Chem. Pharm.
Bull. (Japan), **9**, 207 (1961)

7α-Hydroxycorticosterone

7α, 11β, 21-Trihydroxypregna-
1, 4-diene-3, 20-dione

Nocardia corallina

U. S. Pat. 2,962,512

9α-Fluoro-7α-hydroxycorticosterone

9α-Fluoro-7α, 11β, 21-trihydroxy-
pregna-1, 4-diene-3, 20-dione

Nocardia corallina

U. S. Pat. 2,962,512

9α-Halo-11-dehydrocorticosterone

9α-Halo-21-hydroxypregna-1, 4-
diene-3, 11, 20-trione

Arthrobacter simplex
Corynebacterium hoagii

U. S. Pat. 3,084,103

11β, 21-Dihydroxy-16α, 17α-isopro-
pylidenedioxypregn-4-ene-3, 20-dione

21-Hydroxy-16α, 17α-isopro-
pylidenedioxypregna-1, 4-
diene-3, 11, 20-trione

Nocardia corallina ATCC 999

Sax, K. J., C. E. Holmlund, L. I. Feldman, R. H.
Evans, Jr., R. H. Blank, A. J. Shay, J. S. Schultz
and M. Dann, Steroids, 5, 345 (1965)

CH₂OH
C=O
--OH

CH₂OH
C=O
--OH

11-Deoxycortisol

17α, 21-Dihydroxypregna-
1, 4-diene-3, 20-dione

Bacillus cyclooxydans

U. S. Pat. 2,822,318

Bacillus pulvifaciens IAM N-19-2

Iizuka, H., A. Naito and Y. Sato, J. Gen. Appl. Microbiol. (Japan), **7**, 118 (1961)

Bacillus sphaericus

Stoudt, T. H., W. J. McAleer, J. M. Chemerda, M. A. Kozlowski, R. F. Hirschmann, V. Marlatt and R. Miller, Arch. Biochem. Biophys., **59**, 304 (1955)

Didymella lycopersici

Vischer, E., Ch. Meystre and A. Wettstein, Helv. Chim. Acta, **38**, 1502 (1955)

Flavobacterium aquatile

Japan Pat. 305,166

Fusarium solani

Vischer, E., Ch. Meystre and A. Wettstein, Helv. Chim. Acta, **38**, 835 (1955)

Fusarium solani, conidia

Vézina, C., S. N. Sehgal and K. Singh, Appl. Microbiol., **11**, 50 (1963)

Gliocladium roseum

Shirasaka, M. and M. Tsuruta, Chem. Pharm. Bull. (Japan), **9**, 207 (1961)

Gloeosporium olivarum
Helminthosporium gramineum

Kondo, E. and E. Masuo, J. Agr. Chem. Soc. (Japan), **34**, 847 (1960)

Helminthosporium turcicum

Shirasaka, M. and M. Tsuruta, Chem. Pharm. Bull. (Japan), **9**, 207 (1961)

Helminthosporium zizaniae

Kondo, E. and E. Masuo, J. Agr. Chem. Soc. (Japan), **34**, 847 (1960)

Mixed culture of *Rhizopus nigricans* and *Bacillus subtilis* (80%)

Weisz, E., G. Wix and M. Bodánszky, Naturwiss., **43**, 39 (1956)

Mycobacterium lacticola ATCC 9626

Sutter, D., W. Charney, P. L. O'Neill, F. Carvajal, H. L. Herzog and E. B. Hershberg, J. Org. Chem. **22**, 578 (1957)

Ophiobolus heterostropus

Shirasaka, M. and M. Tsuruta, Chem. Pharm. Bull. (Japan), **9**, 207 (1961)

Protaminobacter alboflavum
Protaminobacter rubrum

U. S. Pat. 2,776,927

Pseudomonas chlororaphis IAM 1511

Naito, A., Y. Sato, H. Iizuka and K. Tsuda, Steroids, **3**, 327 (1964)

Pseudomonas dacunhae

Shirasaka, M., M. Ozaki and S. Sugawara, J. Ferm. Assoc. (Japan), **19**, 335 (1961)

Septomyxa affinis, conidia

Vézina, C., S. N. Sehgal and K. Singh, Appl. Microbiol., **11**, 50 (1963)

Serratia marcescens

Japan Pat. 289,343

Stereum fasciatum

Japan Pat. 307,724

Streptomyces lavendulae, conidia

Vézina, C., S. N. Sehgal and K. Singh, Appl. Microbiol., **11**, 50 (1963)

11-Deoxycortisol   11β, 17α, 21-Trihydroxypregna-1, 4-diene-3, 20-dione (Prednisolone)

Absidia orchidis

Hung. Pat. 150,009

Mixed culture of *Corticium sasakii* and *Pseudomonas boreopolis*

Japan Pat. 303,584

The actions of *Helminthosporium sativum* and *Bacillus pulvifaciens* IAM N-19-2 in one and the same fermentation vessel in sequence

U. S. Pat. 2,993,839

11-Deoxycortisol   17α, 20β, 21-Trihydroxypregna-1, 4-dien-3-one

Alcaligenes sp.

Corynebacterium simplex

Mycobacterium lacticola ATCC 9626

Sutter, D., W. Charney, P. L. O'Neill, F. Carvajal, H. L. Herzog and E. B. Hershberg, J. Org. Chem., **22**, 578 (1957)

Pseudomonas oleovorans

U. S. Pat. 3,037,915

CH₂OAc → CH₂OH structures

11-Deoxycortisol 21-acetate

**17α, 21-Dihydroxypregna-
1, 4-diene-3, 20-dione**

Mycobacterium lacticola
Mycobacterium smegmatis

Belg. Pat. 538,327

**11α, 17α, 21-Trihydroxypregn-
4-ene-3, 20-dione**

**11α, 17α, 21-Trihydroxypregna-
1, 4-diene-3, 20-dione**

Corynebacterium simplex

U. S. Pat. 2,957,893

Fusarium solani, conidia

Vézina, C., S. N. Sehgal and K. Singh, Appl.
Microbiol., **11**, 50 (1963)

Rhizoctonia ferrugena

U. S. Pat. 2,968,595

15β-Hydroxy-11-deoxycortisol

**15β, 17α, 21-Trihydroxypregna-
1, 4-diene-3, 20-dione**

Bacillus sphaericus

U. S. Pat. 2,958,631

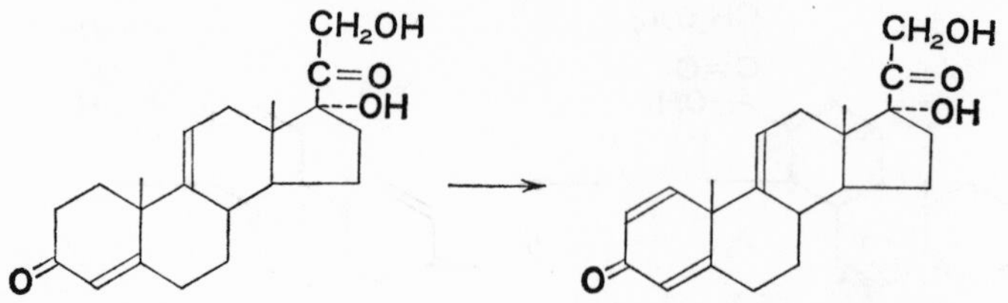

9(11)-Dehydro-11-deoxycortisol

17α, 21-Dihydroxypregna-1,
4, 9(11)-triene-3, 20-dione

Protaminobacter alboflavum
Protaminobacter rubrum

U. S. Pat. 2,776,927

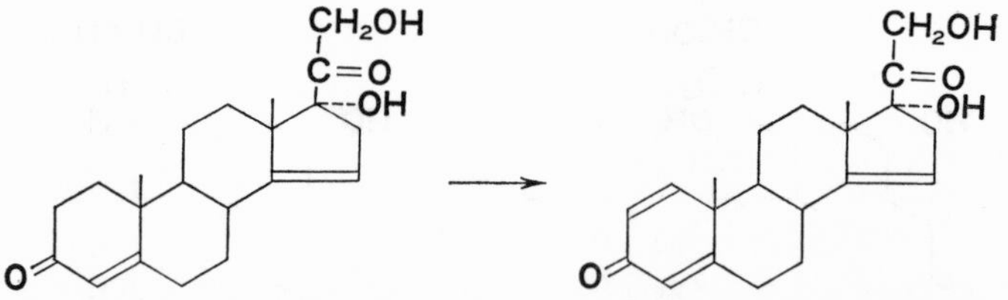

14-Dehydro-11-deoxycortisol

17α, 21-Dihydroxypregna-
1, 4, 14-triene-3, 20-dione

Protaminobacter alboflavum
Protaminobacter rubrum

U. S. Pat. 2,776,927

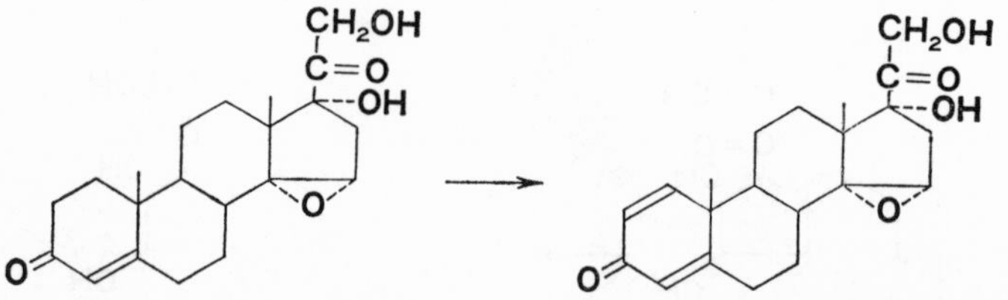

14α, 15α-Oxido-11-deoxycortisol

17α, 21-Dihydroxy-14α, 15α-oxido-
pregna-1, 4-diene-3, 20-dione

Protaminobacter alboflavum
Protaminobacter rubrum

U. S. Pat. 2,776,927

11-Deoxycortisol → 1-Dehydrotestololactone

Cylindrocarpon radicicola ATCC 11011 (50%) — Fried, J., R. W. Thoma and A. Klingsberg, J. Am. Chem. Soc., **75**, 5764 (1953)

Pseudomonas chlororaphis IAM 1511 — Naito, A., Y. Sato, H. Iizuka and K. Tsuda, Steroids, **3**, 327 (1964)

Cortisone → 17α, 21-Dihydroxypregna-1, 4-diene-3, 11, 20-trione (Prednisone)

Bacillus cyclooxydans — U. S. Pat. 2,822,318

Bacillus pulvifaciens IAM N-19-2 — Iizuka, H., A. Naito and Y. Sato, J. Gen. Appl. Microbiol. (Japan), **7**, 118 (1961)

Bacillus sphaericus — Stoudt, T. H., W. J. McAleer, J. M. Chemerda, M. A. Kozlowski, R. F. Hirschmann, V. Marlatt and R. Miller, Arch. Biochem. Biophys., **59**, 304 (1955)

Corynebacterium simplex ATCC 6946 (70%) — Nobile, A., W. Charney, P. L. Perlman, H. L. Herzog, C. C. Payne, M. E. Tully, M. A. Jevnik and E. B. Hershberg, J. Am. Chem. Soc., **77**, 4184 (1955)

Didymella lycopersici — Vischer, E., Ch. Meystre and A. Wettstein, Helv. Chim. Acta, **38**, 1502 (1955)

Fusarium oxysporum — U. S. Pat. 2,951,016

Fusarium solani — Vischer, E., Ch. Meystre and A. Wettstein, Helv. Chim. Acta, **38**, 835 (1955)

Gliocladium roseum — Shirasaka, M. and M. Tsuruta, Chem. Pharm. Bull. (Japan), **9**, 207 (1961)

Gloeosporium olivarum — Kondo, E. and E. Masuo, J. Agr. Chem. Soc. (Japan), **34**, 847 (1960)

Helminthosporium turcicum — Shirasaka, M. and M. Tsuruta, Chem. Pharm. Bull. (Japan), **9**, 207 (1961)

Mixed culture of *Rhizopus nigricans* and *Bacillus subtilis*

Weisz, E., G. Wix and M. Bodánszky, Naturwiss., **43**, 39 (1956)

Ophiobolus heterostropus

Shirasaka, M. and M. Tsuruta, Chem. Pharm. Bull. (Japan), **9**, 207 (1961)

Protaminobacter alboflavum

U. S. Pat. 2,776,927

Protaminobacter rubrum

Pseudomonas boreopolis

Japan Pat. 303,583

Cortisone

17α, 20β, 21-Trihydroxypregna-1, 4-diene-3, 11-dione

Fusarium solani var. *eumartii*

Szpilfogel, S. A., M. S. DeWinter and W. J. Alsche, Rec. Trav. chim., **75**, 402 (1956)

Gloeosporium olivarum

Kondo, E. and E. Masuo, J. Agr. Chem. Soc. (Japan), **34**, 847 (1960)

14α-Hydroxycortisone

14α, 17α, 21-Trihydroxypregna-1, 4-diene-3, 11, 20-trione

Protaminobacter alboflavum

U. S. Pat. 2,776,927

Protaminobacter rubrum

dl-Cortisone

d-17α, 21-Dihydroxypregna-1, 4-diene-3, 11, 20-trione

Didymella lycopersici

Vischer, E., J. Schmidlin and A. Wettstein, Experientia, **12**, 50 (1956)

Cortisol → 11β, 17α, 21-Trihydroxypregna-1, 4-diene-3, 20-dione (Prednisolone)

Azotomonas fluorescens	U. S. Pat. 2,992,973
Bacillus cyclooxydans	U. S. Pat. 2,822,318
Bacillus pulvifaciens IAM N-19-2 (80%)	Iizuka, H., A. Naito and Y. Sato, J. Gen. Appl. Microbiol. (Japan), **7**, 118 (1961)
Bacillus sphaericus	Stoudt, T. H., W. J. McAleer, J. M. Chemerda, M. A. Kozlowski, R. F. Hirschmann, V. Marlatt and R. Miller, Arch. Biochem. Biophys., **59**, 304 (1955)
Bacterium aromaticus	Japan Pat. 289,323
Corynebacterium equi B-58-1	Japan Pat. 414,359
Corynebacterium simplex ATCC 6946 (Pseudo-crystallofermentation)	Kondo, E. and E. Masuo, J. Gen. Appl. Microbiol. (Japan), **7**, 113 (1961)
Corynebacterium simplex ATCC 6946	Nobile, A., W. Charney, P. L. Perlman, H. L. Herzog, C. C. Payne, M. E. Tully, M. A. Jevnik and E. B. Hershberg, J. Am. Chem. Soc., **77**, 4184 (1955)
Flavobacterium aquatile	Japan Pat. 305,166
Graphiola cylindrica	Kondo, E. and E. Masuo, J. Agr. Chem. Soc. (Japan), **34**, 847 (1960)
Mixed culture of *Rhizopus nigricans* and *Bacillus subtilis*	Weisz, E., G. Wix and M. Bodánszky, Naturwiss, **43**, 39 (1956)
Mycobacterium smegmatis	Brit. Pat. 787,410
Mycobacterium sp.	Japan Pat. 271,310
Nocardia corallina	U. S. Pat. 3,087,864
Nocardia sp.	Peterson, G. E., R. W. Thoma, D. Perlman and J. Fried, J. Bacteriol., **74**, 684 (1957)
Nocardia sp.	Japan Pat. 272,229
Protaminobacter alboflavum	U. S. Pat. 2,776,927
Protaminobacter rubrum	
Pseudomonas chlororaphis IAM 1511	Naito, A., Y. Sato, H. Iizuka and K. Tsuda, Steroids, **3**, 327 (1964)
Pseudomonas fluorescens	Brit. Pat. 859,694
Rhizoctonia ferrugena	U. S. Pat. 2,968,595
Streptomyces lavendulae	U. S. Pat. 2,793,164

14α-Hydroxycortisol

11β, 14α, 17α, 21-Tetrahydroxy-
pregna-1, 4-diene-3, 20-dione

Protaminobacter alboflavum
Protaminobacter rubrum

U. S. Pat. 2,776,927

14α, 15α-Oxidocortisol

11β, 17α, 21-Trihydroxy-14α, 15α-
oxidopregna-1, 4-diene-3, 20-dione

Protaminobacter alboflavum
Protaminobacter rubrum

U. S. Pat. 2,776,927

9α-Fluorocortisol

9α-Fluoro-11β, 17α, 21-trihydroxy-
pregna-1, 4-diene-3, 20-dione

Bacillus cyclooxydans
Bacillus sphaericus

U. S. Pat. 2,822,318

Stoudt, T. H., W. J. McAleer, J. M. Chemerda,
M. A. Kozlowski, R. F. Hirschmann, V. Marlatt
and R. Miller, Arch. Biochem. Biophys., **59**, 304
(1955)

Protaminobacter alboflavum
Protaminobacter rubrum

U. S. Pat. 2,776,927

CH₂OAc

9α-Fluorocortisol 21-acetate

Didymella lycopersici

9α-Fluoro-11β, 17α, 21-trihydroxy-
pregna-1, 4-diene-3, 20-dione

Vischer, E., Ch. Meystre and A. Wettstein, Helv.
Chim. Acta, **38**, 1502 (1955)

9α-Fluoro-16α-hydroxycortisol

Bacterium havaniensis

Bacterium mycoides

Mycobacterium rhodochrous (65%)

9α-Fluoro-11β, 16α, 17α, 21-tetrahydroxy-
pregna-1, 4-diene-3, 20-dione

U. S. Pat. 3,037,914

U. S. Pat. 3,037,912

Thoma, R. W., J. Fried, S. Bonanno and P.
Grabowich, J. Am. Chem. Soc., **79**, 4818 (1957)

2-Methyl-11β, 21-dihydroxy-
pregna-4, 17(20)-dien-3-one

Septomyxa affinis

2-Methyl-11β, 21-dihydroxypregna-
1, 4, 17(20)-trien-3-one

U. S. Pat. 3,009,937

(d) $-CH_2-CH< \longrightarrow -CH=C<$

Androst-1-ene-3, 17-dione   Androsta-1, 4-diene-3, 17-dione

Pseudomonas testosteroni   ATCC 11996   Levy, H. R. and P. Talalay, J. Am. Chem. Soc., 79, 2658 (1957)

3β-Hydroxy-5α, 6α-oxido-androstan-17-one   6α-Hydroxyandrost-4-ene-3, 17-dione

Nocardia restrictus   No. 545   Lee, S. S. and C. J. Sih, Biochemistry, 3, 1267 (1964)

5α-Androstane-3, 17-dione   Androsta-1, 4-diene-3, 17-dione

Mycobacterium smegmatis   Brit. Pat. 850,951

Pseudomonas testosteroni   ATCC 11996   Levy, H. R. and P. Talalay, J. Am. Chem. Soc., 79, 2658 (1957)

C. Reduction

(a) $\text{>C=O} \longrightarrow \text{>CH-OH}$

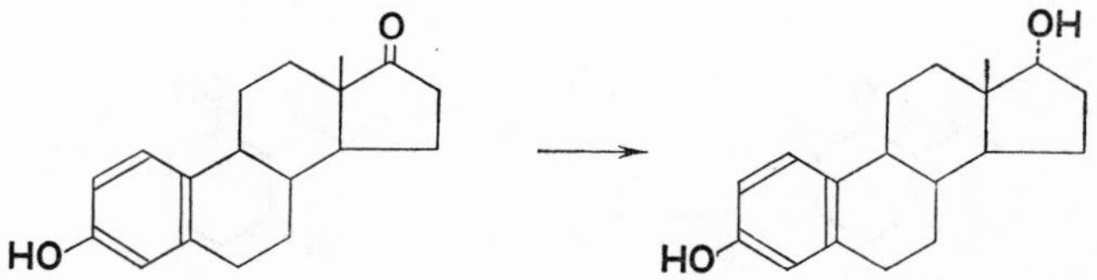

Estrone

α-Estradiol

Baker's yeast (67%)

Press yeast (70%)

Mamoli L., Ber., **71B**, 2696 (1938)
Wettstein A., Helv. Chim. Acta, **22**, 250 (1939)

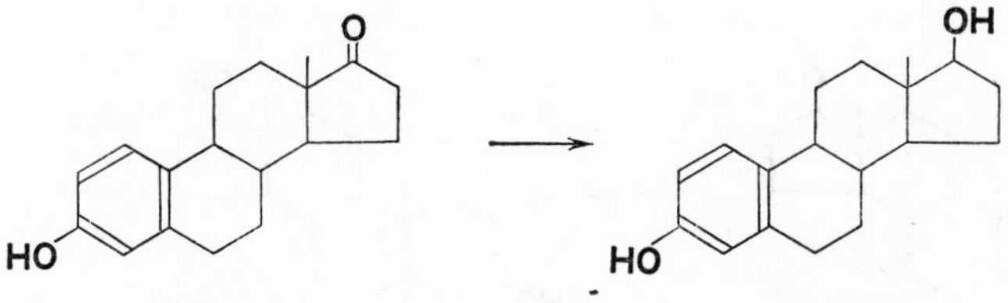

dl-Estrone

d-Estradiol

Press yeast (*Saccharomyces* sp.)

Vischer, E., J. Schmidlin, and A. Wettstein, Experientia, **12**, 50 (1956)

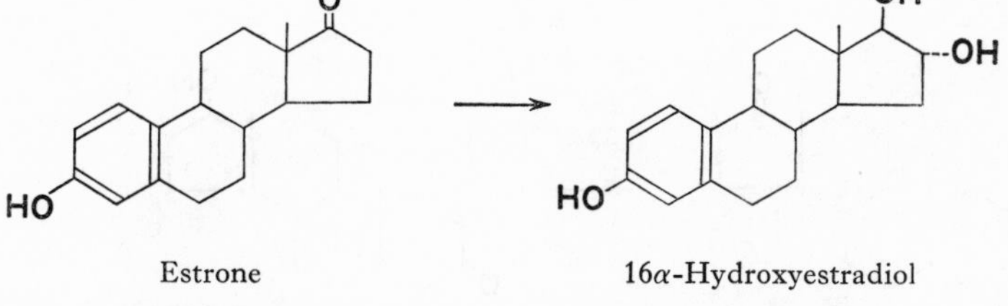

Estrone

16α-Hydroxyestradiol

Streptomyces halstedii ATCC 13499, NRRL B-2138

Streptomyces mediocidicus ATCC 13278

Kita, D. A., J. L. Sardinas and G. M. Shull, Nature, **190**, 627 (1961)

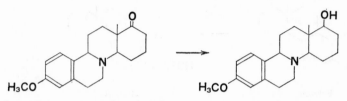

8-Aza-D-homoestrone 3-methylether

8-Aza-D-homoestradiol
3-methylether (17α-OH)

Aspergillus ochraceus

Curtis, P. J., Biochem. J. **97**, 148 (1965)

8-Aza-D-homoestrone 3-methylether

8-Aza-D-homoestradiol
3-methylether (17β-OH)

Aspergillus ochraceus

Curtis, P. J., Biochem. J., **97**, 148 (1965)

Androst-1-ene-3, 17-dione

5β-Androstane-3β, 17β-diol

Baker's yeast (25%)

Butenandt, A., H. Dannenberg and L. A. Surányi,
Ber., **73B**, 818 (1940)

Androst-1-ene-3, 17-dione

17β-Hydroxyandrost-1-en-3-one

Baker's yeast (83%)

Butenandt, A. and H. Dannenberg, Ber., **71B**, 1681
(1938)

17β-Hydroxyandrost-1-en-3-one

Baker's yeast

5β-Androstane-3β, 17β-diol

Butenandt, A., H. Dannenberg and L. A. Surányi, Ber, **73B**, 818 (1940)

Androst-4-ene-3, 17-dione

Testosterone

Yeast

Top yeast

Mamoli, L. and A. Vercellone, Ber. **70B**, 470 (1937)

Mamoli, L. and A. Vercellone, **70B**, 2079 (1937)

Androst-4-ene-3, 17-dione

17β-Hydroxy-5β-Androstan-3-one

Clostridium   lentoputrescens   (Bacillus putrificus) (59%)

Mamoli, L., R. Koch and H. Teschen, Z. Physiol. Chem., **261**, 287 (1939)

Androst-4-ene-3, 17-dione

5α-Androstane-3α, 17β-diol

Clostridium   lentoputrescens   (Bacillus putrificus) (13%)

Mamoli, L., R. Koch and H. Teschen, Z. Physiol. Chem., **261**, 287 (1939)

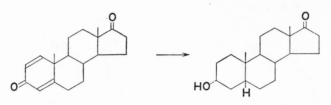

Androsta-1, 4-diene-3, 17-dione   17β-Hydroxyandrosta-1, 4-dien-3-one

Fusarium lateritium   Čapek, A., O. Hanč and M. Tadra, Folia Micro-
                                               biol., **8**, 120 (1963)

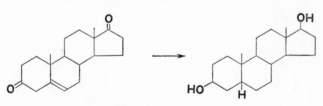

Androsta-1, 4-diene-3, 17-dione   3α-Hydroxy-5β-androstan-17-one

Clostridium paraputrificum   Schubert, K., J. Schlegel and C. Hörhold, Z.
                                               Physiol. Chem., **332**, 310 (1963)

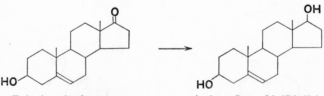

Androst-5-ene-3, 17-dione   5β-Androstane-3β, 17β-diol

Top yeast   Mamoli, L. and A. Vercellone, Ber., **70B**, 2079 (1937)

Dehydroepiandrosterone   Androst-5-ene-3β, 17β-diol

Clostridium lentoputrescens (Bacillus   Mamoli, L., R. Koch and H. Teschen, Z. Physiol.
putrificus) (67%)   Chem., **261**, 287 (1939)

Yeast (18%)   Mamoli, L. and A. Vercellone, Z. Physiol. Chem.,
                                               245, 93 (1937)

Yeast   U. S. Pat. 2,186,906

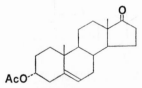

3α-Hydroxyandrost-5-en-17-one

Baker's yeast (81%)
Impoverished yeast
Oxidizing bacteria

Testosterone

Mamoli, L., Ber., **71B**, 2278 (1938)
U. S. Pat. 2,236,574
Mamoli, L., Ber., **71B**, 2278 (1938)

3α-Hydroxyandrost-5-en-17-one

Bacteria

5α-Androstane-3α, 17β-diol

Schramm, G. and L. Mamoli, Ber., **71B**, 1322 (1938)

3α-Hydroxyandrost-5-en-
17-one 3-acetate

Yeast

3α, 17β-Dihydroxyandrost-
5-ene 3-acetate

Mamoli, L. Ber., **71B**, 2696 (1938)

3, 5-Cycloandrostane-6, 17-dione

Yeast (50%)

3, 5-Cyclo-17β-hydroxyandrostan-6-one

Butenandt, A. and L. A. Surányi, Ber., **75B**, 591 (1942)

Testosterone   5α-Androstane-3α, 17β-diol

Clostridium lentoputrescens (*Bacillus putrificus*)

Mamoli, L., R. Koch and H. Teschen, Z. Physiol. Chem., **261**, 287 (1939)

Putrefactive bacteria (60%)

Mamoli, L. and G. Schramm, Ber., **71B**, 2083 (1938)

Testosterone   5β-Androstane-3β, 17β-diol

Bacteria (14%)

Mamoli, L. and G. Schramm, Ber., **71B**, 2698 (1938)

5α-Androstane-3, 17-dione   5α-Androstane-3β, 17β-diol

Clostridium lentoputrescens (*Bacillus putrificus*) (35.5%)

Mamoli, L., R. Koch and H. Teschen, Z. Physiol. Chem., **261**, 287 (1939)

Top yeast

Mamoli, L. and A. Vercellone, Z. Physiol. Chem., **245**, 93 (1937)

5β-Androstane-3, 17-dione   3α-Hydroxy-5β-androstan-17-one

Clostridium lentoputrescens (*Bacillus putrificus*) (36.4%)

Mamoli, L., R. Koch and H. Teschen, Z. Physiol. Chem., **261**, 287 (1939)

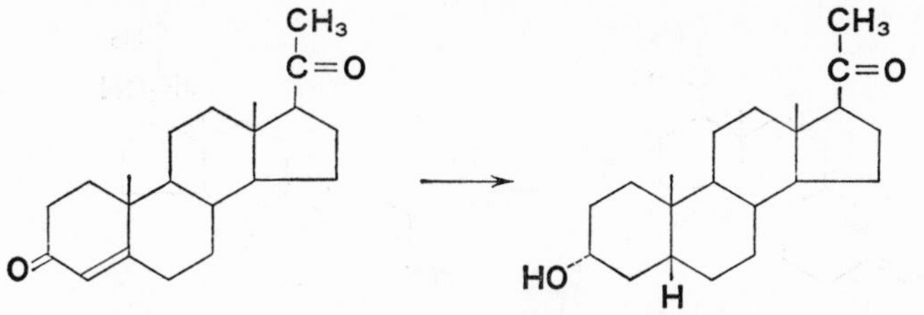

Progesterone

3α-Hydroxy-5β-pregnan-20-one

Alternaria bataticola

Shirasaka, M. and M. Ozaki, J. Agr. Chem. Soc.,
(Japan), **35**, 200 (1961)

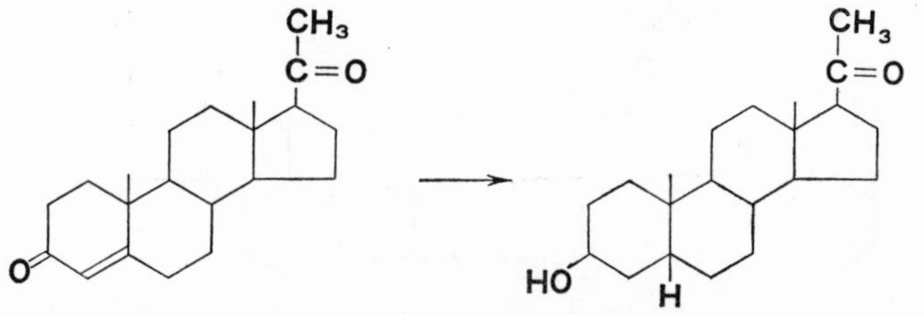

Progesterone

3β-Hydroxy-5β-pregnan-20-one

Alternaria bataticola

Shirasaka, M. and M. Ozaki, J. Agr. Chem. Soc.,
(Japan), **35**, 200 (1961)

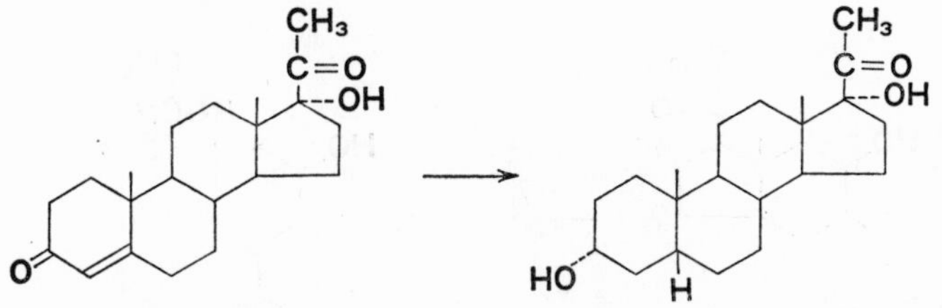

17α-Hydroxyprogesterone

3α, 17α-Dihydroxy-5β-pregnan-20-one

Alternaria bataticola

Shirasaka, M. and M. Ozaki, J. Agr. Chem. Soc.,
(Japan), **35**, 200 (1961)

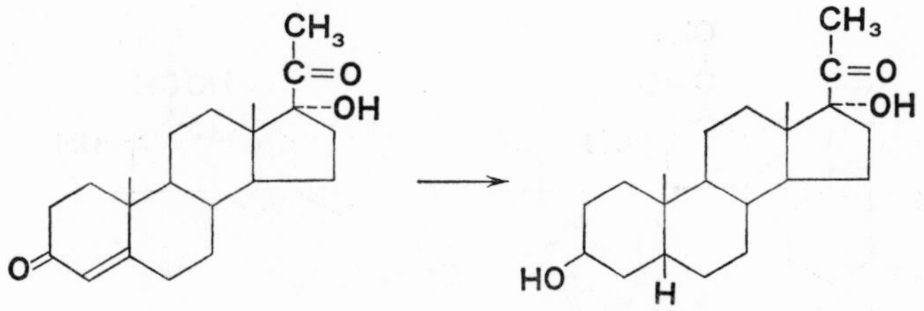

17α-Hydroxyprogesterone

3β, 17α-Dihydroxy-5β-pregnan-20-one

Alternaria bataticola

Shirasaka, M. and M. Ozaki, J. Agr. Chem. Soc.,
(Japan), **35**, 200 (1961)

Progesterone → 20α-Hydroxypregn-4-en-3-one

Rhodotorula longissima strain Schering OFU No. 2

Chang, V. M. and D. R. Idler, Can. J. Biochem. Physiol., **39**, 1277 (1961)

Progesterone → 20β-Hydroxypregn-4-en-3-one

Penicillium lilacinum

Sebek, O. K., L. M. Reineke and D. H. Peterson, J. Bacteriol., **83**, 1327 (1962)

Streptomyces lavendulae strain Rutgers Univ. No. 3440-14

Fried, J., R. W. Thoma and A. Klingsberg, J. Am. Chem. Soc., **75**, 5764 (1953)

11α-Hydroxyprogesterone → 11α, 20β-Dihydroxypregn-4-en-3-one

Penicillium lilacinum

Sebek, O. K., L. M. Reineke and D. H. Peterson, J. Bacteriol., **83**, 1327 (1962)

16α-Hydroxyprogesterone → 16α, 20β-Dihydroxypregn-4-en-3-one

Streptomyces lavendulae

Fried, J., R. W. Thoma, D. Perlman, J. E. Herz and A. Borman, Recent Progr. Hormone Res., **11**, 149 (1955)

16α-Hydroxyprogesterone

16α, 20β-Dihydroxypregna-
1, 4-dien-3-one

Streptomyces lavendulae

Fried, J., R. W. Thoma, D. Perlman, J. E. Herz
and A. Borman, Recent Progr. Hormone Res.,
11, 149 (1955)

11β, 17α-Dihydroxyprogesterone

11β, 17α, 20α-Trihydroxypregn-
4-en-3-one

Rhodotorula glutinis IFO 0395 (45%)

Takahashi, T. and Y. Uchibori, Agr. Biol. Chem.
(Japan), **26**, 89 (1962)

16α, 17α-Oxidoprogesterone

17β-Methyl-16α, 20α-dihydroxy-
18-nor-17α-pregna-4, 13(14)-
dien-3-one

Yeast (60%)

Camerino, B. and R. Modelli, Gazz. Chim. Ital.,
86, 1219 (1956)

16α, 17α-Oxidopregnenolone

17β-Methyl-18-nor-17α-pregna-5, 13(14)-
diene-3β, 16α, 20α-triol

Yeast (20%)

Camerino, B., R. Modelli and C. Spalla, Gazz.
Chim. Ital., **86**, 1226 (1956)

5α-Pregnane-3, 11, 20-trione

3α-Hydroxy-5α-pregnane-11, 20-dione

Yeast (44%)

Camerino, B., C. G. Alberti and A. Vercellone, Helv. Chim. Acta, **36**, 1945 (1953)

5β-Pregnane-3, 11, 20-trione

3α-Hydroxy-5β-pregnane-11, 20-dione

Yeast (60%)

Camerino, B., C. G. Alberti and A. Vercellone, Helv. Chim. Acta, **36**, 1945 (1953)

11α-Hydroxy-5α-pregnane-3, 20-dione

3β, 11α-Dihydroxy-5α-pregnan-20-one

Yeast (60%)

Camerino, B., C. G. Alberti and A. Vercellone, Helv. Chim. Acta, **36**, 1945 (1953)

16α, 17α-Oxido-5β-pregnane-3, 20-dione

17β-Methyl-16α, 20α-dihydroxy-18-nor-5β-pregn-13(14)-en-3-one

Yeast

Camerino, B. and A. Vercellone, Gazz. Chim. Ital., **86**, 260 (1956)

16α, 17α-Oxido-5β-pregnane-3, 20-dione

17β-Methyl-18-nor-5α-pegn-
13(14)-ene-3β, 16α, 20α-triol

Yeast

Camerino, B. and A. Vercellone, Gazz. Chim. Ital.,
86, 260 (1956)

11-Deoxycorticosterone

3α, 21-Dihydroxy-5β-pregnan-20-one

Alternaria bataticola

Shirasaka, M. and M. Ozaki, J. Agr. Chem. Soc.
(Japan), **35**, 200 (1961)

11-Deoxycorticosterone

3β, 21-Dihydroxy-5β-pregnan-20-one

Alternaria bataticola

Shirasaka, M. and M. Ozaki, J. Agr. Chem. Soc.
(Japan), **35**, 200 (1961)

11-Deoxycorticosterone

20β, 21-Dihydroxypregn-4-en-3-one

Streptomyces sp.

Peterson, D. H., Perspectives and Horizons in
Microbiology p121 (1955)

— 149 —

Corticosterone

Alternaria bataticola

3α, 11β, 21-Trihydroxy-5β-pregnan-20-one

Shirasaka, M. and M. Ozaki, J. Agr. Chem. Soc. (Japan), **35**, 200 (1961)

11-Deoxycortisol

Alternaria bataticola

3α, 17α, 21-Trihydroxy-5β-pregnan-20-one

Shirasaka, M. and M. Ozaki, J. Agr. Chem. Soc. (Japan), **35**, 200 (1961)

11-Deoxycortisol

Alternaria bataticola

3β, 17α, 20-Trihydroxy-5β-pregnan-20-one

Shirasaka, M. and M. Ozaki, J. Agr. Chem. Soc. (Japan), **35**, 200 (1961)

11-Deoxycortisol

Streptomyces aureus ATCC 3309

3β, 17α, 21-Trihydroxy-5α-pregnan-20-one

Kondo, E., T. Mitsugi and E. Masuo, Agr. Biol. Chem. (Japan), **26**, 22 (1962)

11-Deoxycortisol → 17α, 20α, 21-Trihydroxypregn-4-en-3-one

Rhodotorula glutinis IFO 0395 (65%)   Takahashi, T. and Y. Uchibori, Agr. Biol. Chem. (Japan), **26**, 89 (1962)

11-Deoxycortisol → 17α, 20β, 21-Trihydroxypregn-4-en-3-one

Candida pulcherrima IFO 0964	Takahashi, T. and Y. Uchibori, Agr. Biol. Chem. (Japan), **26**, 89 (1962)
Curvularia lunata NRRL 2380	Townsley, J. D., H. J. Brodie, M. Hayano and R. I. Dorfman, Steroids, **3**, 341 (1964)
Didymella lycopersici ATCC 11847 (5%)	Sehgal, S. N., K. Singh and C. Vézina, Steroids, **2**, 93 (1963)
Didymella lycopersici, conidia	Vézina, C., S. N. Sehgal and K. Singh, Appl. Microbiol., **11**, 50 (1963)
Epicoccum oryzae	Shull, G. M., Trans. N. Y. Acad. Sci., **19**, 147 (1956)
Pseudomonas fluorescens	Brit. Pat. 859,694
Pythium ultimum	Shirasaka, M. and M. Ozaki, J. Agr. Chem. Soc. (Japan), **35**, 206 (1961)
Sporotrichum gougeroti IFO 5982 (60~70%)	Takahashi, T. and Y. Uchibori, Agr. Biol. Chem., (Japan), **26**, 89 (1962)

11-Deoxycortisol → 17α, 20β, 21-Trihydroxypregna-1, 4-dien-3-one

Alcaligenes sp.

Corynebacterium simplex

Mycobacterium lacticola

Pseudomonas oleovorans

Sutter, D., W. Charney, P. L. O'Neill, F. Carvajal, H. L. Herzog and E. B. Hershberg, J. Org. Chem., **22**, 578, (1957)

U. S. Pat. 3,037,915

1-Dehydro-11-deoxycortisol

17α, 20α, 21-Trihydroxypregna-1, 4-dien-3-one

Rhodotorula glutinis IFO 0395 (80%)

Takahashi, T. and Y. Uchibori, Agr. Biol. Chem. (Japan), **26**, 89 (1962)

1-Dehydro-11-deoxycortisol

17α, 20β, 21-Trihydroxypregna-1, 4-dien-3-one

Candida pulcherrima IFO 0964 (40~80%)

Sporotrichum gougeroti IFO 5982 (40~80%)

Takahashi, T. and Y. Uchibori, Agr. Biol. Chem. (Japan), **26**, 89 (1962)

11-Deoxycortisol

11β, 17α, 20β, 21-Tetrahydroxypregn-4-en-3-one

Curvularia lunata

Shull, G. M., Trans, N. Y. Acad. Sci., **19**, 147 (1956)

19-Hydroxy-11-deoxycortisol

Rhodotorula glutinis IFO 0395 (10%)

17α, 19, 20α, 21-Tetrahydroxypregn-
4-en-3-one

Takahashi, T. and Y. Uchibori, Agr. Biol. Chem.
(Japan), **26**, 89 (1962)

17α, 21-Dihydroxypregna-4, 6-
diene-3, 11, 20-trione

Curvularia lunata NRRL 2380 (20~25%)

17α, 20β, 21-Trihydroxypregna-
4, 6-diene-3, 11-dione

Gould, D., J. Ilavsky, R. Gutekunst and E. B.
Hershberg, J. Org. Chem., **22**, 829 (1957)

17α, 21-Dihydroxypregna-4, 9(11)-
diene-3, 20-dione

Curvularia lunata

17α, 20β, 21-Trihydroxy-9β, 11β-
oxidopregn-4-en-3-one

Shull, G. M., Trans. N. Y. Acad. Sci., **19**, 147 (1956)

Cortisone

3α, 17α, 21-Trihydroxy-5β-pregnane-
11, 20-dione

Alternaria bataticola

Shirasaka, M. and M. Ozaki, J. Agr. Chem. Soc.
(Japan), **35**, 200 (1961)

Catenabacterium catenaforme

Prévot, A.-R., M.-M. Janot and N. D. Tam,
Compt. Rend., Soc. Biol., **256**, 3785 (1963)

Cortisone

17α, 20β, 21-Trihydroxypregn-
4-ene-3, 11-dione

Fusarium solani var. *eumartii*

Szpilfogel, S. A., M. S. DeWinter and W. J. Alsche,
Rec. Trav. chim., **75**, 402 (1956)

Gloeosporium olivarum

Kondo, E. and E. Masuo, J. Agr. Chem. Soc.
(Japan), **34**, 847 (1960)

Cortisol

3α, 11β, 17α, 21-Tetrahydroxy-
5β-pregnan-20-one

Alternaria bataticola

Shirasaka, M. and M. Ozaki, J. Agr. Chem. Soc.
(Japan), **35**, 200 (1961)

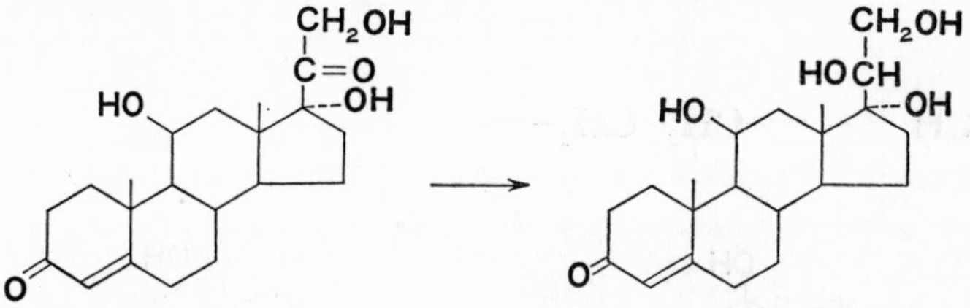

Cortisol

11β, 17α, 20β, 21-Tetrahydroxypregn-
4-en-3-one

Streptomyces hydrogenans

Schmidt-Thomé, J., Angew. Chem., **69**, 238 (1957)

(b) $-CH=CH- \longrightarrow -CH_2-CH_2-$

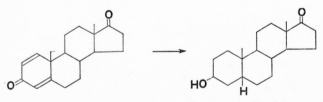

17β-Hydroxyandrost-1-en-3-one

Baker's yeast

5β-Androstane-3β, 17β-diol

Butenandt, A., H. Dannenberg and L. A. Surányi, Ber., **73 B**, 818 (1940)

Androst-1-ene-3, 17-dione

Baker's yeast

5β-Androstane-3β, 17β-diol

Butenandt, A., H. Dannenberg and L. A. Surányi, Ber., **73 B**, 818 (1940)

Androsta-1, 4-diene-3, 17-dione

Clostridium paraputrificum

3α-Hydroxy-5β-androstan-17-one

Schubert, K., J. Schlegel and C. Hörhold, Z. physiol. Chem., **332**, 310 (1963)

(c) $-CH=C\langle \longrightarrow -CH_2-CH\langle$

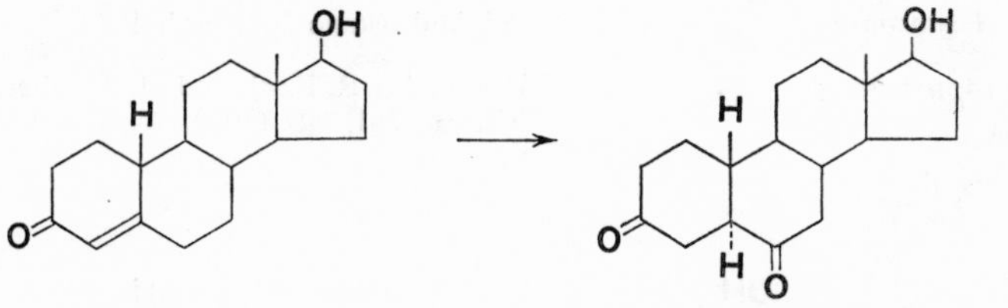

19-Nortestosterone → 17β-Hydroxy-19-nor-5α-androstane-3, 6-dione

Rhizopus reflexus

U. S. 2,692,273

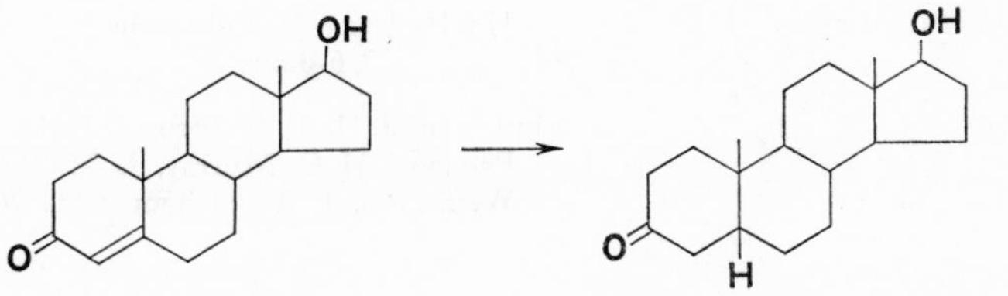

Testosterone → 17β-Hydroxy-5β-androstan-3-one

Clostridium lentoputrescens (*Bacillus putrificus*) (70~80%)

Mamoli, L., R. Koch and H. Teschen, Z. Physiol. Chem., **261**, 287 (1939)

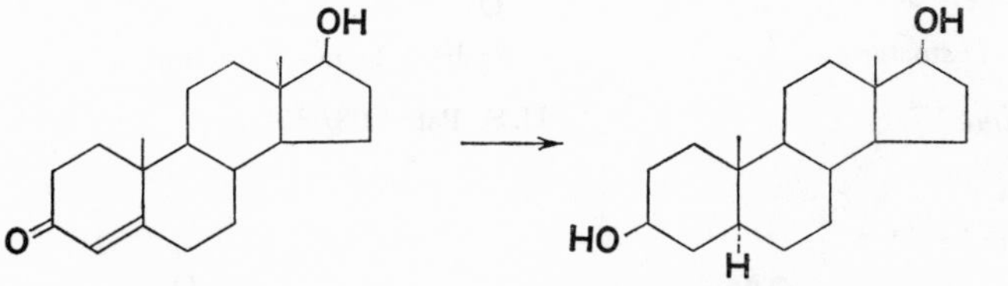

Testosterone → 5α-Androstane-3β, 17β-diol

Putrefactive bacteria

Mamoli, L. and G. Schramm, Ber., **71B**, 2698 (1938)

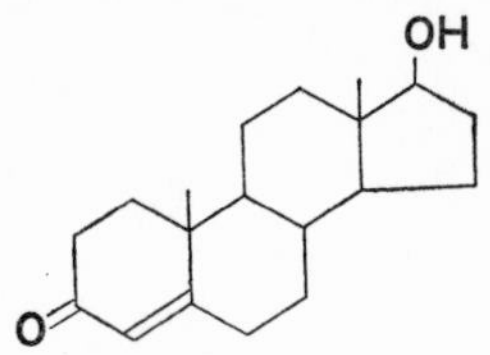

Testosterone

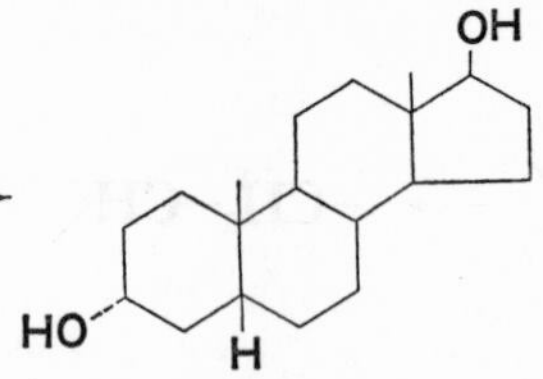

5β-Androstane-3α-17β-diol

Clostridium lentoputrescens (Bacillus putrificus) (10%)

Mamoli, L., R. Koch and H. Teschen, Z. Physiol. Chem., **261**, 287 (1939)

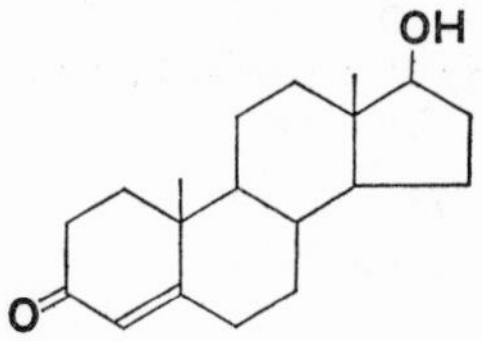

Testosterone

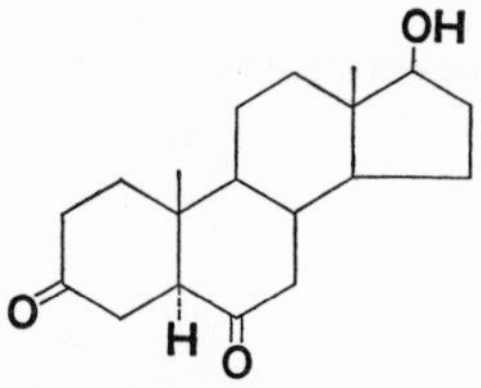

17β-Hydroxy-5α-androstane-3, 6-dione

Rhizopus reflexus

Eppstein, S. H., P. D. Meister, H. M. Leigh, D. H. Peterson, H. C. Murray, L. M. Reineke and A. Weintraub, J. Am. Chem. Soc., **76**, 3174 (1954)

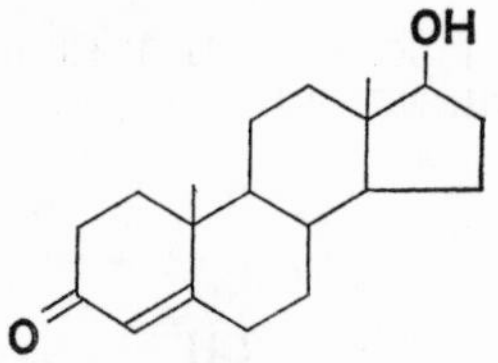

Testosterone

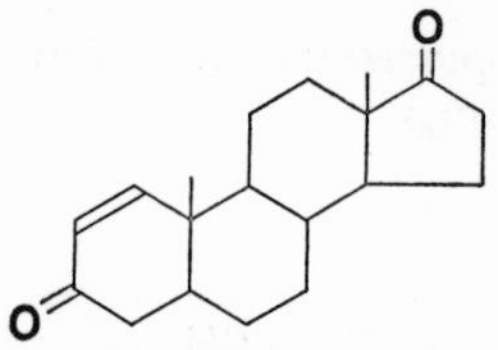

Androst-1-ene-3, 17-dione

Nocardia corallina

U. S. Pat. 3,087,864

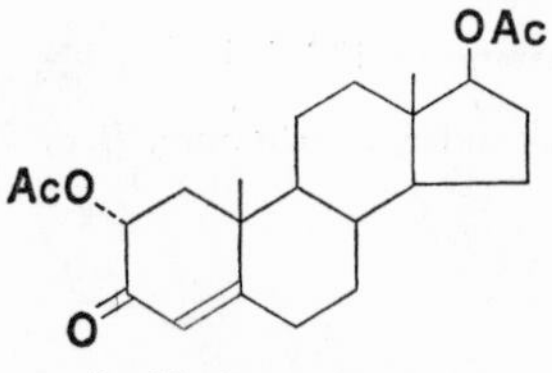

2α-Hydroxytestosterone 2α, 17β-diacetate

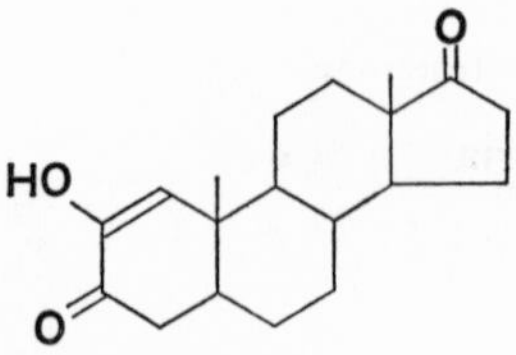

2-Hydroxyandrost-1-ene-3, 17-dione

Nocardia corallina

U. S. Pat. 3,087,864

Androst-4-ene-3, 17-dione

5β-Androstane-3, 17-dione

Clostridium lentoputrescens (*Bacillus putrificus*) (70~80%)

Mamoli, L., R. Koch and H. Teschen, Z. Physiol. Chem., **261**, 287 (1939)

Putrefactive bacteria

Mamoli, L. and G. Schramm, Ber., **71 B**, 2083 (1938)

Androst-4-ene-3, 17-dione

5β-Androstane-3α, 17β-diol

Clostridium lentoputrescens (*Bacillus putrificus*) (13%)

Mamoli, L., R. Koch and H. Teschen, Z. Physiol. Chem., **261**, 287 (1939)

Androst-4-ene-3, 17-dione

17β-Hydroxy-5β-androstan-3-one

Clostridium lentoputrescens (*Bacillus putrificus*) (39%)

Mamoli, L., R. Koch and H. Teschen, Z. Physiol. Chem., **261**, 287 (1939)

Androst-4-ene-3, 17-dione

1α-Hydroxy-5α-androstane-3, 17-dione

Penicillium sp. ATCC 12556

Dodson, R. M., A. H. Goldkamp and R. D. Muir, J. Am. Chem. Soc., **82**, 4026 (1960)

Androst-4-ene-3, 17-dione

Penicillium sp. ATCC 12556

1α, 3β-Dihydroxy-5α-androstan-17-one

Dodson, R. M., A. H. Goldkamp and R. D. Muir, J. Am. Chem. Soc., **82**, 4026 (1960)

Androsta-1, 4-diene-3, 17-dione

Clostridium paraputrificum

3α-Hydroxy-5β-androstan-17-one

Schubert, K., J. Schlegel and C. Hörhold, Z. Physiol. Chem., **332**, 310 (1963)

Androsta-1, 4-diene-3, 17-dione

Clostridium paraputrificum

Androst-1-ene-3, 17-dione

Schubert, K., J. Schlegel and C. Hörhold, Z. Physiol. Chem., **332**, 310 (1963)

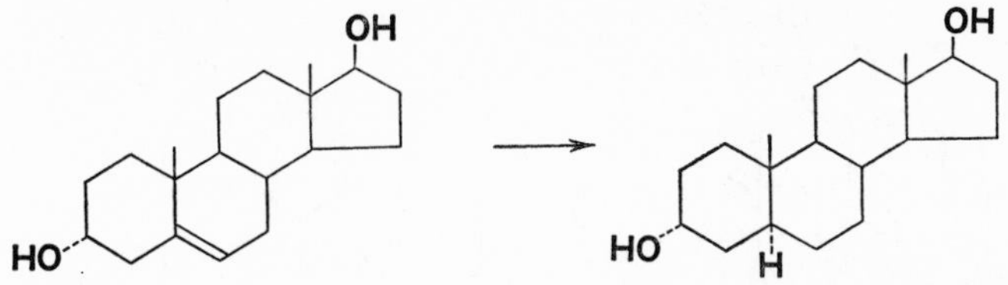

Androst-5-ene-3α, 17β-diol

5α-Androstane-3α, 17β-diol

Bacteria

Schramm, G. and L. Mamoli, Ber., **71 B,** 1322 (1938)

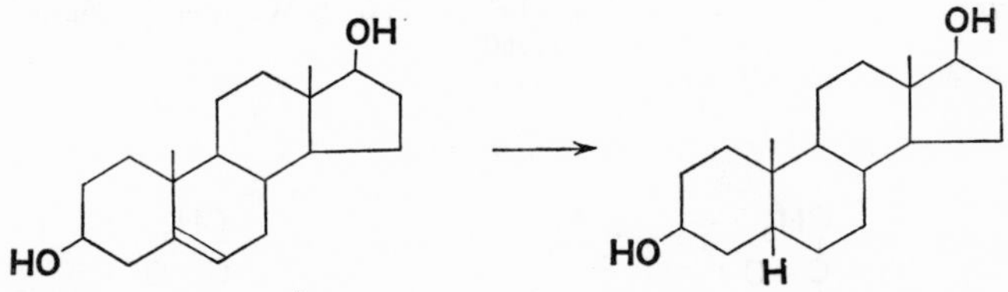

Androst-5-ene-3β, 17β-diol

5β-Androstane-3β, 17β-diol

Yeast

U. S. Pat. 2,186,906

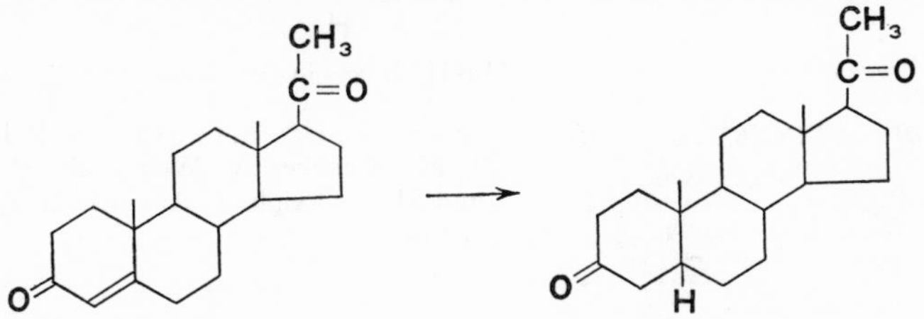

Progesterone

5β-Pregnane-3, 20-dione

Clostridium lentoputrescens (*Bacillus putrificus*) (86%)

Mamoli, L., R. Koch and H. Teschen, Z. Physiol. Chem., **261,** 287 (1939)

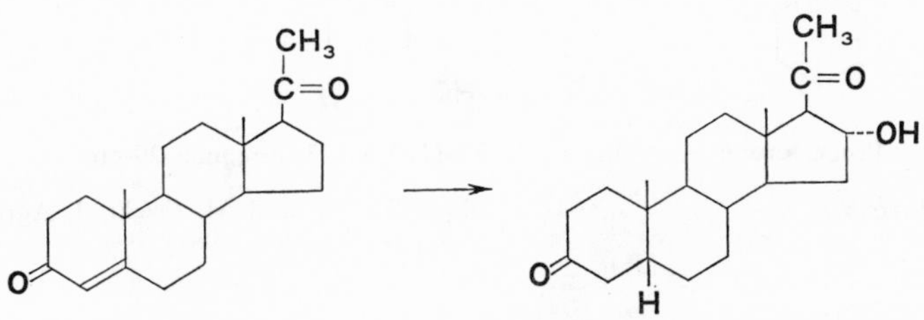

Progesterone

16α-Hydroxy-5β-pregnane-3, 20-dione

Unidentified Actinomycetes

Perlman, D., E. Titus and J. Fried, J. Am. Chem. Soc., **74,** 2126 (1952)

Progesterone

5α-Pregnane-3, 20-dione

Cortinarius evernius C-351

Schuytema, E. C., M. P. Hargie, D. J. Siehr, I.
Merits, J. R. Schenck, M. S. Smith and E. L.
Varner, Appl. Microbiol., **11**, 256 (1963)

Streptomyces griseus

Vischer, E. and A. Wettstein, Experientia, **16**, 355
(1960)

Progesterone

11α-Hydroxy-5α-pregnane-3, 20-dione

Rhizopus nigricans ATCC 6227b (4.0%)

Peterson, D. H., H. C. Murray, S. H. Eppstein,
L. M. Reineke, A. Weintraub, P. D. Meister
and H. M. Leigh, J. Am. Chem. Soc., **74**, 5933
(1952)

Progesterone

3α-Hydroxy-5β-pregnan-20-one

Alternaria bataticola

Shirasaka, M. and M. Ozaki, J. Agr. Chem. Soc.
(Japan), **35**, 200 (1961)

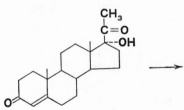

Progesterone

Streptomyces griseus

3β-Hydroxy-5α-pregnan-20-one

Vischer, E. and A. Wettstein, Experientia, **16**, 355 (1960)

Progesterone

Alternaria bataticola

3β-Hydroxy-5β-pregnan-20-one

Shirasaka, M. and M. Ozaki, J. Agr. Chem. Soc. (Japan), **35** 200 (1961)

17α-Hydroxyprogesterone

Alternaria bataticola

3α, 17α-Dihydroxy-5β-pregnan-20-one

Shirasaka, M. and M. Ozaki, J. Agr. Chem. Soc. (Japan), **35**, 200 (1961)

17α-Hydroxyprogesterone

Alternaria bataticola

3β, 17α-Dihydroxy-5β-pregnan-20-one

Shirasaka, M. and M. Ozaki, J. Agr. Chem. Soc. (Japan), **35**, 200 (1961)

16-dehydroprogesterone

11α-Hydroxy-17α-progesterone

Rhizopus nigricans ATCC 6227b (24%)

Meister, P. D., D. H. Peterson, H. C. Murray, S. H. Eppstein, L. M. Reineke, A. Weintraub and H. M. Leigh, J. Am. Chem. Soc., **75**, 55 (1953)

11-Deoxycorticosterone

21-Hydroxy-5α-pregnane-3, 20-dione

Streptomyces griseus (40%)

Vischer, E. and A. Wettstein, Experientia, **16**, 355 (1960)

11-Deoxycorticosterone

3α, 21-Dihydroxy-5β-pregnan-20-one

Alternaria bataticola

Shirasaka, M. and M. Ozaki, J. Agr. Chem. Soc. (Japan), **35**, 200 (1961)

11-Deoxycorticosterone

3β, 21-Dihydroxy-5β-pregnan-20-one

Alternaria bataticola

Shirasaka, M. and M. Ozaki, J. Agr. Chem. Soc. (Japan), **35**, 200 (1961)

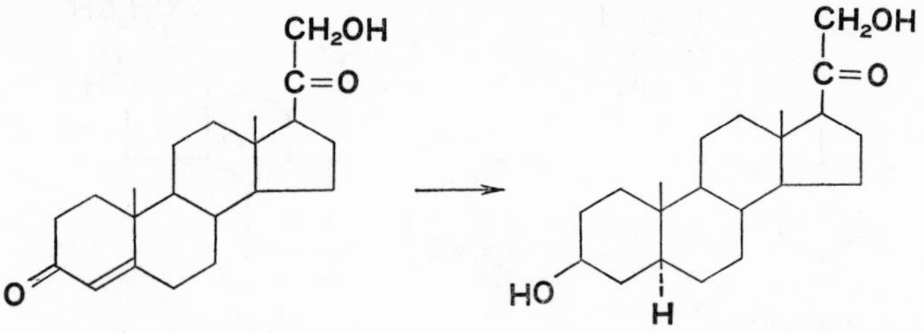

11-Deoxycorticosterone

Streptomyces griseus (85%)

3β, 21-Dihydroxy-5α-pregnan-20-one

Vischer, E. and A. Wettstein, Experientia, **16**, 355 (1960)

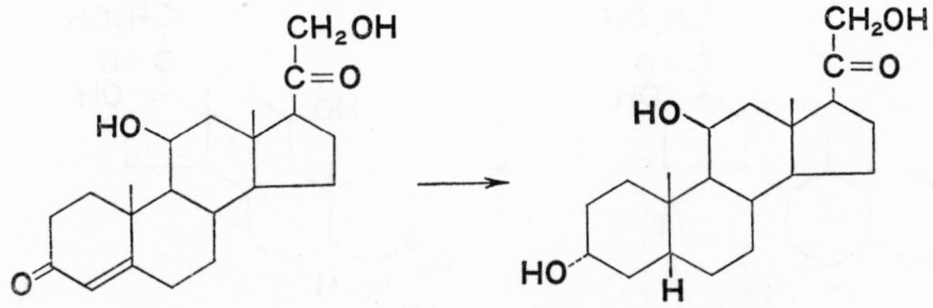

Corticosterone

Alternaria bataticola

3α, 11β, 21-Trihydroxy-5β-pregnan-20-one

Shirasaka, M. and M. Ozaki, J. Agr. Chem. Soc. (Japan), **35**, 200 (1961)

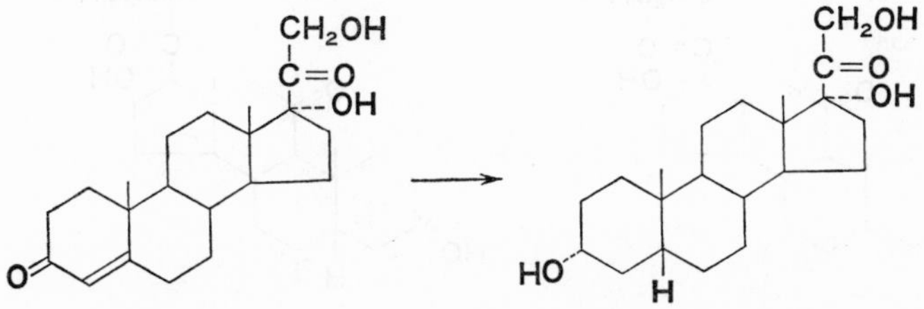

11-Deoxycortisol

Alternaria bataticola

3α, 17α, 21-Trihydroxy-5β-pregnan-20-one

Shirasaka, M. and M. Ozaki, J. Agr. Chem. Soc. (Japan), **35**, 200 (1961)

11-Deoxycortisol

3β, 17α, 21-Trihydroxy-
5β-pregnan-20-one

Alternaria bataticola

Shirasaka, M. and M. Ozaki, J. Agr. Chem. Soc.
(Japan), **35**, 200 (1961)

11-Deoxycortisol

11α, 17α, 21-Trihydroxy-5α-
pregnane-3, 20-dione

Rhizopus nigricans (8.2%)

U. S. Pat. 2,602,769

Cortisone

3α, 17α, 21-Trihydroxy-5β-pregnane-
11, 20-dione

Alternaria bataticola

Shirasaka, M. and M. Ozaki, J. Agr. Chem. Soc.
(Japan), **35**, 200 (1961)

Catenabacterium catenaforme

Prévot, A.-R., M.-M. Janot and N.-D. Tam,
Compt. Rend. Soc. Biol., **256**, 3785 (1963)

Cortisol

3α, 11β, 17α, 21-Tetrahydroxy-5β-
pregnan-20-one

Alternaria bataticola

Shirasaka, M. and M. Ozaki, J. Agr. Chem. Soc.
(Japan), **35**, 200 (1961)

Prednisone

17α, 21-Dihydroxypregn-1-ene-
3, 11, 20-trione

Streptomyces sp. W-3808

Greenspan, G., C. P. Schaffner, W. Charney,
M. J. Gentles and H. L., Herzog, J. Org. Chem.,
26, 1676 (1961)

16α-Methylprednisone

16α-Methyl-17α, 21-dihydroxy-
pregn-1-ene-3, 11, 20-trione

Streptomyces sp. W-3808

Greenspan, G., C. P. Schaffner, W. Charney,
M. J. Gentles and H. L. Herzog, J. Org. Chem.,
26, 1676 (1961)

D. Side Chain Degradation

(a) 17-Alcohol formation

Progesterone → Testosterone

Cladosporium resinae

Fonken, G. S., H. C. Murray and L. M. Reineke, J. Am. Chem. Soc., **82**, 5507 (1960)

Penicillium citrinum (20%)
Penicillium decumbens (60%)

Hanč, O., A. Čapek, M. Tadra, K. Macek and A. Šimek, Arzneimittel-Forsch., **7**, 175 (1957)

Penicillium lilacinum

Sebek, O. K., L. M. Reineke and D. H. Peterson, J. Bacteriol., **83**, 1327 (1962)

Penicillium notatum (62%)

Hanč, O., A. Čapek, M. Tadra, K. Macek and A. Šimek, Arzneimittel-Forsch., **7**, 175 (1957)

Progesterone → 17β-Hydroxyandrosta-1,4-dien-3-one

Cylindrocarpon radicicola ATCC 11011

Fried, J., R. W. Thoma and A. Klingsberg, J. Am. Chem. Soc., **75**, 5764 (1953)

Fusarium solani

Nishikawa, M., S. Noguchi and T. Hasegawa, Pharm. Bull. (Japan), **3**, 322 (1955)

Streptomyces lavendulae strain Rutgers Univ. No. 3440-14 (12%)

Fried, J., R. W. Thoma and A. Klingsberg, J. Am. Chem. Soc., **75**, 5764 (1953)

Progesterone → 9α-Hydroxytestosterone

Nocardia corallina

Brit. Pat. 862,701

Progesterone → 11β-Hydroxytestosterone

Aspergillus tamarii (14%)

Brannon, D. R., J. Martin, A. C. Oehlschlager,
N. N. Durham and L. H. Zalkow, J. Org. Chem.
30, 760 (1965)

11α-Hydroxyprogesterone → 11α-Hydroxytestosterone

Aspergillus chevalieri

Aspergillus oryzae (45%)

Penicillium citrinum

Čapek, A., O. Hanč, K. Macek, M. Tadra and
E. Riedl-Tůmová, Naturwiss, **43**, 471 (1956)

Penicillium citrinum

Penicillium decumbens

Hanč, O., A. Čapek, M. Tadra, K. Macek and
A. Šimek, Arzneimittel-Forsch., **7**, 175 (1957)

Penicillium lilacinum

Sebek, O. K., L. M. Reineke and D. H. Peterson,
J. Bacteriol., **83**, 1327 (1962)

Penicillium notatum

Hanč, O., A. Čapek, M. Tadra, K. Macek and
A. Šimek, Arzneimittel-Forsch., **7**, 175 (1957)

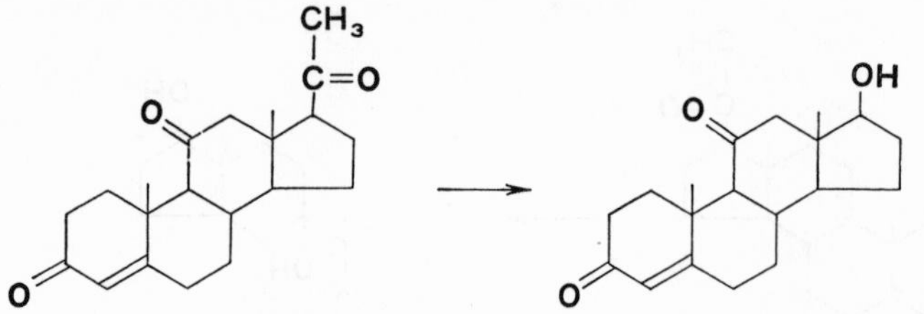

11-Oxoprogesterone → 11-Oxotestosterone

Penicillium citrinum
Penicillium decumbens
Penicillium notatum (51%)

Hanč, O., A. Čapek, M. Tadra, K. Macek and A. Šimek, Arzneimittel-Forsch., **7**, 175 (1957)

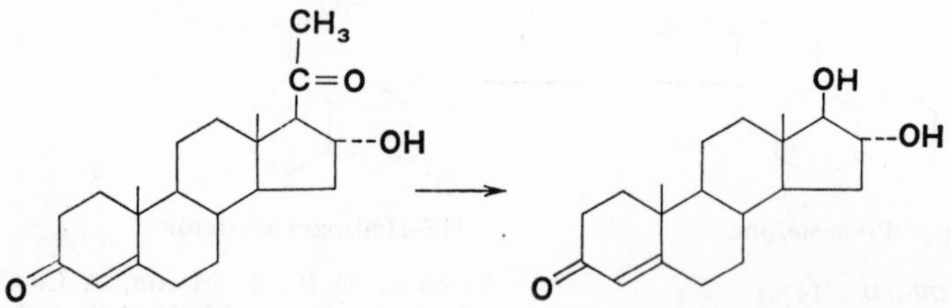

16α-Hydroxyprogesterone → 16α-Hydroxytestosterone

Streptomyces lavendulae

Fried, J. R. W. Thoma, D. Perlman, J. E. Herz and A. Borman, Rec. Progr. Hormone Res., **11**, 149 (1955)

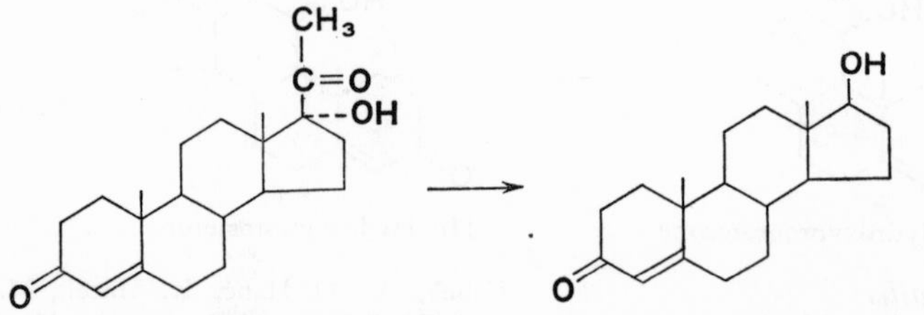

17α-Hydroxyprogesterone → Testosterone

Penicillium citrinum
Penicillium decumbens
Penicillium notatum

Hanč, O., A. Čapek, M. Tadra, K. Macek and A. Šimek, Arzneimittel-Forsch., **7**, 175 (1957)

11β-Hydroxy-3, 20-dioxopregn-
4-en-18-oic acid-18, 11-lactone

11β, 17β-Dihydroxy-3-oxoandrosta-
1, 4-dien-18-oic acid-18, 11-lactone

Fusarium solani

Urech, J., E. Vischer and A. Wettstein, Paper,
Meeting Swiss Chem. Soc., September (1961)

(b) 17-Ketone formation

| 19-Norprogesterone | 19-Norandrost-4-ene-3, 17-dione |

Streptomyces lavendulae ATCC 8664 — Gaul, C., R. I. Dorfman and S. R. Stitch, Biochem. Biophys. Acta., **49**, 387 (1961)

| Progesterone | Androst-4-ene-3, 17-dione |

Aspergillus flavus

Peterson, D. H., S. H. Eppstein, P. D. Meister, H. C. Murray, H. M. Leigh, A. Weintraub and L. M. Reineke, J. Am. Chem. Soc., **75** 5768 (1953)

Cephalosporium subverticillatum (40%)

Bodánszky, A., J. Kollonitsch and G. Wix, Experientia, **11**, 384 (1955)

Cladosporium resinae

Fonken, G. S., H. C. Murray and L. M. Reineke, J. Am. Chem. Soc., **82**, 5507 (1960)

Fusarium solani

Szpilfogel, S. A. et al., Rec. Trav. Chim., **75**, 402 (1956)

Gliocladium catenulatum ATCC 10523
Penicillium lilacinum

Peterson, D. H., S. H. Eppstein, P. D. Meister, H. C. Murray, H. M. Leigh, A. Weintraub and L. M. Reineke, J. Am. Chem. Soc., **75**, 5768 (1953)

Penicillium lilacinum

Sebek, O. K., L. M. Reineke and D. H. Peterson, J. Bacteriol., **83**, 1327 (1962)

Progesterone

6β-Hydroxyandrost-4-ene-3, 17-dione

Gliocladium catenulatum

Peterson, D. H., S. H. Eppstein, P. D. Meister, H. C. Murray, H. M. Leigh, A. Weintraub and L. M. Reineke, J. Am. Chem. Soc., **75**, 5768 (1953)

Progesterone

Androsta-1, 4-diene-3, 17-dione

Calonectria decora

Vischer, E., Ch. Meystre and A. Wettstein, Helv. Chim. Acta., **38**, 835 (1955)

Cylindrocarpon radicicola ATCC 11011

Peterson, G. E., R. W. Thoma, D. Perlman and J. Fried, J. Bacteriol., **74**, 684 (1957)

Fusarium caucasicum

Fusarium solani

Vischer, E. and A. Wettstein, Experientia, **9**, 371 (1953)

Fusarium solani

Nishikawa, M., S. Noguchi and T. Hasegawa, Pharm. Bull. (Japan), **3**, 322 (1955)

Streptomyces lavendulae strain Rutgers Univ. No. 3440-14 (7%)

Fried, J., R. W. Thoma and A. Klingsberg, J. Am. Chem. Soc., **75**, 5764 (1953)

11α-Hydroxyprogesterone

11α-Hydroxyandrost-4-ene-3, 17-dione

Aspergillus chevalieri

Čapek, A., O. Hanč, K. Macek, M. Tadra and E. Riedl-Tůmová, Naturwiss, **43**, 471 (1956)

Aspergillus oryzae (20%)

Penicillium citrinum

Penicillium lilacinum

Sebek, O. K., L. M. Reineke and D. H. Peterson, J. Bacteriol., 83, 1327 (1962)

11-Oxoprogesterone   Adrenosterone

Aspergillus chevalieri

Aspergillus oryzae (20%)

Penicillium citrinum

Čapek, A., O. Hanč, K. Macek, M. Tadra and E. Riedl-Tůmová, Naturwiss., 43, 471 (1956)

14α-Hydroxyprogesterone   14α-Hydroxyandrost-4-ene-3, 17-dione

Penicillium lilacinum

Peterson, D. H., S. H. Eppstein, P. D. Meister, H. C. Murray, H. M. Leigh, A. Weintraub and L. M. Reineke, J. Am. Chem. Soc., 75, 5768 (1953)

9α-Fluoro-11β-hydoxyprogesterone   9α-Fluoro-11β-hydroxyandrost-4-ene-3, 17-dione

Cylindrocarpon radicicola

U. S. Pat. 2,955,075

9α-Fluoro-11-oxoprogesterone

Cylindrocarpon radicicola

9α-Fluoroandrost-4-ene-3, 11, 17-trione

U. S. Pat. 2,955,075

11β-Hydroxy-3, 20-dioxopregn-
4-en-18-oic acid-18, 11-lactone

Fusarium solani

11β-Hydroxy-3, 17-dioxoandrosta-1, 4-
dien-18-oic acid-18, 11-lactone

Urech, J., E. Vischer and A. Wettstein, Paper,
Meeting Swiss Chem. Soc., September (1961)

11β-Hydroxy-3, 20-dioxopregn-
4-en-18-oic acid-18, 11-lactone

Fusarium solani

11β-Hydroxy-18-norandrosta-1, 4-
diene-3, 17-dione

Urech, J., E. Vischer and A. Wettstein, Paper,
Meeting Swiss Chem. Soc., September (1961)

11β-Hydroxy-3, 20-dioxopregn
4-en-18-oic acid-18, 11-lactone

Fusarium solani

11β-Hydroxy-18-nor-18-isoandrosta-
1, 4-diene-3, 17-dione

Urech, J., E. Vischer and A. Wettstein, Paper,
Meeting Swiss Chem. Soc., September (1961)

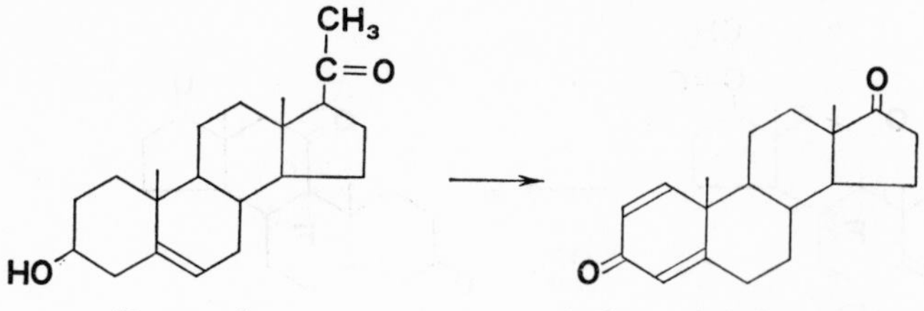

Pregnenolone

Androsta-1, 4-diene-3, 17-dione

Fusarium caucasicum
Fusarium solani

Vischer, E. and A. Wettstein, Experientia, **9**, 371 (1953)

Pycnodothis sp.

Shull, G. M., Trans. N. Y. Acad. Sci., **19**, 147 (1956)

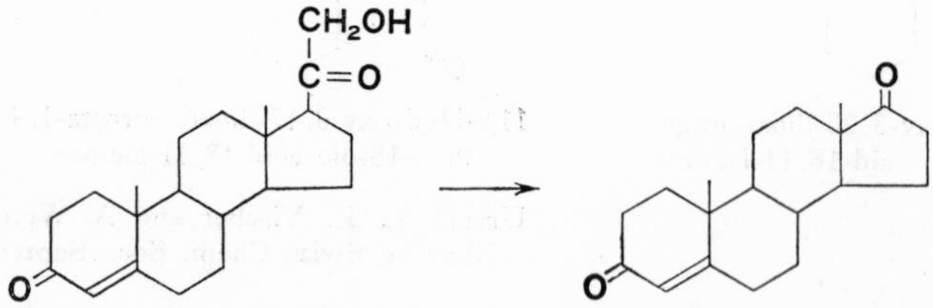

11-Deoxycorticosterone

Androst-4-ene-3, 17-dione

Aspergillus sp.
Penicillium sp.

Peterson, D. H., S. H. Eppstein, P. D. Meister, H. C. Murray, H. M. Leigh, A. Weintraub and L. M. Reineke, J. Am. Chem Soc., **75**, 5768 (1953)

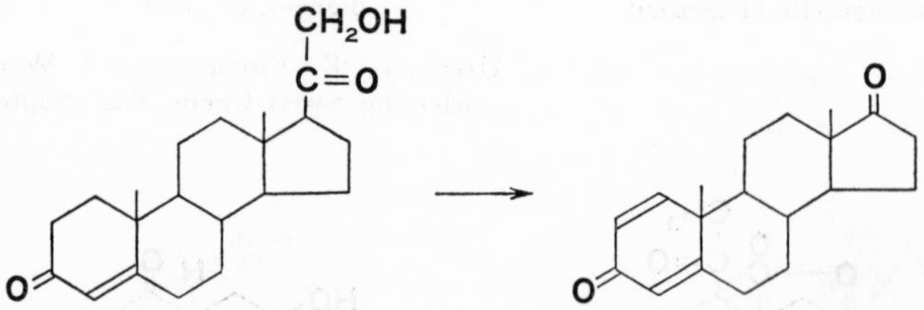

11-Deoxycorticosterone

Androsta-1, 4-diene-3, 17-dione

Fusarium caucasicum
Fusarium solani

Vischer, E. and A. Wettstein, Experientia, **9**, 371 (1953)

CH₂OH
C=O
--OH

11-Deoxycortisol

Androst-4-ene-3, 17-dione

Didymella lycopersici, conidia

Penicillium chrysogenum, conidia

Pseudomonas chlororaphis IAM 1511

Vezina, C., S. N. Sehgal and K. Singh, Appl. Microbiol., **11**, 50 (1963)

Naito, A., Y. Sato, H. Iizuka and K. Tsuda, Steroids, **3**, 327 (1964)

CH₂OH
C=O
--OH
OH

15α-Hydroxy-11-deoxycortisol

15α-Hydroxyandrost-4-ene-3, 17-dione

Pseudomonas chlororaphis IAM 1511

Naito, A., Y. Sato, H. Iizuka and K. Tsuda, Steroids, **3**, 327 (1964)

CH₂OH
C=O
--OH
HO

Cortisol

11β-Hydroxyandrost-4-ene-3, 17-dione

Pseudomonas chlororaphis IAM 1511

Naito, A., Y. Sato, H. Iizuka and K. Tsuda, Steroids, **3**, 327 (1964)

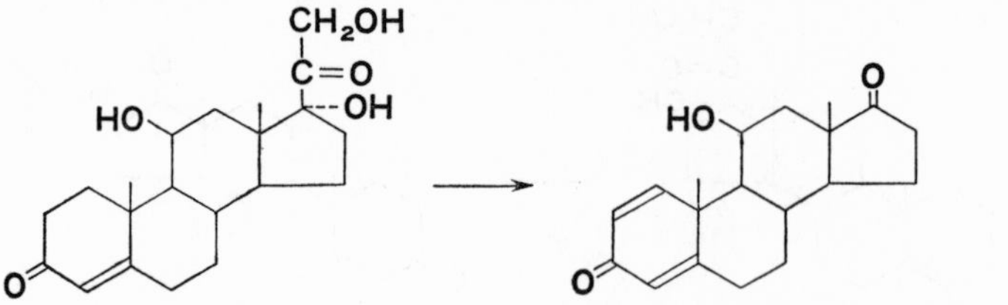

Cortisol

11β-Hydroxyandrosta-1, 4-diene-
3, 17-dione

Pseudomonas chlororaphis IAM 1511

Naito, A., Y. Sato, H. Iizuka and K. Tsuda,
Steroids, **3**, 327 (1964)

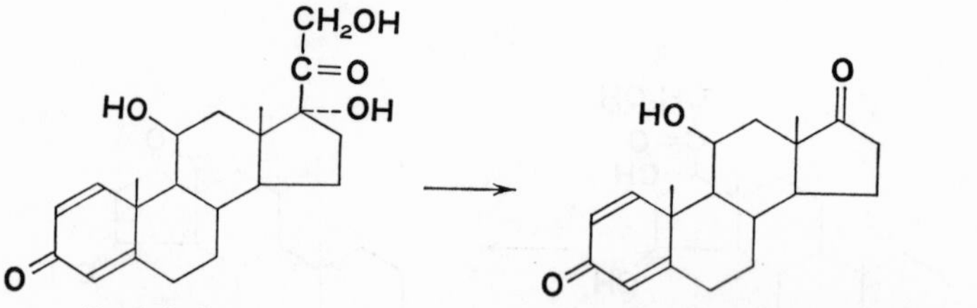

Prednisolone

11β-Hydroxyandrosta-1, 4-diene-
3, 17-dione

Pseudomonas chlororaphis IAM 1511

Naito, A., Y. Sato, H. Iizuka and K. Tsuda,
Steroids, **3**, 327 (1964)

E. Lactone Formation

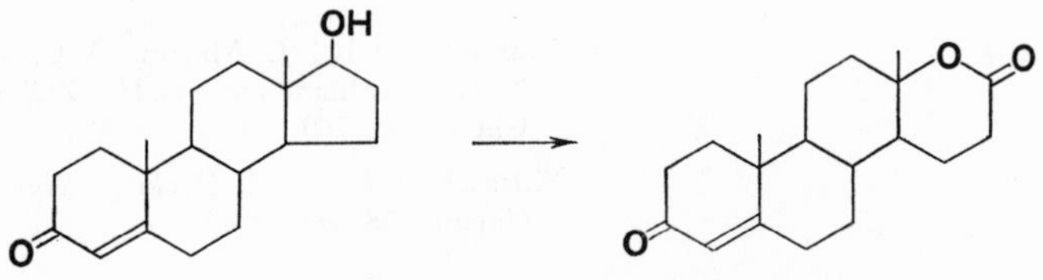

Testosterone

Testololactone

Aspergillus tamarii (41%)

Brannon, D. R., J. Martin, A. C. Oehlschlager, N. N. Durham and L. H. Zalkow, J. Org. Chem., **30**, 760 (1965)

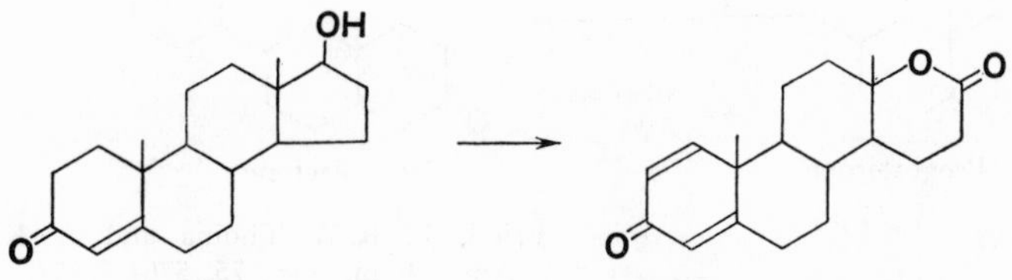

Testosterone

1-Dehydrotestololactone

Cylindrocarpon radicicola ATCC 11011 (50%)

Fried, J., R. W. Thoma and A. Klingsberg, J. Am. Chem. Soc., **75**, 5764 (1953)

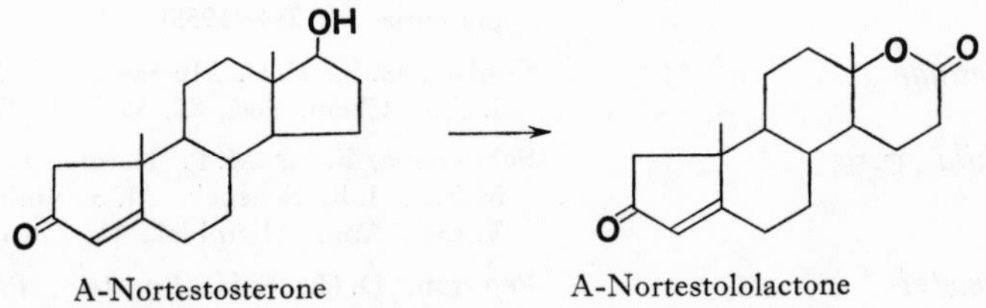

A-Nortestosterone

A-Nortestololactone

Penicillium citrinum

U. S. Pat. 2,998,428

Androst-4-ene-3,17-dione   Testololactone

Aspergillus tamarii

Brannon, D. R., J. Martin, A. C. Oehlschlager, N. N. Durham and L. H. Zalkow, J. Org. Chem., **30**, 760 (1965)

Pythium ultimum

Shirasaka, M. and M. Ozaki, J. Agr. Chem. Soc. (Japan), **35**, 206 (1961)

Progesterone   Testololactone

Aspergillus flavus

Fried, J., R. W. Thoma and A. Klingsberg, J. Am. Chem. Soc., **75**, 5764 (1953)

Aspergillus oryzae

Čapek, A., O. Hanč, K. Macek, M. Tadra and E. Riedl-Tůmová, Naturwiss., **43**, 471 (1956)

Aspergillus tamarii (70%)

Brannon, D. R., J. Martin, A. C. Oehlschlager, N. N. Durham and L. H. Zalkow, J. Org. Chem., **30**, 760 (1965)

Cephalosporium subverticillatum (54%)

Bodánszky, A., J. Kollonitsch and G. Wix, Experientia, **11**, 384 (1955)

Cladosporium resinae

Fonken, G. S., H. C. Murray and L. M. Reineke, J. Am. Chem. Soc., **82**, 5507 (1960)

Collybia dryophila C-59

Schuytema, E. C., M. P. Hargie, D. J. Siehr, I. Merits, J. R. Schenck, M. S. Smith and E. L. Varner, Appl. Microbiol., **11**, 256 (1963)

Penicillium adametzi

Peterson, D. H., S. H. Eppstein, P. D. Meister, H. C. Murray, H. M. Leigh, A. Weintraub and L. M. Reineke, J. Am. Chem. Soc., **75**, 5768 (1953)

Penicillium chrysogenum (70%)

Fried, J., R. W. Thoma and A. Klingsberg, J. Am. Chem. Soc., **75**, 5764 (1953)

Penicillium lilacinum

Sebek, O. K., L. M. Reineke and D. H. Peterson, J. Bacteriol., **83**, 1327 (1962)

Pythium ultimum

Shirasaka, M. and M. Ozaki, J. Agr. Chem. Soc. (Japan), **35**, 206 (1961)

Progesterone

1-Dehydrotestololactone

Cylindrocarpon radicicola ATCC 11011
(50%)

Fusarium lateritium (40%)

Fusarium solani

Fried, J., R. W. Thoma and A. Klingsberg, J. Am. Chem. Soc., **75**, 5764 (1953)

Čapek, A., O. Hanč and M. Tadra, Folia Microbiol., **8**, 120 (1963)

Nishikawa, M., S. Noguchi and T. Hasegawa, Pharm. Bull. (Japan), **3**, 322 (1955)

11α-Hydroxyprogesterone

11α-Hydroxytestololactone

Penicillium lilacinum

Sebek, O. K., L. M. Reineke and D. H. Peterson, J. Bacteriol., **83**, 1327 (1962)

17α-Hydroxyprogesterone

Testololactone

Aspergillus flavus

Peterson, D. H., S. H. Eppstein, P. D. Meister, H. C. Murray, H. M. Leigh, A. Weintraub and L. M. Reineke, J. Am. Chem. Soc., **75**, 5768 (1953)

Pythium ultimum

Shirasaka, M. and M. Ozaki, J. Agr. Chem. Soc. (Japan), **35**, 206 (1961)

CH₂OH
C=O

11-Deoxycorticosterone   Testololactone

Fusarium sp.   Shull, G. M., Trans. N. Y. Acad. Sci., **19**, 147
                                          (1956)

Pythim ultimum   Shirasaka, M. and M. Ozaki, J. Agr. Chem. Soc.
                                          (Japan), **35**, 206 (1961)

CH₂OH
C=O
--OH

11-Deoxycortisol   Testololactone

Curvularia lunata   Shull, G. M., Trans. N. Y. Acad. Sci., **19**, 147
                                          (1956)

CH₂OH
C=O
--OH

11-Deoxycortisol   1-Dehydrotestololactone

Cylindrocarpon radicicola ATCC 11011   Fried, J., R. W. Thoma and A. Klingsberg, J.
(50%)   Am. Chem. Soc., **75**, 5764 (1953)

Pseudomonas chlororaphis IAM 1511   Naito, A., Y. Sato, H. Iizuka and K. Tsuda,
                                          Steroids, **3**, 327 (1964)

— 182 —

F. AROMATIZATION

19-Nortestosterone → Estrone

Bacillus sphaericus ATCC 7055

Nocardia corallina

Gaul, C., R. I. Dorfman and S. R. Stitch, Bio-chem. Biophys. Acta, **49** 387 (1961)

U. S. Pat. 3,087,864

19-Nortestosterone → Estradiol

Arthrobacter simplex

Japan Pat. 443,426

19-Nortestosterone 17-acetate → Estradiol 17-acetate

Corynebacterium simplex ATCC 6946

Kushinsky, S., J. Biol. Chem., **230**, 31 (1958)

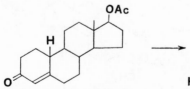

19-Nortestosterone 17-acetate → Estrone

Pseudomonas testosteroni ATCC 11996

Levy, H. R. and P. Talalay, J. Am. Chem. Soc., **79**, 2658 (1957)

2α-Methyl-19-nortestosterone

Septomyxa affinis ATCC 6737 (17%)

2-Methylestrone

Peterson, D. H., L. M. Reineke, H. C. Murray and O. K. Sebek, Chem. & Ind. 1301 (1960)

2α-Methyl-19-nortestosterone

Septomyxa affinis ATCC 6737

2-Methylestradiol

Peterson, D. H., L. M. Reineke, H. C. Murray and O. K. Sebek, Chem. & Ind. 1301 (1960)

4-Methyl-19-nortestosterone

Septomyxa affinis ATCC 6737 (12%)

4-Methylestrone

Peterson, D. H., L. M. Reineke, H. C. Murray and O. K. Sebek, Chem. & Ind. 1301 (1960)

4-Methyl-19-nortestosterone

Septomyxa affinis ATCC 6737

4-Methylestradiol

Peterson, D. H., L. M. Reineke, H. C. Murray and O. K. Sebek, Chem. & Ind. 1301 (1960)

Androst-4-ene-3, 17-dione

9, 10-Seco-3-hydroxyandrosta-
1, 3, 5 (10)-triene-9, 17-dione

Arthrobacter sp. B-22-8 ATCC 13260

Dodson, R. M. and R. D. Muir, J. Am. Chem. Soc., **83**, 4627 (1961)

Nocardia restrictus

Sih, C. J., Biochem. Biophys. Res. Comm. **7**, 87 (1962)

Pseudomonas sp. B-20-184

Dodson, R. M. and R. D. Muir, J. Am. Chem. Soc., **83**, 4627 (1961)

19-Hydroxyandrost-4-ene-3, 17-dione

Estrone

Pseudomonas sp. B-20-184

Dodson, R. M. and R. D. Muir, J. Am. Chem. Soc., **83**, 4627 (1961)

Dehydroepiandrosterone

9, 10-Seco-3-hydroxyandrosta-
1, 3, 5 (10)-triene-9, 17-dione

Mycobacterium smegmatis SG 98

Schubert, K., K.-H. Böhme and C. Hörhold, Z. Naturforsch., **15 B**, 584 (1960)

Dehydroepiandrosterone

9, 10-Seco-3, 9-dihydroxyandrosta-
1, 3, 5 (10)-trien-17-one

Mycobacterium smegmatis SG 98

Schubert, K., K.-H. Böhme and C. Hörhold, Z. Naturforsch., **15 B**, 584 (1960)

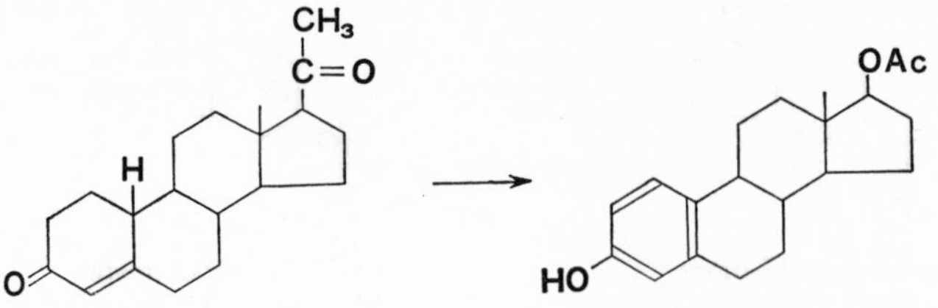

19-Norprogesterone

17β-Acetoxyestra-1, 3, 5(10)-
trien-3-ol

Corynebacterium simplex ATCC 6946

Bowers, A., C. Casas-campillo and C. Djerassi, Tetrahedron, **2**, 165 (1958)

Streptomyces lavendulae ATCC 8664

Gaul, C., R. I. Dorfman and S. R. Stitch, Biochem. Biophys. Acta., **49**, 387 (1961)

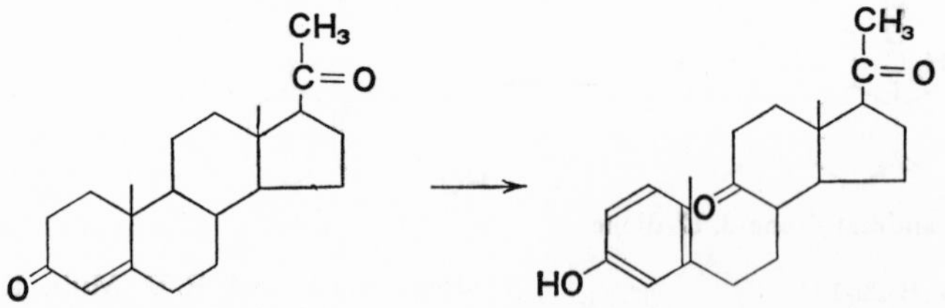

Progesterone

9, 10-Seco-3-hydroxypregna-
1, 3, 5(10)-triene-9, 20-dione

Mycobacterium smegmatis SG 98

Schubert, K., K.-H. Böhme and C. Hörhold, Z. Physiol. Chem., **325**, 260 (1961)

G. ISOMERIZATION

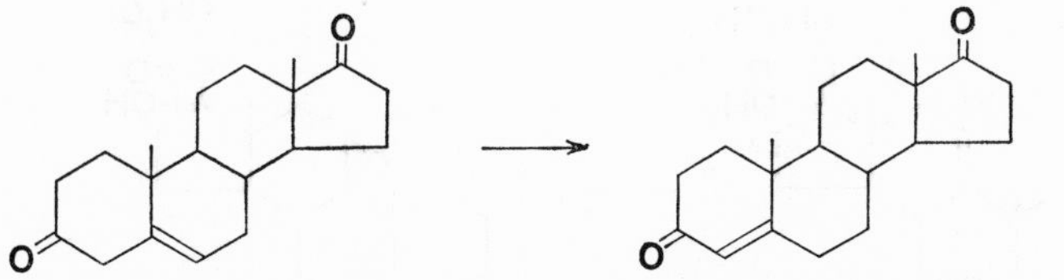

Androst-5-ene-3,17-dione

Androst-4-ene-3,17-dione

Pseudomonas sp.

Talalay, P. and V. S. Wang, Biochem. Biophys. Acta, **18**, 300 (1955)

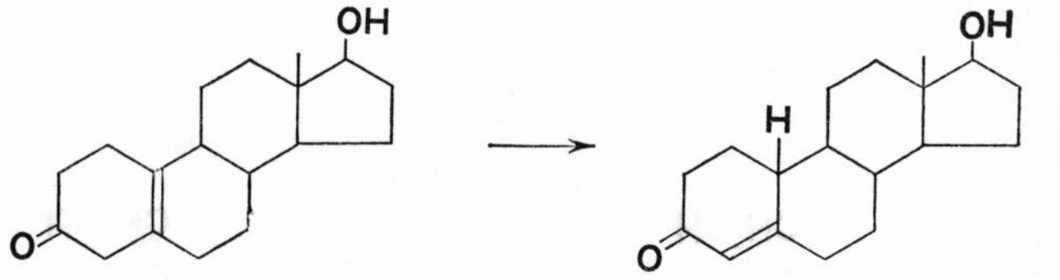

17β-Hydroxy-19-norandrost-5(10)-en-3-one

17β-Hydroxy-19-norandrost-4-en-3-one (19-Nortestosterone)

Pseudomonas sp.

Talalay, P. and V. S. Wang, Biochem. Biophys. Acta, **18**, 300 (1955)

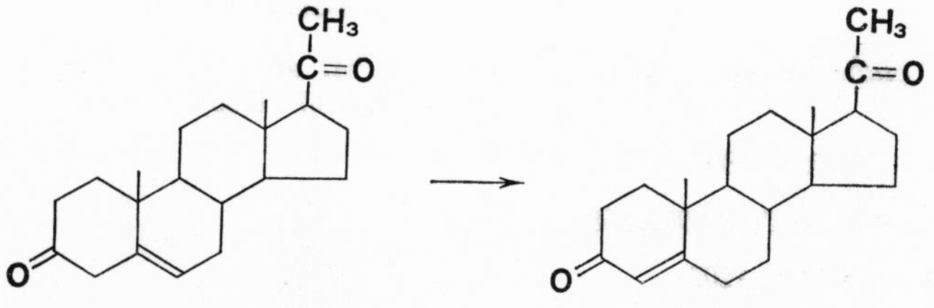

Pregn-5-ene-3,20-dione

Progesterone

Pseudomonas sp.

Talalay, P. and V. S. Wang, Biochem. Biophys, Acta, **18**, 300 (1955)

H. Epoxidation

9(11)-Dehydro-11-deoxycortisol

17α, 21-Dihydroxy-9β, 11β-oxidopregn-
4-ene-3, 20-dione

Cunninghamella blakesleeana ATCC
9245

Curvularia lunata NRRL 2380

Bloom, B. M. and G. M. Shull, J. Am. Chem.
Soc., **77**, 5767 (1955)

14(15)-Dehydro-11-deoxycortisol

17α, 21-Dihydroxy-14α, 15α-oxido-
pregn-4-ene-3, 20-dione

Cunninghamella blakesleeana ATCC
9245

Curvularia lunata NRRL 2380

Helicostylum piriforme ATCC 8992, 8686

Mucor griseocyanus ATCC 1207a

Mucor parasiticus ATCC 6476

Bloom, B. M. and G. M. Shull, J. Am. Chem.
Soc., **77**, 5767 (1955)

I. HYDROLYSIS

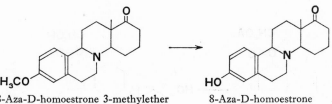

Estrone 3-acetate   ' α '-Estradiol

Baker's yeast   Mamoli, L., Ber., **71 B**, 2696 (1938)

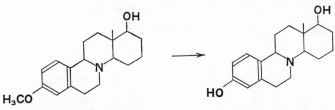

8-Aza-D-homoestrone 3-methylether   8-Aza-D-homoestrone

Aspergillus flavus   Curtis, P. J., Biochem. J., **97**, 148 (1965)

8-Aza-D-homoestradiol 3-methylether   8-Aza-D-homoestradiol

Cunninghamella blakesleeana   Curtis, P. J., Biochem. J., **97**, 148 (1965)

2α-Hydroxytestosterone   2-Hydroxyandrost-1-ene-3, 17-dione
2α, 17β-diacetate

Nocardia carollina   U. S. Pat. 3,087,864

— 189 —

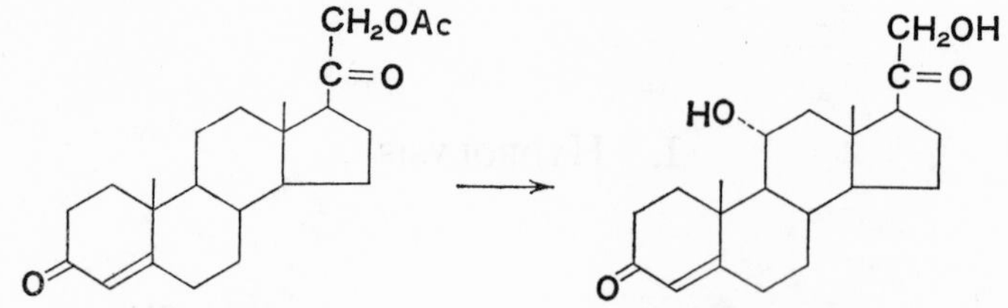

CH₂OAc
C=O

11-Deoxycorticosterone 21-acetate

CH₂OH
C=O

11α, 21-Dihydroxypregn-4-
ene-3, 20-dione

Aspergillus clavatus

Aspergillus fischeri

Aspergillus nidulans (15.5%)

Aspergillus ustus

Rhizopus nigricans

U. S. Pat. 2,649,402

U. S. Pat. 2,602,769

CH₂OAc
C=O

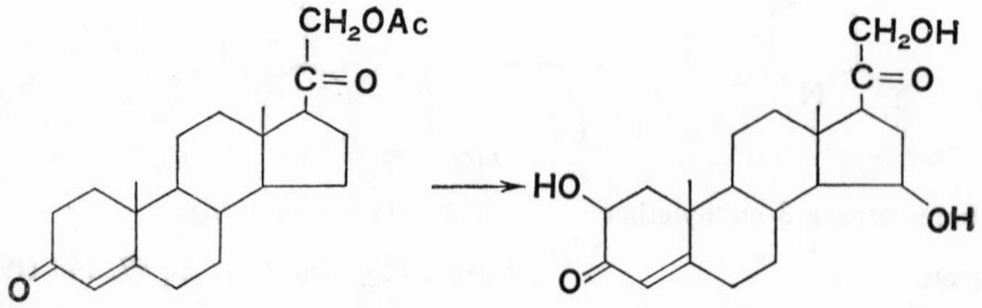

11-Deoxycorticosterone 21-acetate

CH₂OH
C=O

2β, 15β, 21-Trihydroxypregn-
4-ene-3, 20-dione

Sclerotinia sclerotiorum

Japan Pat. 311,627

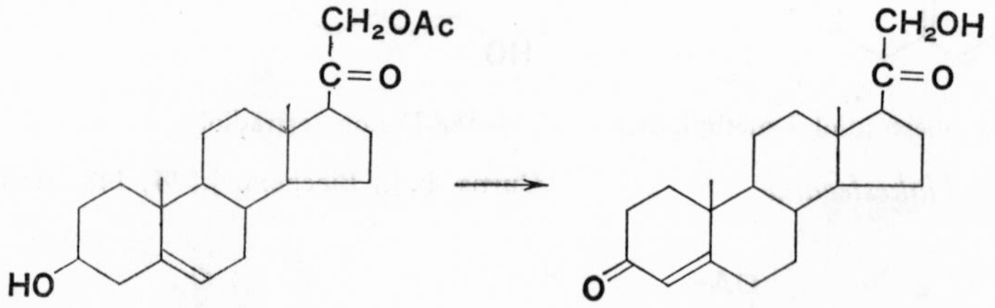

CH₂OAc
C=O

21-Hydroxypregnenolone 21-acetate

Corynebacterium mediolanum

CH₂OH
C=O

21-Hydroxypregn-4-ene-3, 20-dione
(11-Deoxycorticosterone)

Mamoli, L., Ber., **72 B**, 1863 (1939)

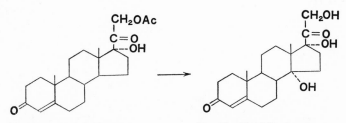

11-Deoxycortisol 21-acetate

11α, 17α, 21-Trihydroxypregn-
4-ene-3, 20-dione

Dactylium dendroides

Dan. Pat. 94,041

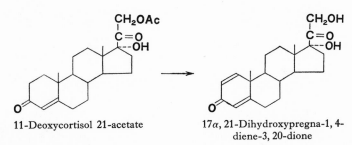

11-Deoxycortisol 21-acetate

14α, 17α, 21-Trihydroxypregn-
4-ene-3, 20-dione

Mycobacterium lacticola
Mycobacterium smegmatis

Belg. Pat. 538,327

11-Deoxycortisol 21-acetate

17α, 21-Dihydroxypregna-1, 4-
diene-3, 20-dione

Mycobacterium lacticola
Mycobacterium smegmatis

Belg. Pat. 538,327

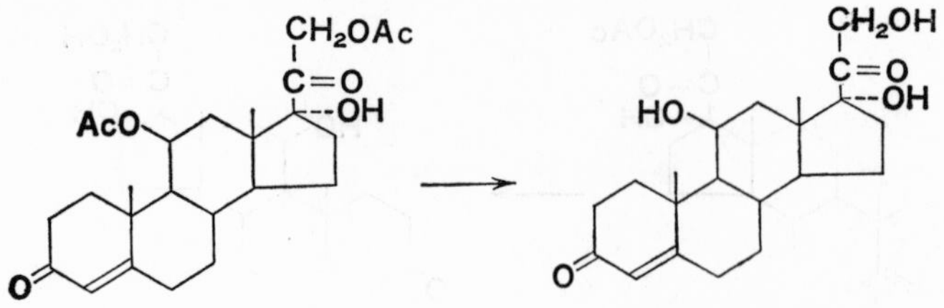

Cortisol 11β, 21-diacetate

11β, 17α, 21-Trihydroxypregn-
4-ene-3, 20-dione
(Cortisol)

Flavobacterium dehydrogenans var. *hydrolyticum* SCH 111

Charney, W., L. Weber and E. Oliveto, Arch.
Biochem. Biophys., **79**, 402 (1959)

J. Esterification

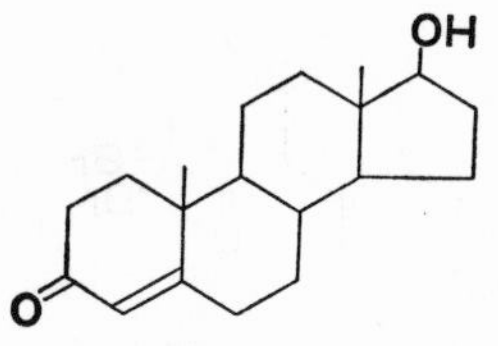

Testosterone

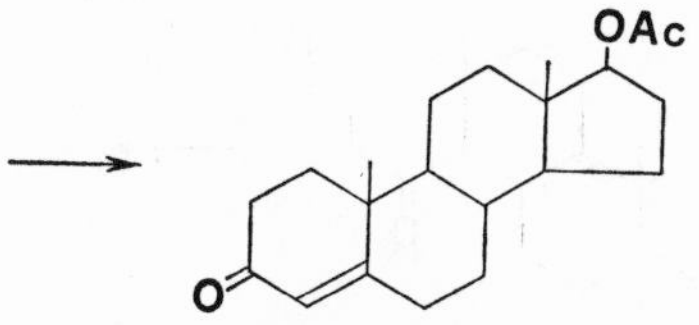

Saccharomyces fragilis ATCC 10022

Testosterone 17-acetate

McGuire, J, S., E. S. Maxwell and G. M. Tomkins, Biochem. Biophys. Acta, **45**, 392 (1960)

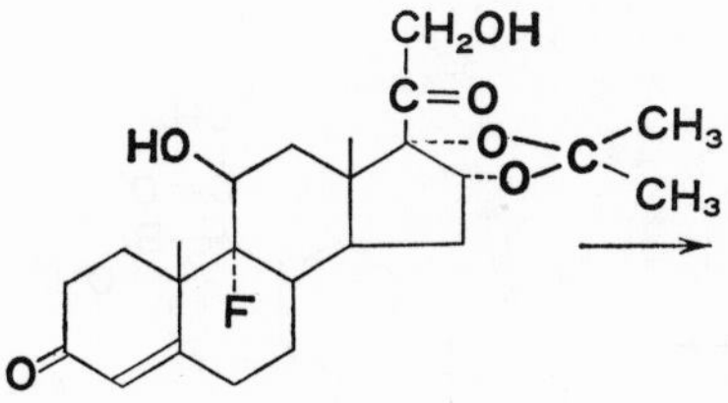

9α-Fluoro-11β, 21-dihydroxy
16α, 17α-isopropylenedioxy-
pregn-4-ene-3, 20-dione

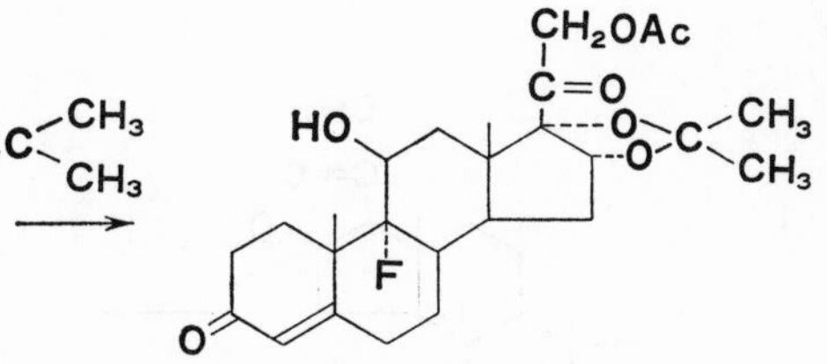

Trichoderma glaucum Lederle culture
No. Z-696

9α-Fluoro-11β, 21-dihydroxy-16α, 17α-
isopropylidenedioxypregn-4-
ene-3, 20-dione 21-acetate

Holmlund, C. E., L. I. Feldman, N. E. Rigler, B. E. Nielsen and R. H. Evans Jr., J. Am. Chem. Soc., **83**, 2586 (1961)

K. HALOGENATION

15-Oxo-1-dehydrotestololactone

16-Dibromo-15-Oxo-1-dehydro-
testololactone

Caldariomyces fumago ATCC 16373

Neidleman, S. L., P. A. Diassi, B. Junta, R. M. Palmere and S. C. Pan, Tetrahedron Letter No. 44, 5337 (1966)

16-Oxo-A-norprogesterone

17α-Bromo-A-norpregn-4-
ene-3, 16, 20-trione

Caldariomyces fumago ATCC 16373

Neidleman, S. L., P. A. Diassi, B. Junta, R. M. Palmere and S. C. Pan, Tetrahedron Letter No. 44, 5337 (1966)

16-Oxo-A-norprogesterone

17α-Chloro-A-norpregn-4-
ene-3, 16, 20-trione

Caldariomyces fumago ATCC 16373

Neidleman, S. L., P. A. Diassi, B. Junta, R. M. Palmere and S. C. Pan, Tetrahedron Letter No. 44, 5337 (1966)

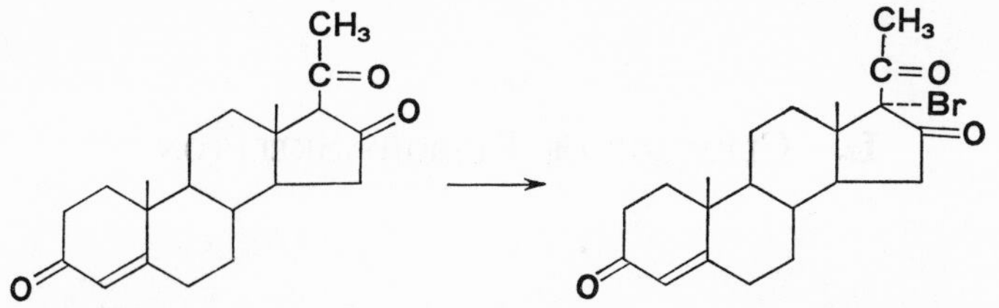

16-Oxoprogesterone

Caldariomyces fumago ATCC 16373 (50%)

17α-Bromopregn-4-ene-3, 16, 20-trione

Neidleman, S. L., P. A. Diassi, B. Junta, R. M. Palmere and S. C. Pan, Tetrahedron Letter No. 44, 5337 (1966)

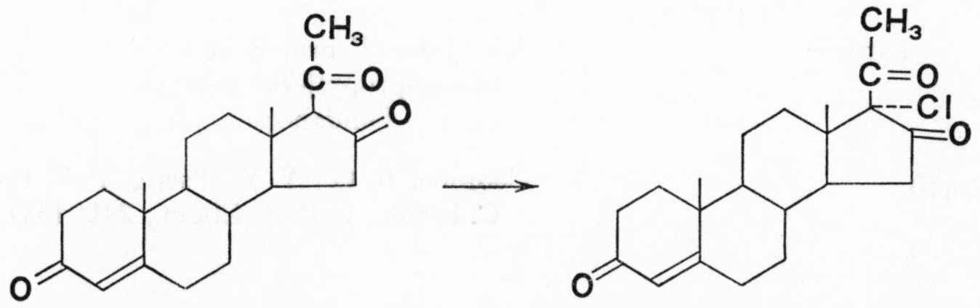

16-Oxoprogesterone

Caldariomyces fumago ATCC 16373 (50%)

17α-Chloropregn-4-ene-3, 16, 20-trione

Neidleman, S. L., P. A. Diassi, B. Junta, R. M. Palmere and S. C. Pan, Tetrahedron Letter No. 44, 5337 (1966)

L. CLEAVAGE OF STEROID SKELETON

Estrone

3aα-H-4α-[3'-propanoic acid]-5β-
[2-ketopropyl]-7aβ-methyl-
1-indanone

Nocardia sp. E 110

Coombe, R. G., Y. Y. Tsong, P. B. Hamilton and
C. J. Sih, J. Biol. Chem., **241**, 1587 (1966)

Estrone

3aα-H-4α-[3'-propanoic acid]-5β-
[4'-but-3-enoic acid]-7aβ-
methyl-1-indanone

Nocardia sp. E 110

Coombe, R. G., Y. Y. Tsong, P. B. Hamilton and
C. J. Sih, J. Biol. Chem., **241**, 1587 (1966)

Estrone

2-Carboxy-7aβ-methyl-7-keto-9aα-H-
indano-[5, 4f]-5aα, 10, 10aβ, 11-
tetrahydroquinoline

Nocardia sp. E 110

Coombe, R. G., Y. Y. Tsong, P. B. Hamilton and
C. J. Sih, J. Biol. Chem., **241**, 1587 (1966)

Androst-4-ene-3, 17-dione

9, 10-Seco-3, 9-dihydroxyandrosta-
1, 3, 5(10)-trien-17-one

Mycobacterium smegmatis SG 98

Schubert, K., K.-H. Böhme and C. Hörhold, Z. Naturforsch., **15B**, 584 (1960)

Androst-4-ene-3, 17-dione

9, 10-Seco-3-hydroxyandrosta-
1, 3, 5(10)-triene-9, 17-dione

Arthrobacter sp. B-22-8 ATCC 13260

Dodson, R. M. and R. D. Muir, J. Am. Chem. Soc., **83**, 4627 (1961)

Mycobacterium smegmatis SG 98

Schubert, K., K.-H. Böhme and C. Hörhold, Z. Naturforsch., **15B**, 584 (1960)

Nocardia restrictus

Sih, C. J., Biochem. Biophys. Res. Comm., **7**, 87 (1962)

Pseudomonas sp. B-20-184

Dodson, R. M. and R. D. Muir, J. Am. Chem. Soc., **83**, 4627 (1961)

Androst-4-ene-3, 17-dione

7aβ-Methylperhydroindane-1, 5-dione-
4α-[3'-propionic acid]

Nocardia restrictus ATCC 14887

Sih, C. J., S. S. Lee, Y. Y. Tsong and K. C. Wang, J. Am. Chem. Soc., **87**, 1385 (1965)

Nocardia restrictus No. 545

Sih, C. J. and K. C. Wang, J. Am. Chem. Soc., **85**, 2135 (1963)

Dehydroepiandrosterone

Mycobacterium smegmatis SG 98

9, 10-Seco-3-hydroxyandrosta-
1, 3, 5(10)-triene-9, 17-dione

Schubert, K., K.-H. Böhme and C. Hörhold, Z
Naturforsch., **15B** 584 (1960)

Dehydroepiandrosterone

Mycobacterium smegmatis SG 98

9, 10-Seco-3, 9-dihydroxyandrosta-
1, 3, 5(10)-trien-17-one

Schubert, K., K.-H. Böhme and C. Hörhold, Z.
Naturforsch., **15B** 584 (1960)

3β, 5α, 6β-Trihydroxy-
androstan-17-one

Nocardia restrictus No. 545

9, 10-Seco-3, 6R-dihydroxyandrosta-
1, 3, 5(10)-triene-9, 17-dione

Lee, S. S. and C. J. Sih, Biochemistry, **3**, 1267
(1964)

3β-Hydroxy-5α, 6α-oxido-
androstan-17-one

Nocardia restrictus No. 545

9, 10-Seco-3, 6S-dihydroxyandrosta-
1, 3, 5(10)-triene-9, 17-dione

Lee, S. S. and C. J. Sih, Biochemistry, **3**, 1267
(1964)

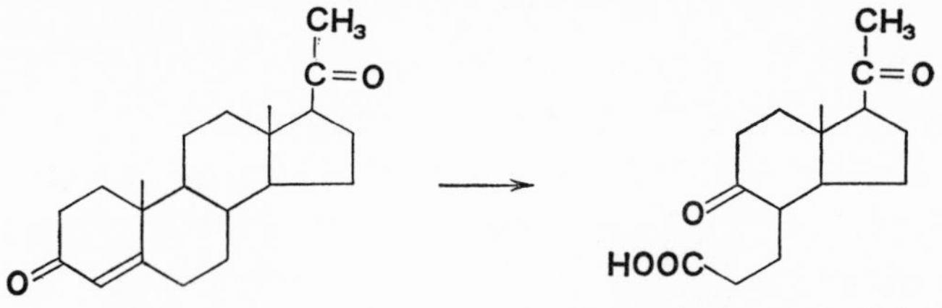

CH₃ C=O ... (structure)

Progesterone

7a-Methyl-1-acetylperhydroindanone-
(5)-[β-propionic acid-(4)]

Mycobacterium smegmatis SG 98

Schubert, K., K.-H. Böhme and C. Hörhold,
Hoppe-Seyler's, Z. Physiol. Chem., **325**, 260
(1961)

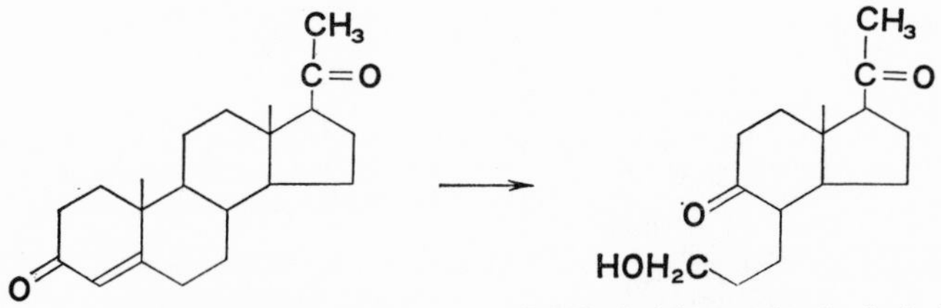

Progesterone

7a-Methyl-1-acetylperhydroindanone-
(5)-[β-propylalcohol-(4)]

Mycobacterium smegmatis SG 98

Schubert, K., K.-H. Böhme and C. Hörhold,
Steroids, **4**, 581 (1964)

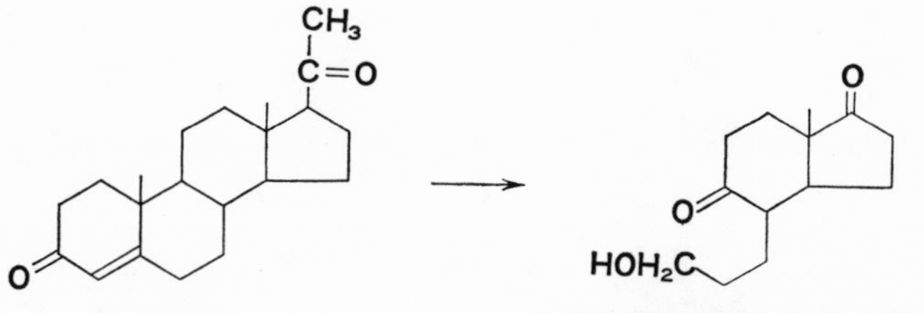

Progesterone

7a-Methylperhydroindanedione-
(1, 5)-[β-propylalcohol-(4)]

Mycobacterium smegmatis SG 98

Schubert, K., K.-H. Böhme and C. Hörhold,
Steroids, **4**, 581 (1964)

II. MICROBIAL TRANSFORMATION
OF BILE ACIDS

Structures of typical bile acids

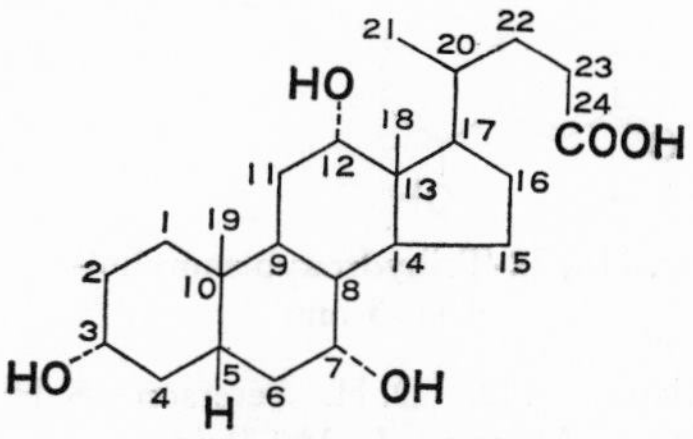

Cholic acid
($3\alpha, 7\alpha, 12\alpha$-Trihydroxy-5$\beta$-cholanic acid)

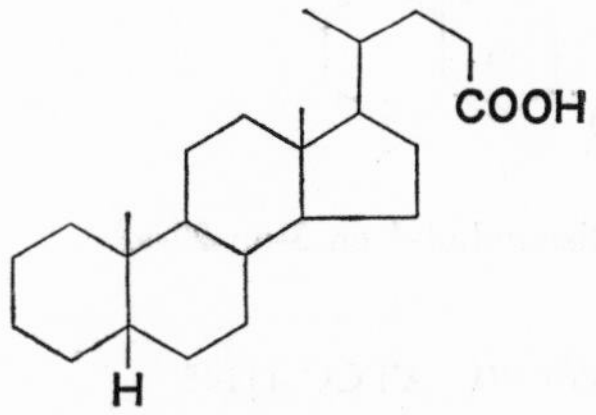

5β-Cholanic acid

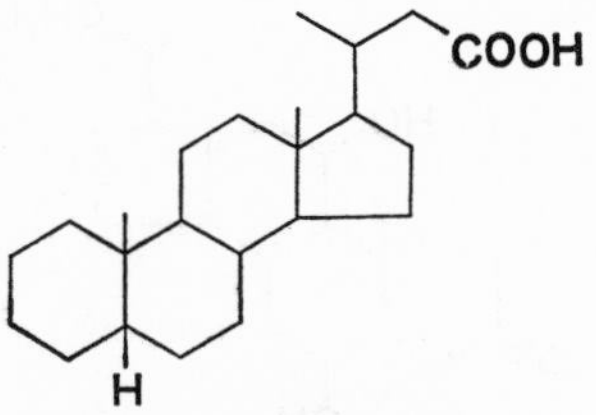

24-Nor-5β-cholanic acid

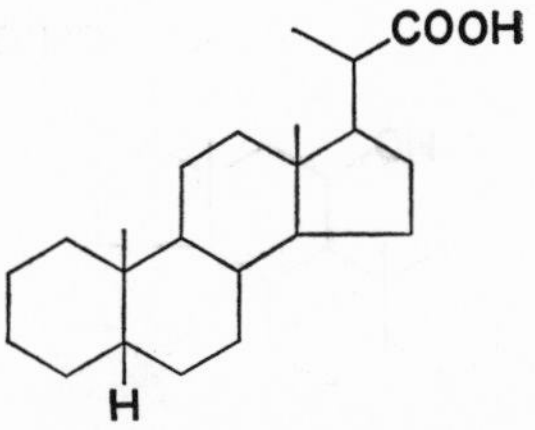

23, 24-Bisnor-5β-cholanic acid

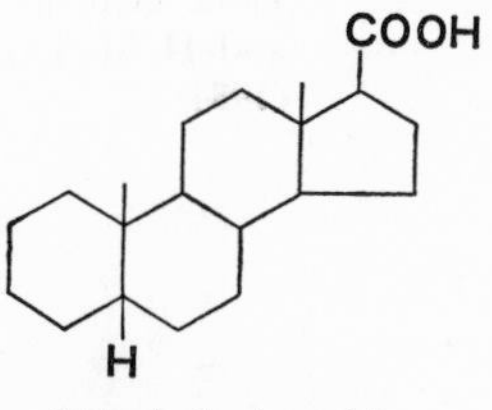

Etiocholanic acid
(5β-Androstane-17β-carboxylic acid)

A. HYDROXYLATION

Bisnorchol-4-en-3-on-22-al

6β, 11α, 22-Trihydroxybisnorchol-
4-en-3-one

Rhizopus arrhizus ATCC 11145

Rhizopus nigricans ATCC 6227b

Meister, P. D., D. H. Peterson, S. H. Eppstein,
H. C. Murray, L. M. Reineke, A. Weintraub
and H. M. Leigh, J. Am. Chem. Soc., **76**, 5679
(1954)

11α, 22-Dihydroxybisnorchol-4-
en-3-one

6β, 11α, 22-Trihydroxybisnorchol-
4-en-3-one

Cunninghamella blakesleeana ATCC
8688a

Meister, P. D., D. H. Peterson, S. H. Eppstein,
H. C. Murray, L. M. Reineke, A. Weintraub
and H. M. Leigh, J. Am. Chem. Soc., **56**, 5679
(1954)

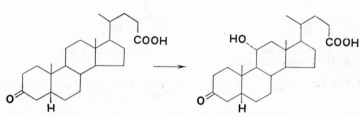

Bisnorchol-4-en-3-on-22-al

11α, 22-Dihydroxybisnorchol-
4-en-3-one

Rhizopus nigricans ATCC 6227b

Meister, P. D., D. H. Peterson, S. H. Eppstein,
H. C. Murray, L. M. Reineke, A. Weintraub
and H. M. Leigh, J. Am. Chem. Soc., **76**, 5679
(1954)

3-Oxocholanic acid

11α-Hydroxy-3-oxocholanic acid

Aspergillus ochraceus

Dulaney, E. L., Mycologia, **47**, 464 (1955)

B. Dehydrogenation

(a) $\text{>CH-OH} \longrightarrow \text{>C=O}$

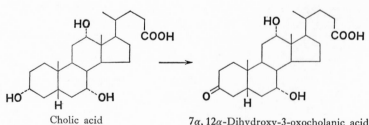

Lithocholic acid
(3α-Hydroxycholanic acid)

Alcaligenes faecalis (25%)

3-Oxocholanic acid

Hughes, H. B. and L. H. Schmidt, Proc. Soc.
Expt. Biol. Med., **51**, 162 (1942)

7-Deoxycholic acid

Alcaligenes faecalis

3, 12-Dioxocholanic acid

Hughes, H. B. and L. H. Schmidt, Proc. Soc.
Expt. Biol. Med., **51**, 162 (1942)

Cholic acid

Streptomyces gelaticus strain 1164

7α, 12α-Dihydroxy-3-oxocholanic acid

Hayakawa, S., Y. Saburi and H. Teraoka, Proc.
Japan Acad., **32**, 519 (1956)

Cholic acid

Alcaligenes faecalis

3α, 12α-Dihydroxy-7-oxocholanic acid

Hoehn, W. M., L. H. Schmidt and H. B. Hughes, J. Biol. Chem., **152**, 59 (1944)

Cholic acid

Streptomyces gelaticus strain 1164

3α, 7α-Dihydroxy-12-oxocholanic acid

Hayakawa, S., Y. Saburi and H. Teraoka, Proc. Japan. Acad., **32**, 519 (1956)

Cholic acid

Streptomyces gelaticus strain 1164 (6.7%)

7α-Hydroxy-3, 12-dioxocholanic acid

Hayakawa, S., Y. Saburi and H. Teraoka, Proc. Japan Acad., **32**, 519 (1956)

Cholic acid

Alcaligenes faecalis

3α-Hydroxy-7, 12-dioxocholanic acid

Hoehn, W. M., L. H. Schmidt and H. B. Hughes, J. Biol. Chem., **152**, 59 (1944)

Cholic acid

3, 7, 12-Trioxocholanic acid

Alcaligenes faecalis (83%)

Schmidt, L. H., H. B. Hughes, M. H. Green and E. Cooper, J. Biol. Chem., **145**, 229 (1942)

Cholic acid

7α, 12α-Dihydroxy-3-oxo-chol-4-enic acid

A soil bacterium strain CE-1

Eguchi, T., J. Biochem. (Japan), **44**, 81 (1957)

Cholic acid

3α, 7α-Dihydroxy-12-oxo-bisnorcholanic acid

Streptomyces gelaticus strain 1164

Hayakawa, S., Y. Saburi and I. Akaeda, J. Biochem. (Japan), **44**, 109 (1957)

Cholic acid

7α-Hydroxy-3, 12-dioxobis-norchol-4-enic acid

Streptomyces gelaticus strain 1164

Hayakawa, S., Y. Saburi, T. Fujii and Y. Sonoda, J. Biochem. (Japan), **43**, 723 (1956)

Cholic acid

7α-Hydroxy-3, 12-dioxobisnorchola-
4, 9(11)-dienic acid

Actinomyces No. 1164 (6.7%)

Hayakawa, S., Proc. Japan Acad., **30**, 133 (1954)

(b) $-CH_2-CH\diagdown \longrightarrow -CH=C\diagdown$

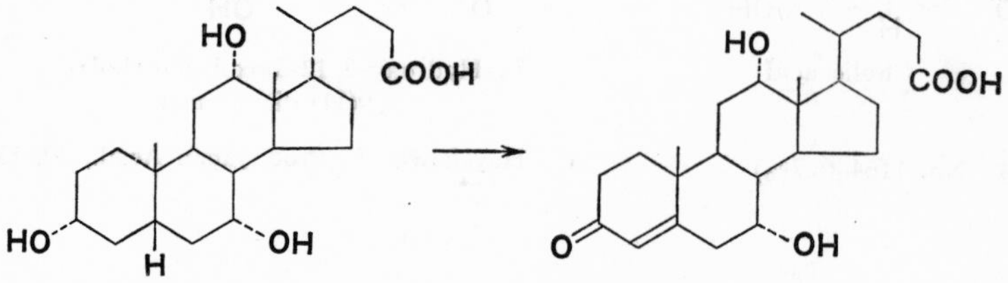

Cholic acid

7α, 12α-Dihydroxy-3-oxochol-
4-enic acid

A soil bacterium CE-1

Eguchi, T., J. Biochem. (Japan), **44**, 81 (1957)

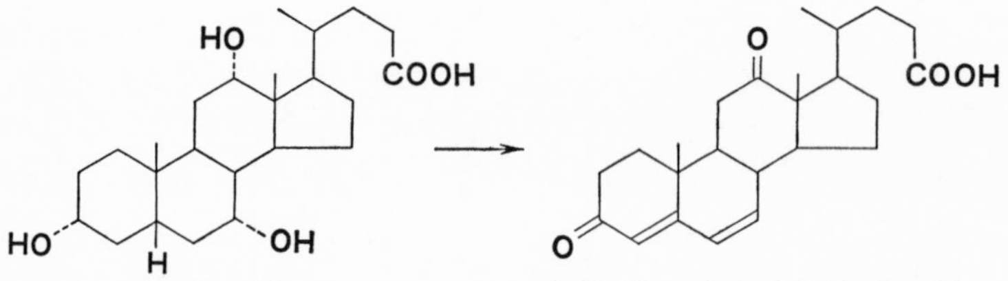

Cholic acid

3, 12-Dioxochola-4, 6-dienic acid

Streptomyces gelaticus strain 1164

Hayakawa, S., Y. Saburi and H. Teraoka, Proc.
Japan Acad., **32**, 519 (1956)

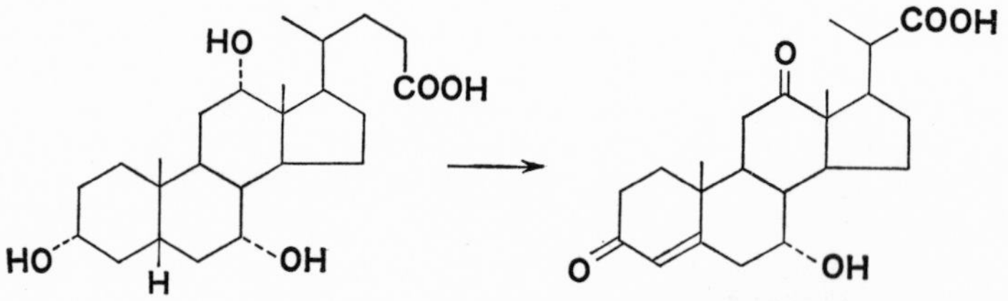

Cholic acid

7α-Hydroxy-3, 12-dioxobisnorchol-
4-enic acid

Streptomyces gelaticus strain 1164

Hayakawa, S., Y. Saburi, T. Fujii and Y. Sonoda, J. Biochem. (Japan), **43**, 723 (1956)

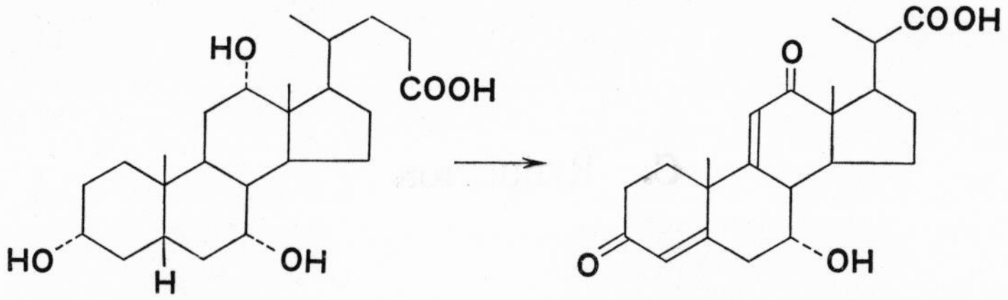

Cholic acid

7α-Hydroxy-3, 12-dioxobisnorchola-
4, 9(11)-dienic acid

Actinomyces sp. (7.3%)

Hayakawa, S., Proc. Japan Acad., **30**, 133 (1954)

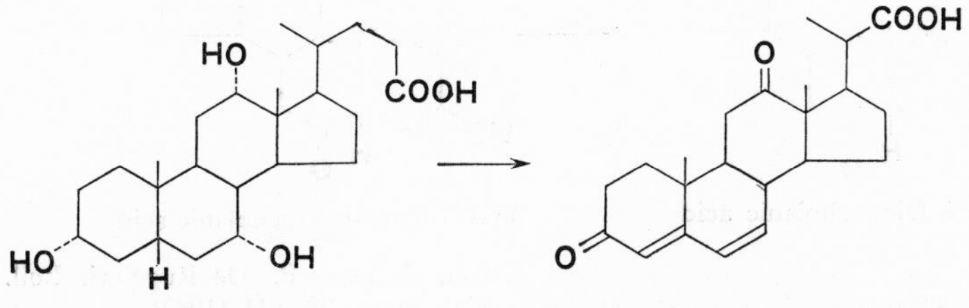

Cholic acid

3, 12-Dioxobisnorchola-4, 6-dienic acid

Streptomyces gelaticus strain 1164

Hayakawa, S., Y. Saburi and I. Akaeda, J. Biochem. (Japan), **44**, 109 (1957)

C. REDUCTION

(a) $\text{>}C{=}O \longrightarrow \text{>}CH{-}OH$

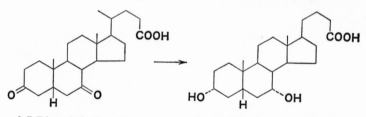

3, 6-Dioxocholanic acid   3α-Hydroxy-6-oxocholanic acid

Yeast

Ercoli, A. and P. De Ruggieri, Boll. Soc. Ital. Biol. Sper., **28**, 611 (1952)

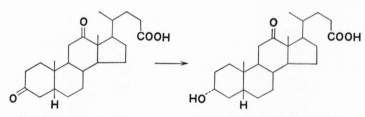

3, 7-Dioxocholanic acid   3α, 7α-Dihydroxycholanic acid

Escherichia coli

Sihn, T. S., J. Biochem. (Japan), **28**, 165 (1938)

3, 12-Dioxocholanic acid   3α-Hydroxy-12-oxocholanic acid

Press yeast (11%)   Kim, C. H., Enzymologia, **4**, 119 (1937)

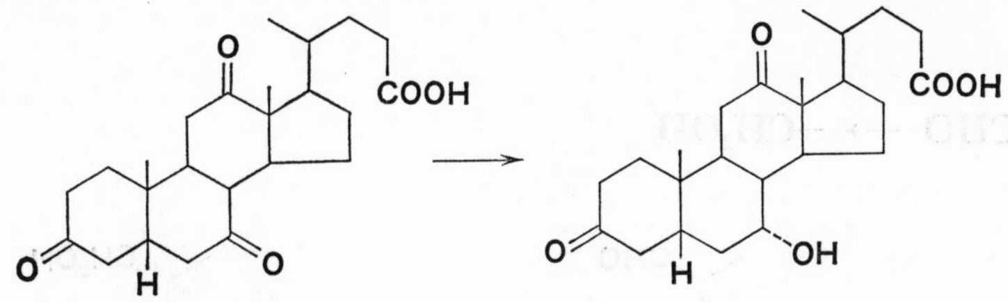

3, 7, 12-Trioxocholanic acid

7α-Hydroxy-3, 12-dioxocholanic acid

Escherichia coli

Fukui, T., J. Biochem. (Japan), **25**, 61 (1937)

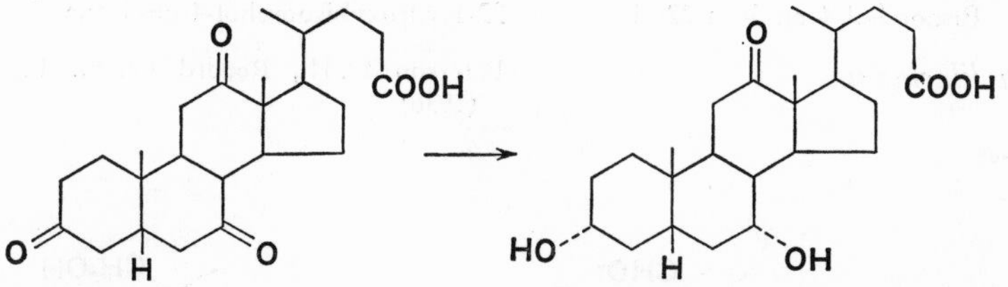

3, 7, 12-Trioxocholanic acid

3α, 7α-Dihydroxy-12-oxocholanic acid

Bacillus coli

Machida, M., J. Biochem. (Japan), **40**, 435 (1953)

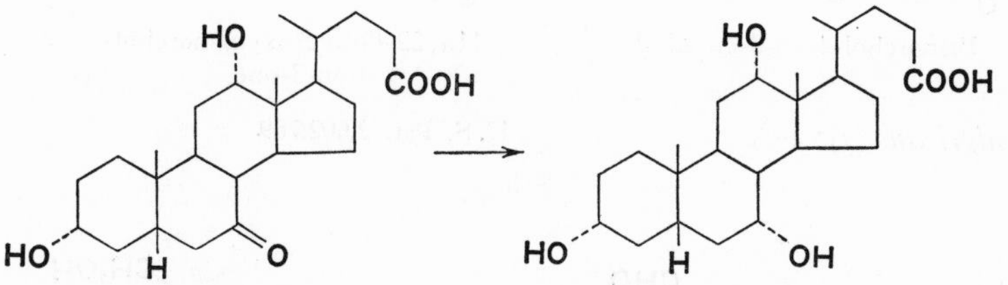

3α, 12α-Dihydroxy-7-oxo-
cholanic acid

Cholic acid

Escherichia coli

Machida, M., J. Med. Sci., **2**, 291 (1953)

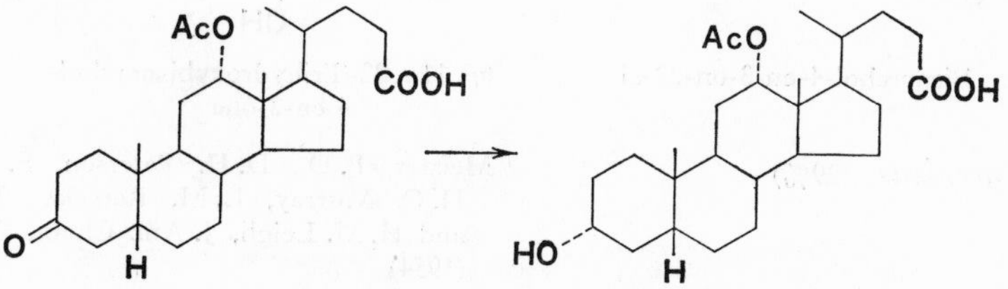

12α-Acetoxy-3-oxocholanic acid

12α-Acetoxy-3α-hydroxycholanic acid

Beer yeast (33%)

Kim, C. H., Enzymologia, **6**, 105 (1939)

(b) $-CHO \longrightarrow -CH_2OH$

Bisnorchol-4-en-3-on-22-al

22-Hydroxybisnorchol-4-en-3-one

Penicillium lilacinum

Peterson, D. H., Record Chem. Progr., **17**, 211 (1956)

Bisnorchol-4-en-3-on-22-al

11α, 22-Dihydroxybisnorchol-4-en-3-one

Rhizopus nigricans (17.4%)

U. S. Pat. 2,602,769

Bisnorchol-4-en-3-on-22-al

6β, 11α, 22-Trihydroxybisnorchol-4-en-3-one

Rhizopus arrhizus (29%)

Meister, P. D., D. H. Peterson, S. H. Eppstein, H. C. Murray, L. M. Reineke, A. Weintraub and H. M. Leigh, J. Am. Chem. Soc., **76**, 5679 (1954)

(c) $-CHOH- \longrightarrow -CH_2-$

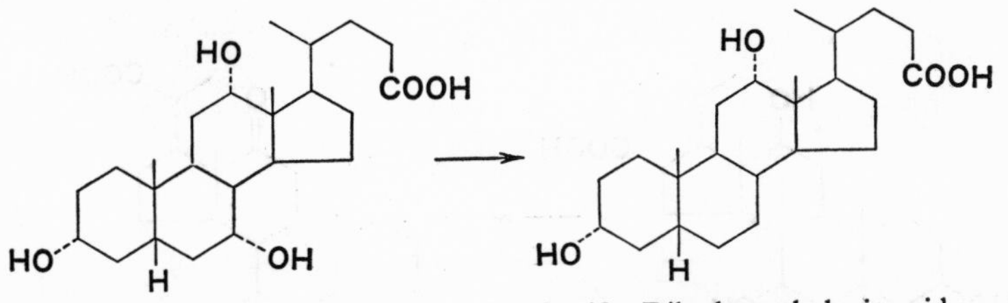

Cholic acid

Intestinal bacteria

$3\alpha, 12\alpha$-Dihydroxycholanic acid

Baumgärtel et al., Deut. Z. Verdauungs-u. Stoffwechselkrankh., **11**, 257 (1951)

D. SIDE CHAIN DEGRADATION

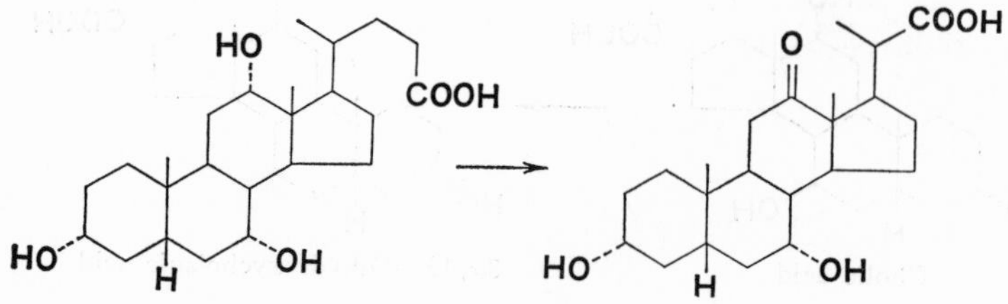

Cholic acid

3α, 7α-Dihydroxy-12-oxobisnor-
cholanic acid

Streptomyces gelaticus strain 1164

Hayakawa, S., Y. Saburi and I. Akaeda, J. Biochem. (Japan), **44**, 109 (1957)

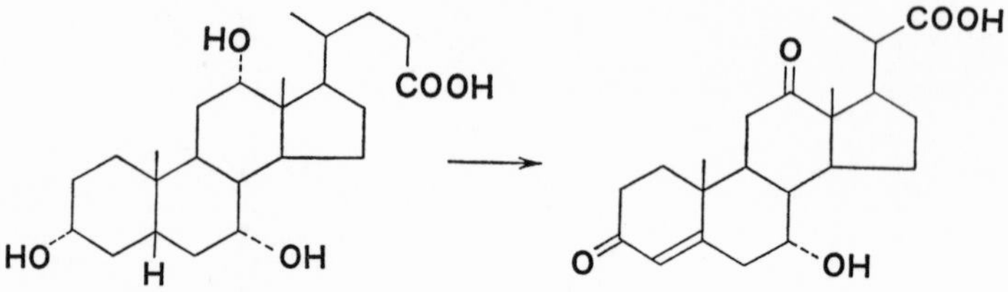

Cholic acid

7α-Hydroxy-3, 12-dioxobisnorchol-
4-enic acid

Streptomyces gelaticus strain 1164

Hayakawa, S., Y. Saburi, T. Fujii and Y. Sonoda,
J. Biochem. (Japan), **43**, 723 (1956)

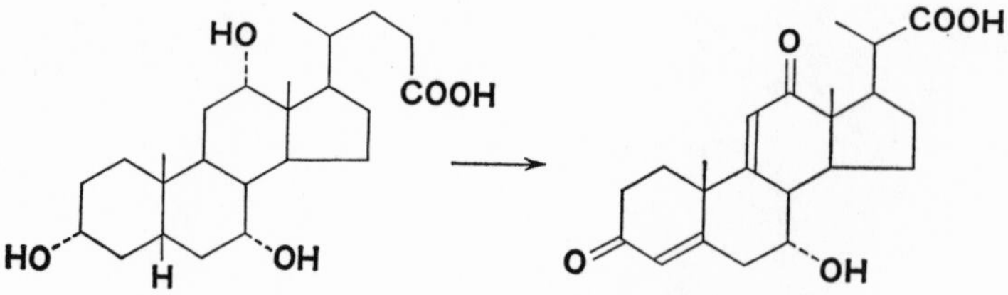

Cholic acid

7α-Hydroxy-3, 12-dioxobisnorchola-
4, 9(11)-dienic acid

Actinomyces sp. No. 1164 (6.7%)

Hayakawa, S., Proc. Japan Acad., **30**, 133 (1954)

III. MICROBIAL TRANSFORMATION OF STEROLS

Structures of typical sterols

Cholesterol
(Cholest-5-en-3β-ol)

β-Sitosterol
(β-Sitost-5-en-3β-ol)

3α, 5-Cyclo-6β, 19-oxido-5α-cholestane

A. HYDROXYLATION

Cholesterol → 4-Hydroxycholest-4-en-3-one

Streptomyces sp.

Peterson, G. E. and J. R. Davis, Steroids, **4**, 677 (1964)

Cholesterol → 7ξ-Hydroxycholesterol

Proactinomyces roseus

Krámli, A. and J. Horváth, Nature, **162**, 619 (1948)

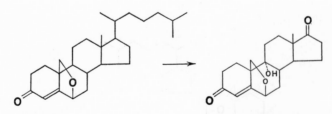

6β, 19-Oxidocholest-4-en-3-one → 9α-Hydroxy-6β, 19-oxido-androst-4-ene-3, 17-dione

CSD-10

Sih, C. J., S. S. Lee, Y. Y. Tsong, K. C. Wang and F. N. Chang, J. Am. Chem. Soc., **87**, 2765 (1965)

B. Dehydrogenation

3-Hydroxynorcholest-5-en-25-one → Norcholest-4-en-3, 25-dione

Flavobacterium dehydrogenans (14%)
(*Micococcus dehydrogenans*)

Ercoli, A., Boll. Sci. Facolata Chim. Ind. Bologna 279 (1940)

Cholesterol → Cholest-4-en-3-one

Arthrobacter simplex (30~40%)

Nagasawa, M., T. Hai, G. Tamura and K. Arima, Abstr. paper (39th and 40th Meeting Agr. Chem. Soc., Japan) p. 81, No. 415, 416 (1964) p. 63, No. 366 (1965)

Azotobacter sp.

Horváth, J. and A. Krámli, Nature, **160**, 639 (1947)

Flavobacterium maris (11~13%)

Arnaudi, C. and C. Colla, Experientia, **5**, 120 (1949)

Mycobacterium cholesterolicum

Stadtman, T. C., A. Cherkes and C. B. Anfinsen, J. Biol. Chem., **206**, 511 (1954)

Nocardia restrictus ATCC 14887

Sih, C. J. and K. C. Wang, J. Am. Chem. Soc., **87**, 1387 (1965)

Proactinomyces erythropolis

Turfitt, G. E., Biochem. J., **42**, 376 (1948)

Proactinomyces roseus

Krámli, A. and J. Horváth, Nature, **162**, 619 (1948)

Streptomyces sp.

Peterson, G. E. and J. R. Davis, Steroids, **4**, 677 (1964)

Cholesterol

Cholesta-5, 7-dien-3β-ol
(7-Dehydrocholesterol)

Azotobacter ozydans

Horváth, J. and A. Krámli, Nature, **160**, 639 (1947)

Cholesterol

Cholesta-1, 4-dien-3-one

Arthrobacter simplex

Nagasawa, M., T. Hai, G. Tamura and K. Arima, Abstr. paper (39th Meeting Agr. Chem. Soc., Japan) p. 81, No. 415, 416 (1964)

Cholesterol

Cholest-4-ene-3, 6-dione

Mycobacterium cholesterolicum

Stadtman, T. C., A. Cherkes and C. B. Anfinsen, J. Biol. Chem., **206**, 511 (1954)

C. REDUCTION

Cholesterol   5β-Cholestan-3β-ol

Intestinal bacteria

Snog-kjaer, A., I. Prange and H. Dam, J. Gen. Microbiol., **14**, 256 (1956)

7-Dehydrocholesterol   5β-Cholest-7-en-3β-ol

Fecal microorganisms

Coleman, D. L. and C. A. Baumann, Arch. Biochem. Biophys, **72**, 219 (1957)

β-Sitosterol   5β-Sitostan-3β-ol

Fecal microorganisms

Coleman, D. L. and C. A. Baumann, Arch. Biochem. Biophys., **72**, 219 (1957)

D. SIDE CHAIN DEGRADATION

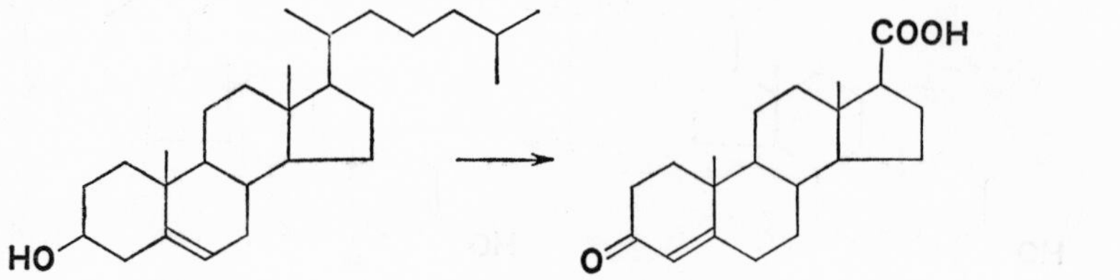

Cholesterol

3-Oxo-etiochol-4-enic acid
(Androst-4-en-3-one-17β-carboxylic acid)

Proactinomyces erythropolis

Turfitt, G. E., Biochem. J., **42**, 376 (1948)

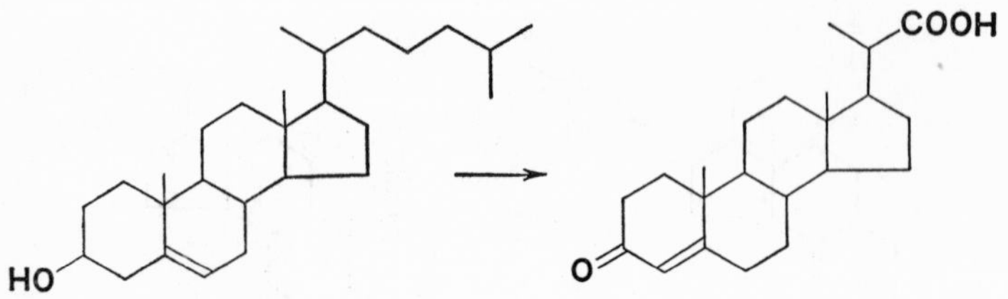

Cholesterol

3-Oxobisnorchol-4-enic acid

Nocardia sp.

Whitmarsh, J. M., Biochem. J., **90**, 23p. (1964)

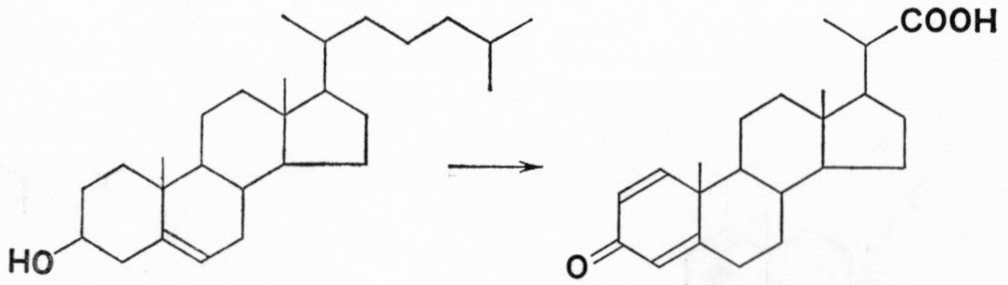

Cholesterol

3-Oxobisnorchola-1, 4-dienic acid

Nocardia sp.

Whitmarsh, J. M., Biochem. J., **90**, 23p. (1964)

Cholesterol

Androst-4-ene-3, 17-dione

Nocardia sp. (low yield)

Arthrobacter simplex

Whitmarsh, J. M., Biochem. J., **90**, 23p. (1964)

Nagasawa, M., T. Hai, G. Tamura and K. Arima, Abstr. paper (39th and 40th Meeting Agr. Chem. Soc., Japan) p. 81, No. 415, 416 (1964) p. 63, No. 366 (1965)

Cholesterol

Androsta-1, 4-diene-3, 17-dione

Nocardia sp. (low yield)

Arthrobacter simplex

Whitmarsh, J. M., Biochem. J., **90**, 23p. (1964)

Nagasawa, M., T. Hai, G. Tamura and K. Arima, Abstr. paper (39th and 40th Meeting Agr. Chem. Soc., Japan) p. 81, No. 415, 416 (1964) p. 63, No. 366 (1965)

19-Hydroxycholest-4-en-3-one

Estrone

Nocardia restrictus ATCC 14887 (8%)

CSD-10 (30%)

Sih, C. J. and K. C. Wang, J. Am. Chem. Soc., **87**, 1387 (1965)

19-Hydroxy-β-sitost-4-en-3-one

Estrone

CSD-10 (10%)

Sih, C. J. and K. C. Wang, J. Am. Chem. Soc., **87**, 1387 (1965)

19-Hydroxycholesterol 3-acetate

Estrone

CSD-10 (72%)

Sih, C. J., S. S. Lee, Y. Y. Tsong, K. C. Wang and F. N. Chang, J. Am. Chem. Soc., **87**, 2765 (1965)

6β, 19-Oxidocholest-4-en-3-one

6β, 19-Oxido-androst-4-ene-3, 17-dione

CSD-10 (57%)

Sih, C. J., S. S. Lee, Y. Y. Tsong, K. C. Wang and F. N. Chang, J. Am. Chem. Soc., **87**, 2765 (1965)

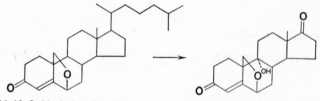

6β, 19-Oxidocholest-4-en-3-one

9α-Hydroxy-6β, 19-oxido-androst-4-ene-3, 17-dione

CSD-10

Sih, C. J., S. S. Lee, Y. Y. Tsong, K. C. Wang and F. N. Chang, J. Am. Chem. Soc., **87**, 2765 (1965)

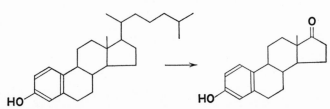

6β, 19-Oxidocholest-4-en-3-one   9α-Hydroxy-6β, 19-oxido-androstane-
                                          3, 17-dione

CSD-10   Sih, C. J., S. S. Lee, Y. Y. Tsong, K. C. Wang
                                 and F. N. Chang, J. Am. Chem. Soc., **87, 2765**
                                 (1965)

5α-Chloro-6β, 19-oxidocholestane   6β, 19-Oxido-androst-4-ene-3, 17-dione
          3-acetate

CSD-10 (36%)   Sih, C. J., S. S. Lee, Y. Y. Tsong, K. C. Wang
                                 and F. N. Chang, J. Am. Chem. Soc., **87, 2765**
                                 (1965)

19-Norcholesta-1, 3, 5(10)-trien-3-ol   Estrone

Corynebacterium sp. (*Nocardia restric-*   Afonso, A., H. L. Herzog, C. Federbush and
tus) ATCC 14887 (8%)   W. Charney, Steroids, **7, 429** (1966)

3α, 5-Cyclo-6β, 19-oxido-
5α-cholestane

3α, 5-Cyclo-6β, 19-oxido-5α-
androstan-17-one

Corynebacterium equi B-58-1

Naito, A., M. Shirasaka, K. Tanabe, Abstr. paper
(41st Meeting Agr. Chem. Soc., Japan) p. 139,
No. 756 (1966)

E. Cleavage of Steroid Skeleton

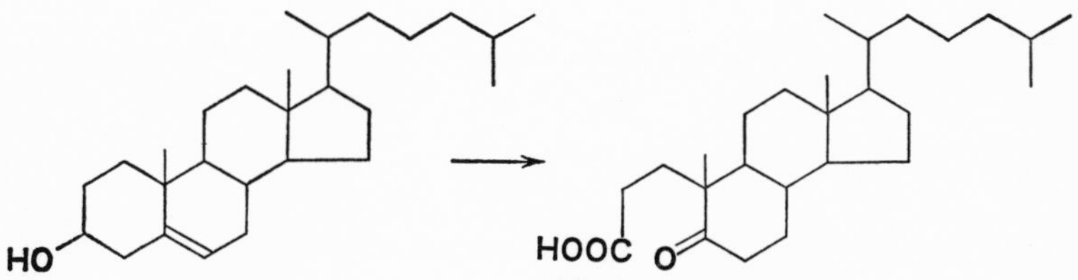

Cholesterol

Proactinomyces erythropolis

Windaus keto acid
(5-Oxo-3, 5-seco-A-norcholestan-
3-oic acid)

Turfitt, G. E., Biochem. J., **42**, 376 (1948)

IV. MICROBIAL TRANSFORMATION
OF SAPOGENINS

A. HYDROXYLATION

Diosgenin
(Spirost-5-en-3β-ol)

Helicostylum piriforme ATCC 8992 (10~ 15%)

7β, 11α-Dihydroxydiosgenin

Sato, Y. and S. Hayakawa, J. Org. Chem., **28**, 2742 (1963)

Diosgenin

Helicostylum piriforme ATCC 8992 (5~ 10%)

11α-Hydroxy-7-oxodiosgenin

Sato, Y. and S. Hayakawa, J. Org. Chem., **28**, 2742 (1963)

B. DEHYDROGENATION

Diosgenin

Diosgenon
(Spirost-4-en-3-one)

Brevibacterium maris A 126

Iizuka, H. and S. Iwado, Abstr. paper (40th Meeting Agr. Chem. Soc., Japan) p. 64 No. 367 (1965)

Corynebacterium simplex ATCC 6946

U. S. Pat. 3,134,718

Penicillium chrysogenum MF 2133 (3.6%)

Rothrock, J. W. and J. D. Garber, Arch. Biochem. Biophys, **57**, 151 (1955)

Diosgenin

Diosgedienon
(Spirosta-1, 4-dien-3-one)

Brevibacterium maris A 126

Iizuka, H. and S. Iwado, Abstr. paper (40th Meeting Agr. Chem. Soc., Japan) p. 64 No. 367 (1965)

Corynebacterium simplex ATCC 6946

U. S. Pat. 3,134,718

C. Degradation of Spiroketal Ring

Diosgenon

Fusarium solani No. 101 (65%)

Androsta-1, 4-diene-3, 16-dione

Kondo, E. and T. Mitsugi, J. Am. Chem. Soc.,
88, 4737 (1966)

Diosgenon

Fusarium solani No. 101 (5%)

16α-Hydroxyandrosta-1, 4-dien-3-one

Kondo, E. and T. Mitsugi, J. Am. Chem. Soc.,
88, 4737 (1966)

Diosgenon

Fusarium solani No. 101 (5%)

16β-Hydroxyandrosta-1, 4-dien-3-one

Kondo, E. and T. Mitsugi, J. Am. Chem. Soc.,
88, 4737 (1966)

V. MICROBIAL TRANSFORMATION OF CARDENOLIDES AND BUFADIENOLIDES

Structures of typical cardenolides and bufadienolide

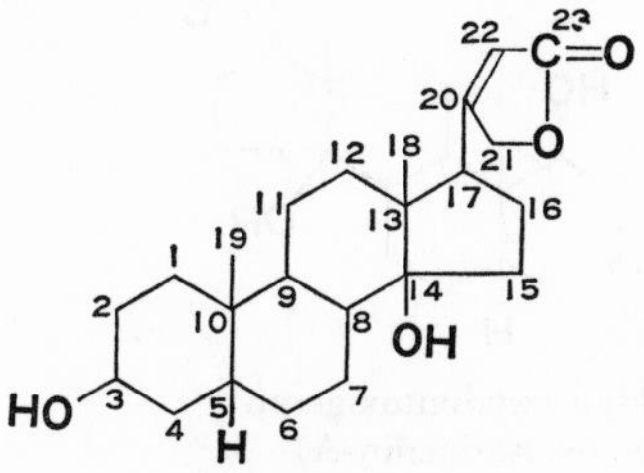

Digitoxigenin
(3β, 14-Dihydroxy-5β-card-
20(22)-enolide)

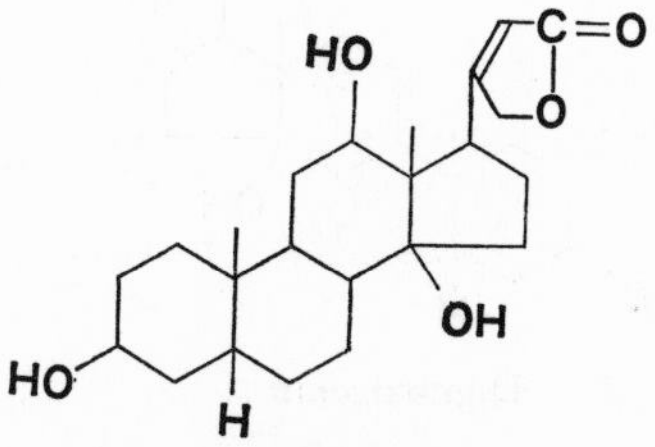

Digoxigenin
(3β, 12β, 14-Trihydroxy-5β-card-
20(22)-enolide)

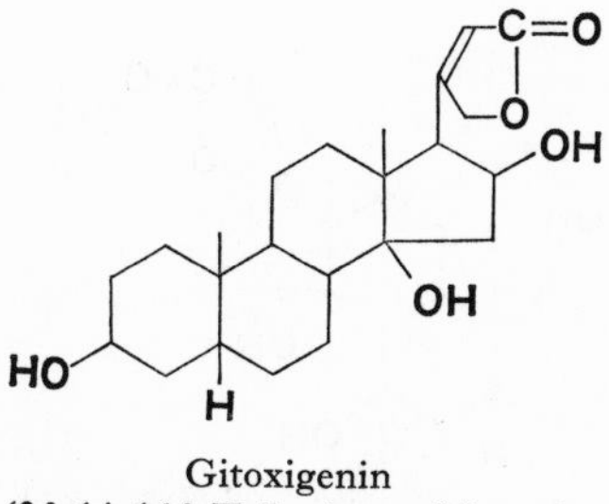

Gitoxigenin
(3β, 14, 16β-Trihydroxy-5β-card-
20(22)-enolide)

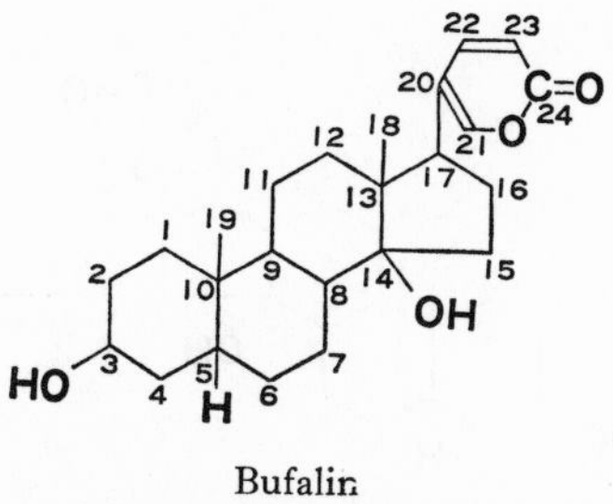

Bufalin
(3β, 14-Dihydroxy-5β-bufa-
20, 22-dienolide)

A. HYDROXYLATION

(a) 1-Hydroxylation

Digitoxigenin → 1β-Hydroxydigitoxigenin (Acovenosigenin-A)

Absidia orchidis

Rhizopus nigricans ATCC 6227b

Nozaki Y. and T. Okumura, Agr. Chem. Soc. (Japan), **25**, 515 (1961)

Nozaki, Y., E. Masuo and D. Satoh, Agr. Chem. Soc. (Japan), **26**, 399 (1962)

Digitoxigenin → 1β, 7β-Dihydroxydigitoxigenin

Absidia orchidis

Ishii, H., Y. Nozaki, T. Okumura and D. Satoh, J. Pharm. Soc. (Japan), **81**, 1051 (1961)

(b) 5-Hydroxylation

Digitoxigenin

Absidia orchidis

Mucor parasiticus ATCC 6476

5β-Hydroxydigitoxigenin
(Periplogenin)

Ishii, H., Y. Nozaki, T. Okumura and D. Satoh,
J. Pharm. Soc. (Japan), **81**, 1051 (1961)

Ishii, H., J. Pharm. Soc. (Japan), **81**, 153, (1961)

Digitoxigenin

Absidia orchidis

5β, 7β-Dihydroxydigitoxigenin

Ishii, H., Y. Nozaki, T. Okumura and D. Satoh,
J. Pharm. Soc. (Japan), **81**, 1051 (1961)

(c) 6-Hydroxylation

Digitoxigenin	6β-Hydroxydigitoxigenin
Trichothecium roseum ATCC 8685	Titus, E., A. W. Murray and H. E. Spiegel, J. Biol. Chem., **235**, 3399 (1960)

(d) 7-Hydroxylation

Digitoxigenin → 7β-Hydroxydigitoxigenin

Absidia orchidis (4%)

Nozaki, Y., E. Masuo and D. Satoh, Agr. Biol. Chem. (Japan), **26**, 399 (1962)

Aspergillus oryzae

Juhasz, G. and Ch. Tamm, Helv. Chim. Acta., **44**, 1063 (1961)

Mucor parasiticus ATCC 6476 (2%)

Nozaki, Y., E. Masuo and D. Satoh, Agr. Biol. Chem. (Japan), **26**, 399 (1962)

Rhizopus arrhizus ATCC 11145

Ishii, H., Y. Nozaki, T. Okumura and D. Satoh, J. Pharm. Soc. (Japan), **81**, 805 (1961)

Rhizopus nigricans ATCC 6227b (59%)

Nozaki, Y., E. Masuo and D. Satoh, Agr. Biol. Chem. (Japan), **26**, 399 (1962)

Trichothecium roseum
(*Cephalothecium roseum*)

Juhasz, G. and Ch. Tamm, Helv. Chim. Acta., **44**, 1063 (1961)

Digitoxigenin → 1β, 7β-Dihydroxydigitoxigenin

Absidia orchidis

Ishii, H., Y. Nozaki, T. Okumura and D. Satoh, J. Pharm. Soc. (Japan), **81**, 1051 (1961)

Digitoxigenin

5β, 7β-Dihydroxydigitoxigenin

Absidia orchidis

Ishii, H., Y. Nozaki, T. Okumura and D. Satoh,
J. Pharm. Soc. (Japan), **81**, 1051 (1961)

(e) 11-Hydroxylation

Digitoxigenin   11α-Hydroxydigitoxigenin
                                (Sarmentogenin)

Aspergillus ochraceus

Nozaki, Y. and K. Akagi, 39th Meeting Agr. Chem. Soc. (Japan), Abstr. paper p. 100 No. 463 (1964)

Trichothecium roseum ATCC 8685

Titus, E., A. W. Murray and H. E. Spiegel, J. Biol. Chem., **235**, 3399 (1960)

(f) 12-Hydroxylation

Digitoxigenin	12β-Hydroxydigitoxigenin (Digoxigenin)
Calonectria decora	Nozaki, Y., E. Masuo, H. Ishii, T. Okumura and D. Satoh, Abstr. Paper (Symposium on the Chem. of Digitalis Cardiac Glycosides, Tokyo) p. 114 (1960)
Fusarium lini	Gubler, A. and Ch. Tamm, Helv. Chim. Acta., **41**, 297 (1958)
Gibberella fujikuroii	Nawa, H., M. Uchibayashi, T. Kamiya, T. Yamano, H. Arai and M. Abe, Nature, **184**, 469 (1959)
Gibberella saubinetti (70%)	Okada, M., A. Yamada and M. Ishidate, Chem. Pharm. Bull. (Japan), **8**, 530 (1960)
Helicostylum piriforme	Nawa, H., M. Uchibayashi, T. Kamiya, T. Yamano, H. Arai and M. Abe Nature, **184**, 469 (1959)
Nigrospora sphaerica	Nozaki, Y., E. Masuo, H. Ishii, T. Okumura and D. Satoh, Abstr. Paper (Symposium on the Chem. of Digitalis Cardiac Glycosides, Tokyo) p. 114 (1960)

3-Dehydrodigitoxigenin	3-Dehydrodigoxigenin
Fusarium lini	Gubler, A. and Ch. Tamm, Helv. Chim. Acta., **41**, 297 (1958)
Gibberella saubinetti (53%)	Okada, M., A. Yamada and M. Ishidate, Chem. Pharm. Bull. (Japan), **8**, 530 (1960)

Gitoxigenin → 12β-Hydroxygitoxigenin (Diginatigenin)

Fusarium lini (0.5%)

Gibberella saubinetti (6%)

Tamm, Ch. and A. Gubler, Helv. Chim. Acta., **41**, 1762 (1958)

Okada, M., A. Yamada and M. Ishidate, Chem. Pharm. Bull. (Japan), **8**, 530 (1960)

14β, 15β-Oxido-14-an-hydrodigitoxigenin → 12β-Hydroxy-14β, 15β-oxido-14-anhydrodigitoxigenin

Fusarium lini

Schüpbach, M. and Ch. Tamm, Helv. Chim. Acta., **47**, 2217 (1964)

Bufalin → 12β-Hydroxybufalin

Fusarium lini

Tamm, Ch. and A. Gubler, Helv. Chim. Acta, **42**, 473 (1959)

3-Dehydrobufalin   12β-Hydroxy-3-dehydrobufalin

Fusarium lini   Tamm, Ch. and A. Gubler, Helv. Chim. Acta,
                                    42, 473 (1959)

Marinobufagin   12β-Hydroxymarinobufagin

Fusarium lini   Schüpbach, M. and Ch. Tamm, Helv. Chim.
                                    Acta, **47**, 2226 (1964)

Resibufogenin   12β-Hydroxyresibufogenin

Fusarium lini   Schüpbach, M. and Ch. Tamm, Helv. Chim.
                                    Acta, **47**, 2217 (1964)

(g) 16-Hydroxylation

Digitoxigenin — Gitoxigenin

Cunninghamella blakesleeana
Helicostylum piriforme

Nawa, H., M. Uchibayashi, T. Kamiya, T. Ya-
mano, H. Arai and M. Abe, Nature, **184**, 469
(1959)

B. DEHYDROGENATION

(a) $\rangle$CH–OH $\longrightarrow$ $\rangle$C=O

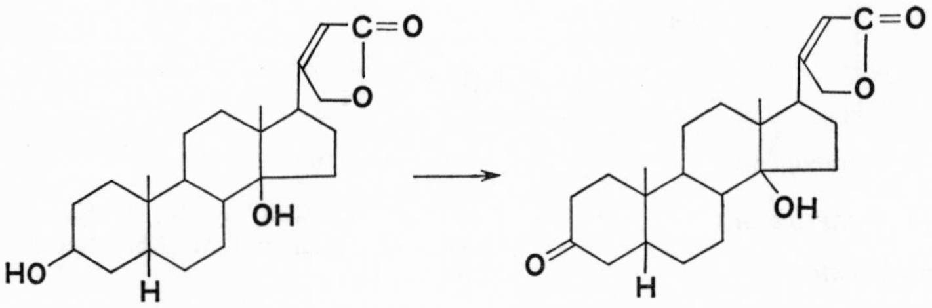

Digitoxigenin

Aspergillus oryzae
Calonectria decora (16%)
Nigrospora sphaerica (12%)

3-Dehydrodigitoxigenin

Nozaki, Y., E. Masuo, H. Ishii, T. Okumura and D. Satoh, Abstr. Paper (Symposium on the Chem. of Digitalis Cardiac Glycosides, Tokyo) p. 114 (1960)

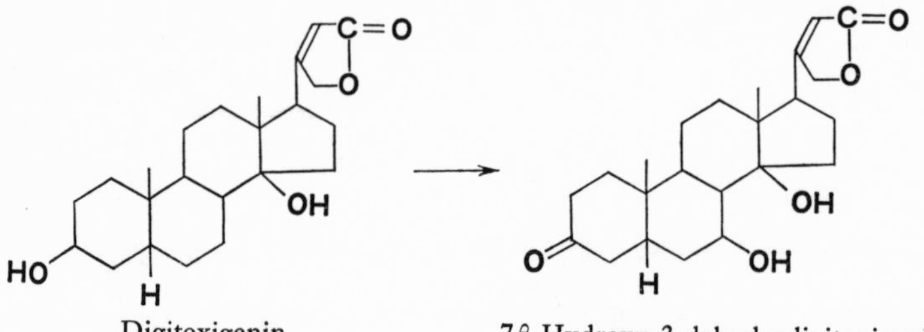

Digitoxigenin

Rhizopus arrhizus

7β-Hydroxy-3-dehydrodigitoxigenin

Juhasz, G. and Ch. Tamm, Helv. Chim. Acta, **44**, 1063 (1961)

(b) $-CH_2-CH{\big\langle} \longrightarrow -CH=C{\big\langle}$

Digitoxigenin

16-Dehydrodigitoxigenin
(Δ^{16}-Anhydrogitoxigenin)

Trichothecium roseum ATCC 8685

Titus, E., A. W. Murray and H. E. Spiegel, J. Biol. Chem., **235**, 3399 (1960)

C. REDUCTION

3-Dehydrodigitoxigenin   3-Epidigitoxigenin

Fusarium lini   Gubler, A. and Ch. Tamm, Helv. Chim. Acta,
                                41, 297 (1958)

Gibberella saubinetti (3.5%) Okada, M., A. Yamada and M. Ishidate, Chem.
                                Pharm. Bull. (Japan), 8, 530 (1960)

3-Dehydrodigitoxigenin   3-Epidigoxigenin

Fusarium lini   Gubler, A. and Ch. Tamm, Helv. Chim. Acta,
                                41, 297 (1958)

Gibberella saubinetti   Okada, M., A. Yamada and M. Ishidate, Chem.
                                Pharm. Bull. (Japan), 8, 530 (1960)

3-Dehydrogitoxigenin   3-Epigitoxigenin

Fusarium lini   Tamm, Ch. and A. Gubler, Helv. Chim. Acta,
                                41, 1762 (1958)

VI. MICROBIAL TRANSFORMATION OF STEROIDAL ALKALOIDS

Structures of typical steroidal alkaloids

Conessine

Solasodine

Tomatidine

A. HYDROXYLATION

(a) 7-Hydroxylation

Conessine → 7α-Hydroxyconessine

Aspergillus ochraceus

Kupchan, S. M., C. J. Sih, S. Kubota and A. M. Rahim, Tetrahedron Letter No. 26, 1767 (1963)

Conessine → 7β-Hydroxyconessine

Aspergillus ochraceus

Kupchan, S. M., C. J. Sih, S. Kubota and A. M. Rahim, Tetrahedron Letter No. 26, 1767 (1963)

Solasodine → 7β-Hydroxysolasodine

Helicostylum piriforme ATCC 8992 (1%)

Sato, Y. and S. Hayakawa, J. Org. Chem., **28**, 2739 (1963)

Solasodine

7ξ, 11α-Dihydroxysolasodine

Helicostylum piriforme ATCC 8992 (0.5%)

Sato, Y. and S. Hayakawa, J. Org. Chem., **28**, 2739 (1963)

Tomatidine

7α-Hydroxytomatidine

Helicostylum piriforme ATCC 8992 (5%)

Sato, Y. and S. Hayakawa, J. Org. Chem., **29**, 198 (1964)

(b) 9-Hydroxylation

Solasodine → 9α-Hydroxysolasodine

Helicostylum piriforme ATCC 8992 (30~ 35%)

Sato, Y. and S. Hayakawa, J. Org. Chem., **28**, 2739 (1963)

Tomatidine → 9α-Hydroxytomatidine

Helicostylum piriforme ATCC 8992 (0.5%)

Sato, Y. and S. Hayakawa, J. Org. Chem., **29**, 198 (1964)

(c) 11-Hydroxylation

Solasodine → 11α-Hydroxysolasodine

Helicostylum piriforme ATCC 8992 (1%)   Sato, Y. and S. Hayakawa, J. Org. Chem., **28**, 2739 (1963)

Solasodine → 7ξ, 11α-Dihydroxysolasodine

Helicostylum piriforme ATCC 8992 (0.5%)   Sato, Y. and S. Hayakawa, J. Org. Chem., **28**, 2739 (1963)

Tomatidine → 7α, 11α-Dihydroxytomatidine

Helicostylum piriforme ATCC 8992 (25~30%)   Sato, Y. and S. Hayakawa, J. Org. Chem., **29**, 198 (1964)

B. DEHYDROGENATION

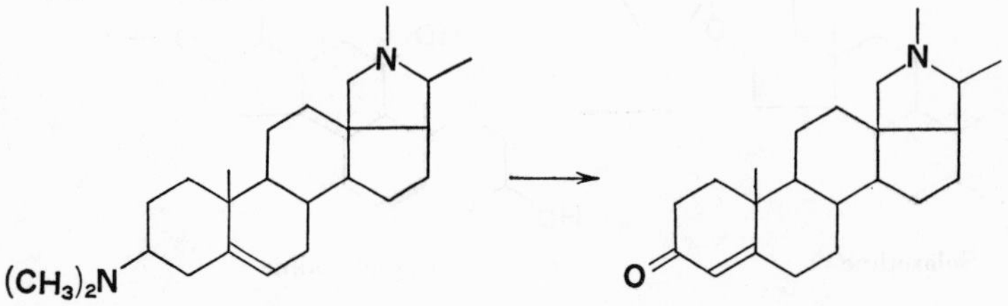

Conessine   4-Dehydroconenin-3-one

Gloeosporium cyclaminis

Hypomyces haematococcus

De Flines, J., A. F. Marx, W. F. van der Waad and D. van der Sijde, Tetrahedron Letter No. 26, 1257 (1962)

VII. MICROBIAL TRANSFORMATION OF ERGOT ALKALOIDS

A. HYDROXYLATION

(a) 8-Hydroxylation

Agroclavin → Setoclavin

Psilocybe semperviva

Brack, A., R. Brunner and H. Kobel, Helv. Chim. Acta, **45**, 276 (1962)

Agroclavin → Isosetoclavin

Psilocybe semperviva

Brack, A., R. Brunner and H. Kobel, Helv. Chim. Acta, **45**, 276 (1962)

Elymoclavin

Penniclavin

Psilocybe semperviva

Brack, A., R. Brunner and H. Kobel, Helv. Chim. Acta., **45**, 276 (1962)

Elymoclavin

Isopenniclavin

Psilocybe semperviva

Brack, A., R. Brunner and H. Kobel, Helv. Chim. Acta, **45**, 276 (1962)

VIII. MICROBIAL TRANSFORMATION OF INDOL ALKALOIDS

Structures of typical indol alkaloids

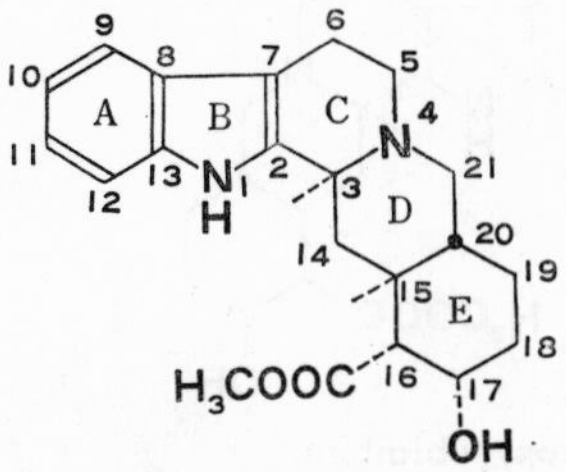

Yohimbine

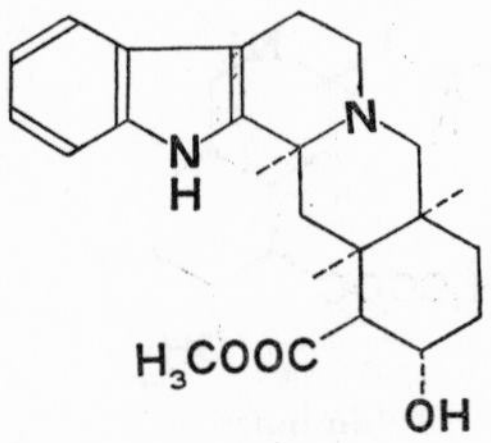

α-Yohimbine

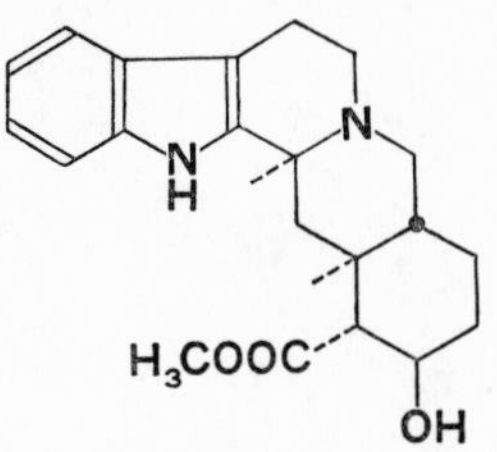

β-Yohimbine

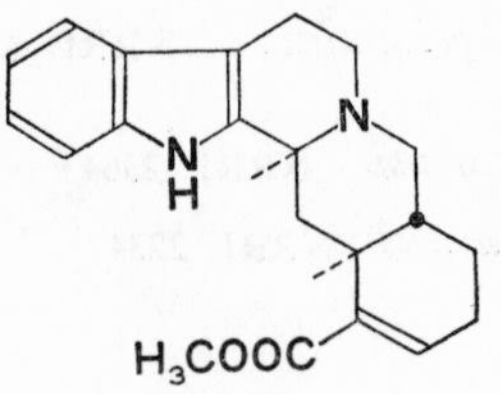

Apoyohimbine

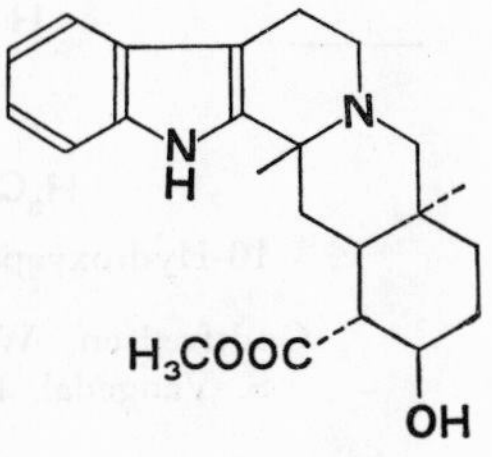

Corynanthine

A. HYDROXYLATION

(a) 10-Hydroxylation

Yohimbine

Cunninghamella bainieri ATCC 924
Cunninghamella blakesleeana ATCC 8688a
Cunninghamella echinulata NRRL A-11498
Streptomyces platensis NRRL 2364
Streptomyces rimosus NRRL 2234

10-Hydroxyyohimbine

Hartman, R. E., E. F. Krause, W. W. Andres and E. L. Patterson, Appl. Microbiol., **12**, 138 (1964)

Apoyohimbine

Cunninghamella blakesleeana

10-Hydroxyapoyohimbine

Godtfredsen, W. O., G. Korsby, H. Lorck and S. Vangedal, Experientia, **14**, 88 (1958) α-Yohimbine

Cunninghamella bainieri ATCC 924

Cunninghamella blakesleeana ATCC 8688a

Cunninghamella echinulata NRRL A-11498

Streptomyces platensis NRRL 2364

10-Hydroxy-α-yohimbine

Hartman, R. E., E. F. Krause, W. W. Andres and E. L. Patterson, Appl. Microbiol., **12**, 138 (1964)

β-Yohimbine

Cunninghamella bainieri ATCC 924

Cunninghamella echinulata NRRL A-11498

Streptomyces platensis NRRL 2364

Streptomyces rimosus NRRL 2234

10-Hydroxy-β-yohimbine

Hartman, R. E., E. F. Krause, W. W. Andres and E. L. Patterson, Appl. Microbiol., **12**, 138 (1964)

Corynanthine

10-Hydroxycorynanthine

Cunninghamella bainieri ATCC 924

Cunninghamella echinulata NRRL A-11498

Streptomyces platensis NRRL 2364

Streptomyces rimosus NRRL 2234

Hartman, R. E., E. F. Krause, W. W. Andres and E. L. Patterson, Appl. Microbiol., **12**, 138 (1964)

β-Yohimbine methylether

10-Hydroxy-β-yohimbine methylether

Cunninghamella blakesleeana

Godtfredsen, W. O., G. Korsby, H. Lorck and S. Vangedal, Experientia, **14**, 88 (1958)

3-Epiapoyohimbine

10-Hydroxy-3-epiapoyohimbine

Cunninghamella blakesleeana

Godtfredsen, W. O., G. Korsby, H. Lorck and S. Vangedal, Experientia, **14**, 88 (1958)

(b) 11-Hydroxylation

Yohimbine

11-Hydroxyyohimbine

Cunninghamella bainieri strain Campbell X-48

Cunninghamella bertholletiae NRRL A-11497

Cunninghamella echinulata

Cunninghamella elegans NRRL A-11499

Hartman, R. E., E. F. Krause, W. W. Andres and E. L. Patterson, Appl. Microbiol., **12**, 138 (1964)

α-Yohimbine

11-Hydroxy-α-yohimbine

Cunninghamella bainieri strain Campbell X-48

Cunninghamella bertholletiae NRRL A-11497

Cunninghamella echinulata

Cunninghamella elegans NRRL A-11499

Streptomyces fulvissimus NRRL B-1453

Hartman, R. E., E. F. Krause, W. W. Andres and E. L. Patterson, Appl. Microbiol., **12**, 138 (1964)

Corynanthine   11-Hydroxycorynanthine

Cunninghamella bertholletiae   NRRL A-11497

Streptomyces fulvissimus   NRRL B-1453

Hartman, R. E., E. F. Krause, W. W. Andres and E. L. Patterson, Appl. Microbiol., **12**, 138 (1964)

(c) 18-Hydroxylation

Yohimbine   18α-Hydroxyyohimbine

Calonectria decora

Hartman, R. E., E. F. Krause, W. W. Andres and E. L. Patterson, Appl. Microbiol., **12**, 138 (1964)

Streptomyces aureofaciens ATCC 11834
Streptomyces rimosus NRRL 2234

Pan, S. C. and F. L. Weisenborn, J. Am. Chem. Soc., **80**, 4749 (1958)

Apoyohimbine   18-Hydroxyapoyohimbine

Cunninghamella blakesleeana

Godtfredsen, W. O., G. Korsby, H. Lorck and S. Vangedal, Experientia, **14**, 88 (1958)

α-Yohimbine   18α-Hydroxy-α-yohimbine

Streptomyces aureofaciens ATCC 11834
Streptomyces rimosus NRRL 2234

Pan, S. C. and F. L. Weisenborn, J. Am. Chem. Soc., **80**, 4749, (1958)

IX. MICROBIAL TRANSFORMATION OF MORPHINE ALKALOIDS

Structures of typical morphine alkaloids

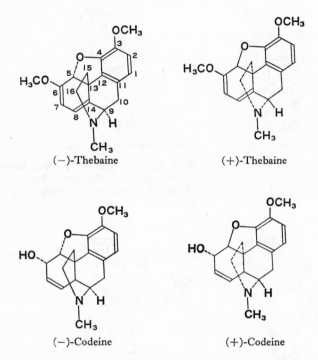

(−)-Thebaine

(+)-Thebaine

(−)-Codeine

(+)-Codeine

A. HYDROXYLATION

(a) 14-Hydroxylation

(+)-Codeinone

Trametes sanguinea (10.9%)

(+)-14-Hydroxycodeinone

Tsuda, K., Chemistry of Microbial Products (6th Symposium of the Inst. Appl. Microbiol. Univ. of Tokyo) p. 167 (1964)

(+)-Codeinone

Trametes sanguinea (3.2%)

(+)-14-Hydroxyisocodeine

Tsuda, K., Chemistry of Microbial Products (6th Symposium of the Inst. Appl. Microbiol. Univ. of Tokyo) p. 167 (1964)

(−)-14-Bromocodeinone

Trametes sanguinea (16%)

(−)-14-Hydroxycodeine

Yamada, M., K. Iizuka, S. Okuda, T. Asai and K. Tsuda, Chem. Pharm. Bull. (Japan), **11**, 206 (1963)

(−)-Thebaine

Trametes sanguinea (Polystictus sanguineus) (40%)

(−)-14-Hydroxycodeinone

Iizuka, K., M. Yamada, J. Suzuki, I. Seki, K. Aida, S. Okuda, T. Asai and K. Tsuda, Chem. Pharm. Bull. (Japan), **10**, 67 (1962)

(+)-Thebaine

Trametes sanguinea (40%)

(+)-14-Hydroxycodeinone

Tsuda, K., Chemistry of Microbial Products (6th Symposium of the Inst. Appl. Microbiol. Univ. of Tokyo) p. 167 (1964)

B. REDUCTION

(a) $\rangle$C=O $\longrightarrow$ $\rangle$CH–OH

(−)-Codeinone

Trametes sanguinea (24.5%)

(−)-Codeine

Tsuda, K., Chemistry of Microbial Products (6th Symposium of the Inst. Appl. Microbiol. Univ. of Tokyo) p. 167 (1964)

(+)-Codeinone

Trametes sanguinea

(+)-Codeine

Tsuda, K., Chemistry of Microbial Products (6th Symposium of the Inst. Appl. Microbiol. Univ. of Tokyo) p. 167 (1964)

(−)-14-Hydroxycodeinone

Trametes sanguinea (Polystictus sanguineus) (55%)

(−)-14-Hydroxycodeine

Iizuka, K., M. Yamada, J. Suzuki, I. Seki, K. Aida, S. Okuda, T. Asai and K. Tsuda, Chem. Pharm. Bull. (Japan), **10**, 67 (1962)

(+)-14-Hydroxycodeinone

Trametes sanguinea

(+)-14-Hydroxyisocodeine

Tsuda, K., Chemistry of Microbial Products (6th Symposium of the Inst. Appl. Microbiol. Univ. of Tokyo) p. 167 (1964)

(−)-Dihydrocodeinone

Trametes sanguinea (31%)

(−)-Dihydrocodeine

Yamada, M., Chem. Pharm. Bull. (Japan), **11,** 356 (1963)

(−)-Dihydrocodeinone

Trametes sanguinea (10%)

(−)-Dihydroisocodeine

Tsuda, K., Chemistry of Microbial Products (6th Symposium of the Inst. Appl. Microbiol. Univ. of Tokyo) p. 167 (1964)

(+)-Dihydrocodeinone

Trametes sanguinea (2.7%)

(+)-Dihydrocodeine

Tsuda, K., Chemistry of Microbial Products (6th Symposium of the Inst. Appl. Microbiol. Univ. of Tokyo) p. 167 (1964)

(−)-14-Hydroxydihydrocodeinone

Trametes sanguinea (38.4%)

(−)-14-Hydroxydihydrocodeine

Tsuda, K., Chemistry of Microbial Products (6th Symposium of the Inst. Appl. Microbiol. Univ. of Tokyo) p. 167 (1964)

(+)-14-Hydroxydihydrocodeinone

Trametes sanguinea

(+)-14-Hydroxydihydrocodeine

Tsuda, K., Chemistry of Microbial Products (6th Symposium of the Inst. Appl. Microbiol. Univ. of Tokyo) p. 167 (1964)

(−)-14-Acetoxycodeinone

(−)-14-Hydroxycodeine

Trametes sanguinea (70%)

Yamada, M., K. Iizuka, S. Okuda, T. Asai and K. Tsuda, Chem. Pharm. Bull. (Japan), **11**, 206 (1963)

(−)-14-Bromocodeinone

(−)-14-Hydroxycodeine

Trametes sanguinea (16%)

Yamada, M., K. Iizuka, S. Okuda, T. Asai and K. Tsuda, Chem. Pharm. Bull. (Japan), **11**, 206 (1963)

(−)-14-Bromocodeinone

(−)-Neopine

Trametes sanguinea (4.3%)

Yamada, M., K. Iizuka, S. Okuda, T. Asai and K. Tsuda, Chem. Pharm. Bull. (Japan), **11**, 206 (1963)

(b) $-CH=CH-$ → $-CH_2-CH_2-$

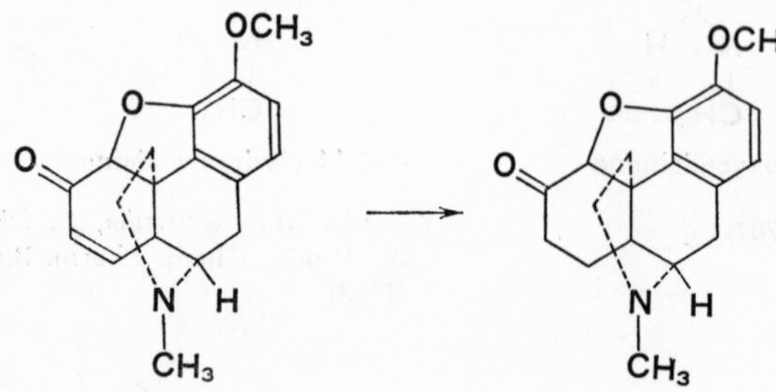

(+)-Codeinone

Trametes sanguinea (4.9%)

(+)-Dihydrocodeinone

Tsuda, K., Chemistry of Microbial Products (6th Symposium of the Inst. Appl. Microbiol. Univ. of Tokyo) p. 167 (1964)

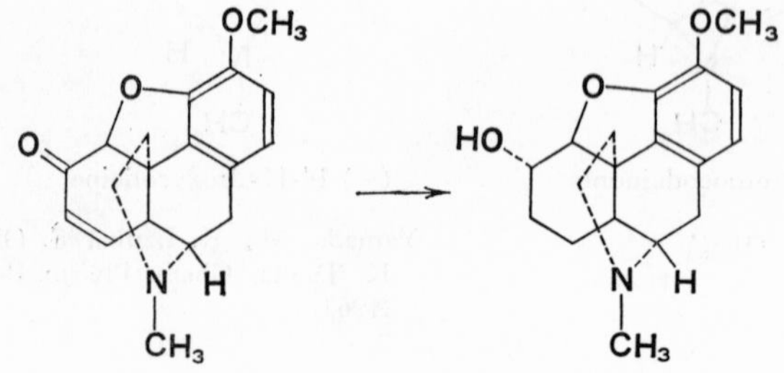

(+)-Codeinone

Trametes sanguinea

(+)-Dihydrocodeine

Tsuda, K., Chemistry of Microbial Products (6th Symposium of the Inst. Appl. Microbiol. Univ. of Tokyo) p. 167 (1964)

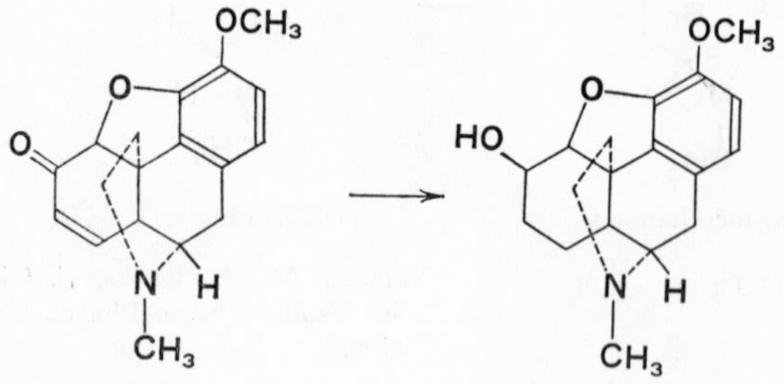

(+)-Codeinone

Trametes sanguinea

(+)-Dihydroisocodeine

Tsuda, K., Chemistry of Microbial Products (6th Symposium of the Inst. Appl. Microbiol. Univ. of Tokyo) p. 167 (1964)

C. Hydrolysis

(−)-14-Acetoxycodeine

Trametes sanguinea (70%)

(−)-14-Hydroxycodeine

Yamada, M., K. Iizuka, S. Okuda, T. Asai and K. Tsuda, Chem. Pharm. Bull. (Japan), **11**, 206 (1963)

(−)-14-Acetoxycodeinone

Trametes sanguinea (70%)

(−)-14-Hydroxycodeine

Yamada, M., K. Iizuka, S. Okuda, T. Asai and K. Tsuda, Chem. Pharm. Bull. (Japan), **11**, 206 (1963)

X. MICROBIAL TRANSFORMATION
OF NICOTINE

Nicotine

1-Methyl-2(6-hydroxy-3-pyridyl)-
pyrrolidine

Unidentified soil bacterium

Hochstein, L. I. and S. C. Rittenberg, J. Biol.
Chem., **235**, 795 (1960)

Nicotine

6-Hydroxypseudooxonicotine

Unidentified soil bacterium

Hochstein L. I. and S. C. Rittenberg, J. Biol.
Chem., **235**, 795 (1960)

Nicotine

3-Succinoylpyridine

Achromobacter denitrificans
Bacillus megaterium var. *nicotinovorus*
Bacterium flavescens
Bacterium mutabile var. *acidoformans*
Bacterium qualis var. *amylophilum*
Pseudomonas nicotinophaga
Pseudomonas cyclosites
Pseudomonas nicotiana
Xanthomonas carotae var. *nicotinovora*

Tabuchi, T., J. Agr. Chem. Soc. (Japan), **28**, 806
(1954)

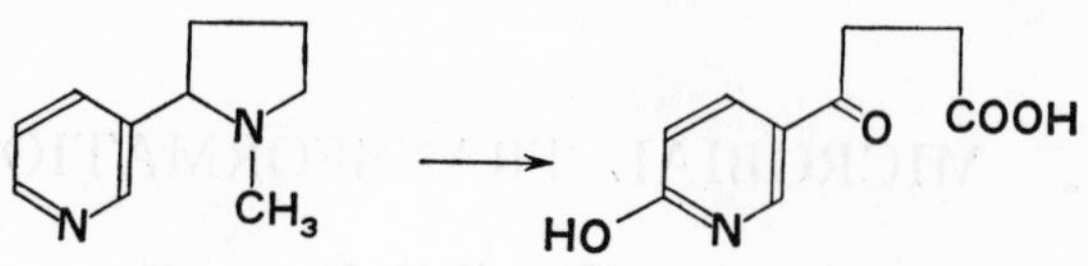

Nicotine   3-Succinoylpyridone-6

Achromobacter denitrificans

Bacillus megaterium var. *nicotinovorus*

Bacterium flavescens

Bacterium mutabile var. *acidoformans*

Bacterium qualis var. *amylophilum*

Pseudomonas cyclosites

Pseudomonas nicotiana

Pseudomonas nicotinophaga

Xanthomonas carotae var. *nicotinovora*

Tabuchi, T., J. Agr. Chem. Soc. (Japan), **28**, 806 (1954)

Author Index

Microorganism Index

N

Naucoria confragosa C-172, 20, 88
Neurospora crassa No. 74-A, 31, 36
Nigrospora oryzae, 73, 74, 77, 80
Nigrospora sphaerica, 238, 242
Nocardia corallina, 33, 35, 36, 102, 103, 104, 116,
   121, 127, 128, 135, 158, 169, 183, 189
Nocardia corallina ATCC 999, 7, 9, 11, 14, 103,
   112, 117, 128
Nocardia sp., 119, 123, 135, 220, 221
Nocardia sp. E 110, 196
Nocardia italica, 86, 87
Nocardia restrictus, 33, 35, 118, 185, 197, 223
Nocardia restrictus ATCC 14887, 34, 197, 217,
   221
Nocardia restrictus No. 545, 15, 107, 108, 138,
   197, 198

O

Ophiobolus herbotrichus, 95, 96, 98, 100
Ophiobolus heterostropus, 125, 127, 129, 134
Oxidizing bacteria, 104, 143

P

Penicillium adametzi, 180
Penicillium chrysogenum, 58, 177, 180
Penicillium chrysogenum MF 2133, 228
Penicillium citrinum, 168, 169, 170, 173, 174, 179
Penicillium corylophilum, 41
Penicillium decumbens, 168, 169, 170
Penicillium expansum, 52
Penicillium lilacinum, 41, 146, 168, 169, 172, 174,
   180, 181, 212
Penicillium notatum, 73, 168, 169, 170
Penicillium sp., 8, 9, 12, 106, 176
Penicillium sp. ATCC 11598, 72
Penicillium sp. ATCC 12556, 8, 9, 12, 159, 160
Penicillium tardum, 41
Penicillium urticae, 73
Pestalotia foedans, 41
Pestalotia funera, 83
Pestalotia royenae, 41
Pestalotia sp., 94
Peziza sp. ETH M-23, 26
Phycomyces blakesleeanus, 28, 78, 109
Polystictus sanguineus→Trametes sanguinea
Press yeast, 139, 210
Press yeast (*Saccharomyces* sp.), 139
Proactinomyces erythropolis, 104, 105, 217, 220,
   225

Proactinomyces roseus, 216, 217
Proactinomyces sp., 101
Protaminobacter alboflavum, 115, 118, 120, 121,
   122, 129, 132, 134, 135, 136
Protaminobacter rubrum, 115, 118, 120, 121, 122,
   129, 132, 134, 135, 136
Pseudodiphtheria bacilli, 101, 105
Pseudomonas boreopolis, 60, 130, 134
Pseudomonas chlororaphis IAM 1511, 103, 115,
   129, 133, 135, 177, 178, 182
Pseudomonas cyclosites, 271, 272
Pseudomonas dacunhae, 129
Pseudomonas fluorescens, 59, 135, 151
Pseudomonas graveolens, 117
Pseudomonas nicotiana, 271, 272
Pseudomonas nicotinophaga, 271, 272
Pseudomonas oleovorans, 130, 152
Pseudomonas sp., 105, 108, 112, 187
Pseudomonas sp. B-20-184, 185, 197
Pseudomonas testosteroni ATCC 11996, 101,
   103, 107, 108, 115, 118, 119, 138, 183
Psilocybe semperviva, 251, 252
Putrefactive bacteria, 144, 157, 159
Pycnodothis sp., 109, 125, 176
Pycnosporium sp., 59
Pythium ultimum, 151, 180, 181, 182

R

Rhizoctonia ferrugena, 131, 135
Rhizoctonia ferrugena CBS, 10, 14
Rhizoctonia solani, 14
Rhizopus arrhizus, 18, 29, 30, 40, 43, 47, 48, 111,
   114, 212, 242
Rhizopus arrhizus PH-176, 41
Rhizopus arrhizus ATCC 11145, 17, 19, 21, 22,
   24, 40, 42, 45, 202, 235
Rhizopus cambodjae, 19, 42
Rhizopus chinensis 10-10, 41
Rhizopus nigricans, 16, 28, 39, 40, 41, 46, 47, 48,
   51, 52, 129, 134, 135, 166, 190, 212
Rhizopus nigricans ATCC 6227b, 16, 19, 21,
   24, 38, 39, 40, 42, 44, 45, 47, 48, 49, 50, 162,
   164, 202, 203, 232, 235
Rhizopus nigricans R-5-4, 41
Rhizopus reflexus, 16, 39, 113, 157, 158
Rhizopus reflexus ATCC 1225, 16, 39
Rhizopus sp., 30
Rhizopus sp. strain SY-152, 41
Rhodoseptoria sp., 59
Rhodotorula glutinis IFO 0395, 147, 151, 152,
   153

Substance Index

A

12α-Acetoxy-3α-hydroxycholanic acid, 211
12α-Acetoxy-3-oxocholanic acid, 211
(−)-14-Acetoxycodeinone, 264, 269
17β-Acetoxyestra-1, 3, 5(10)-trien-3-ol, 186
Acovenosigenin-A, 232
Adrenosterone, 174
Agroclavin, 251
Androst-4-en-3-one-17β-carboxylic acid, 220
Androst-5-ene-3β, 17α-diol, 106
Androst-5-ene-3β, 17β-diol, 105, 142, 161
Androst-1-ene-3, 17-dione, 103, 116, 138, 140, 156, 158, 160
Androst-4-ene-3, 17-dione, 3, 8, 12, 17, 33, 34, 40, 62, 65, 72, 77, 84, 93, 103, 104, 105, 106, 117, 141, 159, 160, 172, 176, 177, 180, 185, 187, 197, 221
Androst-5-ene-3, 17-dione, 107, 142, 187
Androsta-1, 4-diene-3, 16-dione, 229
Androsta-1, 4-diene-3, 17-dione, 109, 115, 117, 118, 119, 124, 125, 126, 138, 142, 156, 160, 173, 176, 221
Androsta-4, 6-diene-3, 17-dione, 118
Androsta-1, 4, 6-triene-3, 17-dione, 118
5β-Androstane-17β-carboxylic acid, 201
5α-Androstane-3α, 17β-diol, 108, 141, 143, 144, 161
5α-Androstane-3β, 17β-diol, 108, 141, 144, 157
5β-Androstane-3α-17β-diol, 158, 159
5β-Androstane-3β, 17β-diol, 140, 141, 142, 144, 156, 161
5α-Androstane-3, 17-dione, 9, 108, 118, 138, 144
5β-Androstane-3, 17-dione, 144, 159
5α-Androstane-3, 6, 17-trione, 113
Androstenedione, 3, 4
Androsterone, 3, 4
Δ16-Anhydrogitoxigenin, 243
Apoyohimbine, 253, 254, 259
8-Aza-D-homoestradiol, 189
8-Aza-D-homoestradiol 3-methylether, 189
8-Aza-D-homoestradiol 3-methylether(17β-OH), 140
8-Aza-D-homoestrone, 189
8-Aza-D-homoestrone 3-methylether, 140, 189

B

23, 24-Bisnor-5β-cholanic acid, 201
Bisnorchol-4-en-3-on-22-al, 202, 203, 212
17α-Bromo-11α-hydroxyprogesterone, 46
17α-Bromo-A-norpregn-4-ene-3, 16, 20-trione, 194
(−)-14-Bromocodeinone, 262, 264, 265
17α-Bromopregn-4-ene-3, 16, 20-trione, 195
17α-Bromoprogesterone, 46
Bufalin, 231, 239

C

2-Carboxy-7aβ-methyl-7-keto-9aα-H-indano-[5, 4f]-5aα, 10, 10aβ, 11-tetrahydroquinoline, 196
6α-Chloro-16α-alkyl-11-deoxycortisol, 54
6α-Chloro-16α-alkyl-11α, 17α, 21-trihydoxy-pregn-4-ene-3, 20-dione, 54
17α-Chloro-A-norpregn-4-ene-3, 16, 20-trione, 194
5α-Chloro-6β, 19-oxidocholestane 3-acetate, 223
17α-Chloropregn-4-ene-3, 16, 20-trione, 195
5β-cholanic acid, 201
Cholest-5-en-3β-ol, 215 →Cholesterol
5β-Cholest-7-en-3β-ol, 219
Cholest-4-en-3-one, 217
Cholest-4-ene-3, 6-dione, 218
Cholesta-5, 7-dien-3β-ol, 218
Cholesta-1, 4-dien-3-one, 218
5β-Cholestan-3β-ol, 219
Cholesterol (Cholest-5-en-3β-ol), 215, 216, 217, 218, 219, 220, 221, 225
Cholic acid, 201, 204, 205, 206, 207, 208, 209, 211, 213, 214
(+)-Codeine, 261, 267
(−)-Codeine, 261, 267
(+)-Codeinone, 263, 267, 268
(−)-Codeinone, 267
Conessine, 245, 246, 250
Corticosterone, 3, 4, 13, 23, 56, 58, 69, 81, 82, 91, 96, 98, 110, 111, 127, 150, 165
Cortisol (Hydrocortisone), 3, 4, 32, 58, 86, 91, 99, 135, 154, 155, 167, 177, 178, 192
Cortisol 11β, 21-diacetate, 192
Cortisone, 3, 4, 91, 92, 110, 114, 133, 134, 154, 166